The M16/AR15 Rifle

A Shooters and Collector's Guide

Joe Poyer

Development History
Military and Civilian Models
Military Service Use
Civilian Usage
Part-by-Part Analysis
Sniper Rifles and Telescopic Sights
Accurizing the M16/AR15
Operating Instructions
Cleaning and Maintenance
Trouble Shooting
Shooting M16/AR15
.22 Caliber AR15s
.308 AR15s
Ammunition

North Cape Publications®, Inc.

Dedicated to the memory of Eugene Stoner

The author wishes to thank all those who helped in the preparation of this book: Jim Gronning and Lisa Gronning of Grúning Precision, Riverside, California; Bruce Bigelow, USMC Ret.; Bob Frushon, USMC Ret.; Fred Johnson; Steve Kehaya, Century International Arms; Mel Kunkle; David Lutz, Knights Manufacturing Co.; Terry Madory, Corona, California Police Department; Roy Marcot, Old Fort Lowell Press; Major Sam Pikula, USAR; Vince Scarlati, Remington Arms and Dan Young, Young Manufacturing, Inc. And to Britt Osgood-Treston for her usual fine copy-editing work. Any mistakes beyond their efforts are entirely the author's responsibility.

This publication is designed to provide authoritative and accurate information of the subject matter covered. However, it should be recognized that serial numbers and dates, as well as other information given within are necessarily limited by the accuracy of source materials, the experimental nature of certain developments and procedures and the military nature of the basic rifle/ammunition system.

The M16/AR15 rifle develops breech pressures in excess of 52,000 pounds per square inch. Use common sense at all times when shooting or working with this or any firearm.

ISBN 1-882391-28-4

North Cape Publications®, Inc. P.O. Box 1027, Tustin, California 92781
714 832-3621

Email: ncape@pacbell.net
Internet website http://www.northcapepubs.com

Printed by KNI, Inc., Anaheim, CA 92806

Table of Contents

Sidebars

Tables

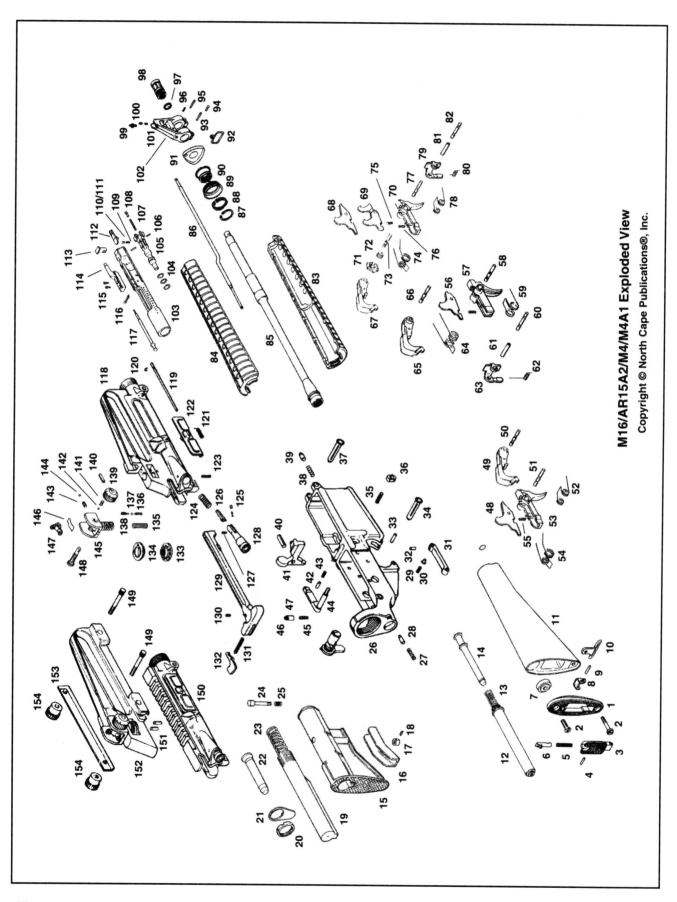

M16/AR15A2/M4/M4A1 Exploded View

Copyright © North Cape Publications®, Inc.

M16/AR15A2/M4/M4A1 EXPLODED VIEW

#		#		#	
1	Butt plate	54	Hammer spring	105	Bolt
2	Butt plate screws	55	Disconnector spring	106	Ejector pin
3	Butt plate door	56	Disconnector (A)**	107	Ejector spring
4	Retaining pin	57	Trigger (A)	108	Ejector
5	Plunger spring	58	Trigger pin (A)	109	Extractor pin
6	Plunger	59	Trigger spring (A)	110	Extractor spring
7	Butt plate spacer	60	Automatic sear pin (A)	111	Rubber insert or 2nd spring
8	Hinge	61	Automatic sear bushing (A)	112	Extractor
9	Hinge pin	62	Automatic sear spring (A)	113	Bolt cam pin
10	Sling swivel	63	Automatic sear (A)	114	Key
11	Butt stock	64	Hammer spring (A)	115	Bolt key screws (2)
12	Receiver extension tube	65	Hammer (A)	116	Firing pin retainer pin
13	Action spring	66	Hammer pin (A)	117	Firing pin
14	Buffer assembly	67	Hammer (B)***	118	Upper receiver
15	Carbine sliding butt stock	68	Semiautomatic disconnector (B)	119	Dust cover pin
16	Release lever			120	Split ring
17	Lock nut	69	Burst disconnector (B)	121	Dust cover spring
18	Pin	70	Trigger (B)	122	Dust cover
19	Receiver extension tube	71	Burst cam (B)	123	Forward Assist Pin
20	Receiver extension nut	72	Clutch spring (B)	124	Plunger spring
21	End plate	73	Hammer pin (B)	125	Pawl and pin
22	Buffer	74	Hammer spring (B)	126	Pawl
23	Action spring	75	Burst disconnector spring (B)	127	Plunger pin
24	Release lever lock pin	76	Semiautomatic disconnector spring (B)	128	Forward assist plunger
25	Spring			129	Charging handle
26	Lower receiver	77	Trigger pin (B)	130	Roll pin
27	Takedown detent spring	78	Trigger spring (B)	131	Charging spring
28	Takedown detent	79	Automatic sear (B)	132	Latch
29	Plunger spring	80	Automatic sear spring (B)	133	Elevation index
30	Trigger guard plunger	81	Automatic sear bushing (B)	134	Elevation knob
31	Trigger guard	82	Automatic sear pin (B)	135	Elevation index screw
32	Trigger guard pin	83	Lower Handguard	136	Helical spring
33	Trigger guard pivot pin	84	Upper handguard	137	Ball bearing
34	Rear receiver pin	85	Barrel	138	Index screw
35	Magazine button spring	86	Gas tube	139	Elevation knob
36	Magazine release button	87	Handguard retaining ring	140	Spring pin
37	Forward takedown pin	88	Slip ring springs	141	Helical spring
38	Detent spring	89	Handguard slip ring	142	Ball bearing
39	Forward takedown pin detent	90	Barrel nut	143	Helical spring
40	Bolt release pin	91	Handguard cap	144	Ball bearing
41	Bolt release	92	Sling swivel	145	Rear sight base
42	Magazine release plunger	93	Front sight taper pin (rear)	146	Flat spring
43	Plunger spring	94	Swivel rivet	147	Aperture
44	Magazine release	95	Front sight taper pin (front)	148	Windage screw
45	Buffer retainer spring	96	Gas tube pin	149	Clamp screws (front & rear)
46	Buffer retainer	97	Compensator spacer or washer	150	Flat top upper receiver
47	Selector			151	Dowel pins
48	Disconnector (SA)*	98	Compensator	152	Carry handle base
49	Hammer (SA)	99	Front sight post	153	Bar clamp
50	Hammer pin (SA)	100	Front sight detent	154	Handle nuts
51	Trigger pin (SA)	101	Detent spring		
52	Trigger spring (SA)	102	Front sight	*	Semiautomatic Trigger (SA)
53	Trigger (SA)	103	Bolt carrier	**	Automatic Trigger (A)
		104	Gas seal rings	***	Burst (B)

ix

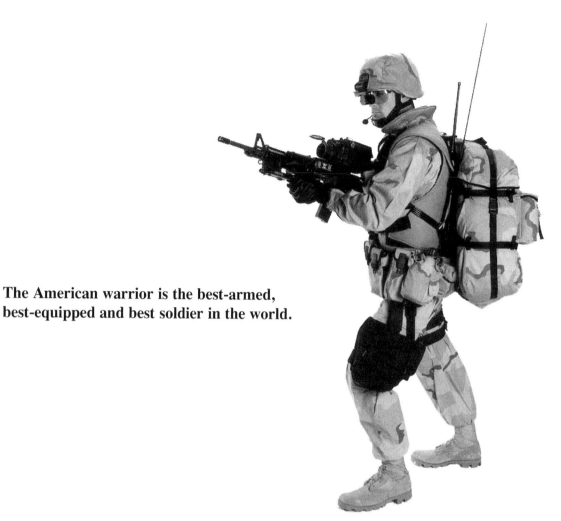

The American warrior is the best-armed, best-equipped and best soldier in the world.

A Chronology of General Issue U.S. Military Shoulder Arms*			
Model	No. of Years in Service	Model	No. of Years in Service
1795 U.S. Flintlock Musket	17	1870 U.S. Springfield Rifle	3
1812 U.S. Flintlock Musket	4	1873 U.S. Springfield Rifle	19
1816 U.S. Flintlock Musket	26	1888 U.S. Springfield Rifle (Ramrod bayonet)	4
1842 U.S. Percussion Musket	13	1892 U.S. Springfield Bolt Action Rifle (Krag)	11
1855 U.S. Percussion Rifle-Musket	6	1903/1903A1 U.S. Springfield Bolt Action Rifle	34
1861 U.S. Percussion Rifle-Musket	2	1903A3 U.S. Springfield Bolt Action Rifle	3
1863 U.S. Percussion Rifle-Musket	2	M1 Garand	21
1865 U.S. Allin Conversion Rifle	1	M14	7
1866 U.S. Allin Conversion Rifle	3	M16A, M16A2, M4 and M4A1	36+
1868 U.S. Springfield Rifle	2	OICW Rifle/Grenade Launcher	ca. 2005

1. THE M16/AR15 RIFLE

Introduction

The M16 has been the service rifle of the United States military for thirty-six years, longer than any other service rifle in the history of the U.S. Army, see Figure 1-1. Only the Model 1903 Springfield, in use from 1906 to 1936 as the first-line weapon, comes close, see Figure 1-2.

confusion in the media as many reporters never understood the difference between the Army's cartridge with its .22 caliber, 55 grain bullet and 28 grains plus of powder that gave it a muzzle velocity of 3,250 feet per second (fps) and the 40 grain .22 caliber bullet propelled by 5 grains of powder to 1,150 fps used in the .22 caliber rimfire standard velocity long rifle cartridge. Many ordnance officials as well as sol-

Fig. 1-1. The M16A2 5.56 x 45 mm rifle. This variation has a three-round burst capability and improved rear sight and was adopted as Standard A in November 1983. Photograph courtesy U.S. Army.

With the exception of its first few years — and the mistaken impressions of not a few pundits, older veterans and those who think the military can never do anything right — the M16 has had a remarkably trouble-free career. Those of us old enough to remember, and perhaps serve during the War in Vietnam, recall the controversy that swirled about the new rifle in 1966 and 1967 when media reports, supplemented by letters home from unlucky G.I.s, castigated the new rifle as unreliable. The reports all noted that the rifle needed frequent cleaning and often jammed during firefights. But the rifle itself was cleared of all charges when it was discovered that the specifications for the type of powder to be used in the ammunition had been changed without sufficient testing. The new powder produced unacceptable levels of calcium carbonate fouling, causing the rifles to jam. Calcium carbonate was included in the powder to extend shelf-life, and when the amount was reduced in the powder composition and new ammunition distributed and proper cleaning instructions issued to the troops, the problem disappeared.

Another major criticism of the M16 was its minuscule cartridge – when compared to the larger and heavier 7.62 mm NATO cartridge used by the M16's predecessor, the M14 rifle, see Figure 1-3. The new cartridge used a .223 caliber (5.56 mm) bullet weighing 55 grains. This caused a deal of

diers felt that the 55 grain bullet was simply too light to be effective against human targets and lacked the range of the 7.62 x 51 mm NATO cartridge and its predecessor, the .30-06 (7.62 x 63 mm) cartridge.

In certain quarters, the idea of distributing full automatic weapons to combat troops had never been popular and resistance to the select fire M16 was vigorous. It was pointed out

Fig. 1-2. The M1903 Springfield, in various models, served in all the nation's wars during the first half of the 20th century. North Cape Publications Collection.

that while the M14 rifle had been developed as a select fire weapon, the selector switch had been removed from most so that they could fire as semiautomatic rifles only. There was enough truth in the accusation that when it came time to incorporate design changes in 1983, the fully-automatic option was dropped in favor of a three-round burst mechanism that helped increase accuracy. The three-round burst device did not, how-

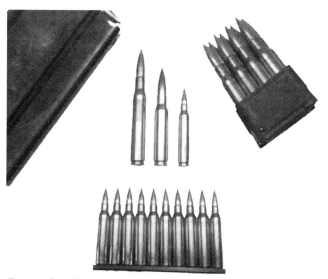

Fig. 1-3. Cartridges in the center are, L-R, the .30-06, the 7.62 x 51 mm NATO and the 5.56 x 45 mm NATO. The M14 magazine for the 76.2 MM NATO cartridges is at the upper left, the en-bloc clip for the .30-06 is at the upper right and 5.56 NATO cartridges in a stripper clip are shown at the bottom.

ever, allow the soldier to lay down the sleet of bullets that forced the enemy to keep their heads down. That job was left to the M60 machine gun and its successor, the M249 squad automatic weapon.

Within a year of its adoption by the U.S. military, a civilian version of the rifle appeared in the market. Designated the AR15, it was identical to its military counterpart in all but one respect – it lacked full automatic capability. As changes were made to the M16 military rifle, most were incorporated into the civilian AR15 as well.

For more than twenty years, the AR15 was considered by many a curiosity that only firearms collectors would want. Few thought the M16/AR15 suitable for serious target shooting and hunters chuckled at the idea of the M16/AR15 as a hunting rifle. Its high capacity magazine and its configuration were wrong for a hunting weapon — too many projections to catch on brush, and its bullet was too light for anything but varmints. Plus it just did not look like a hunting rifle.

And while the M16/AR15 was a very accurate rifle, it was neglected by match shooters for years for a number of reasons but principally for its lack of range. But over the past decade, the combination of new heavier bullets and a stiffer barrel, plus the attentions of custom gunsmiths have changed all that. In 1998, the M16/AR15 swept the service rifle competition at Camp Perry for the first time.

And in spite of being branded an assault rifle by both the media and clueless government politicians and bureaucrats desperate for anything to suggest they are serious about reducing crime except actually jailing criminals, the AR15 has today become a popular target rifle used by many law-abiding shooters at local, state and national matches, as well as a fun plinker for recreational shooting. The M16/AR15 is also showing that it is a serious contender in 1,000 meter shooting.

Conventions

The term M16/AR15 is used in this book when referring to the M16 and AR15 rifles or carbines generically. When referring to a specific model, it will be identified by its suffix, M16A1 or AR15A2, or its prefix, XM16. Note that there is no hyphen between the designator, "M" and the series number, "16."

Military Specification – MIL-Spec

Military specifications or Mil-Specs are a set of descriptive documents and drawings that define a particular product purchased by the United States military through the Department of Defense's procurement agencies. The Mil-Spec that governs the current M16A2 military rifle is MIL-R-63997B(AR). Currently, only M16A2 rifles built by Colt and FNMI conform completely to this Mil-Spec standard, see Appendix H.

Specifications for the current military versions of the M16 rifle are shown in Table 1-1, opposite. The major assemblies of the M16/AR15 rifle are show in Figure 1-4, overleaf.

Commercial AR15 rifles as manufactured for the civilian market by a variety of companies, including Colt, conform in part, but not in all respects to MIL-R-63997B(AR).

M16/AR15 Calibers

The M16/AR15 has been manufactured in six calibers. The U.S. Armed Forces have used the M16/AR15 in two calibers, 5.56 x 45 mm NATO and 9 X 18 mm NATO. Civilian versions known as the AR15 have been manufactured in both of these calibers as well as 7.62 x 39 mm Russian. A commercial variant of the AR15 has also been manufactured in 7.62 x 51 mm NATO for long range shooting. Specialty variations have been manufactured in small quantities in .45 ACP and .40 S&W as carbines for special weapons units of the military and police in the United States, see Figure 1-5.

Fig. 1-5. .45 Caliber M16 built by Tim La France Specialties, San Diego, California.

Table 1 Component Data, M16, M16A1, M16A2 and M16A4				
Part	**M16**	**M16A1**	**M16A2**	**M4**
Weight				
Rifle, w/o magazine and sling	6.35 lbs	6.55 lbs	7.5 lbs	5.65 lbs
Sling	0.4 lb	0.4 lb	0.4 lb	0.4 lbs
Magazine empty	0.16 lb	0.16 lb	0.25 lb	0.25 lbs
Magazine, loaded	0.70 lb	0.70 lb	1.01 lb	1.01 lbs
Rifle, w/sling and loaded magazine	7.76 lb	7.96 lb	8.9 lb	7.06 lbs
M7 Bayonet	0.6 lb	0.6 lb	0.6 lb	0.6lb
M9 Bayonet	15.2 oz	15.2 oz	15.2 oz	15.2 oz
M8A1 Scabbard	0.3 lb	0.3 lb	0.3 lb	0.3 lb
M10 Scabbard	0.3 lb	0.3 lb	0.3 lb	0.3 lb
M9 Scabbard	11.5 oz	11.5 oz	11.5 oz	11.5 oz
Bipod	0.6 lb	0.6 lb	0.6 lb	0.6 lb
Bipod case	0.2 lb	0.2 lb	0.2 lb	0.2 lb
Length				
Rifle w/compensator	39 in	39 in	39.6 in	29.8/33 in
Barrel	20 in	20 in	20 in	14.5 in
Mechanical Features				
Rifling	RH, 6 grooves, 1:12	RH, 6 grooves, 1:12	RH, 6 grooves 1:7 and 1:9	RH, 6 grooves, 1:7
Operational type	Gas	Gas	Gas	Gas
Breech Mechanism	Rotating Bolt	Rotating Bolt	Rotating Bolt	Rotating Bolt
Feed Mechanism	Magazine	Magazine	Magazine	Magazine
Cooling	Air	Air	Air	Air
Trigger Pull Weight	5 - 8.5 lb	5 - 8.5 lb	5-8.5 lb	5-8.5 lb

Firing Characteristics				
Muzzle Velocity (Approximate)	3,250 fps (M193)	3,250 fps (M193)	3,110 fps (M885)	2,970 fps (M885)
Muzzle Energy	1,300 ft-lb	1,300 ft-lb	1,322 ft-lb	1,322 ft
Chamber Pressure	52,000 psi	52,000 psi	52,000 psi	52,000 psi
Cyclic Rate of Fire	800 rpm	800 rpm	800 rpm	800 rpm
Max Rate of Fire, Semiautomatic	45-65 rpm	45-65 rpm	45-65 rpm	45-65 rpm
Max Rate of Fire, 3-round Burst	N/A	N/A	90 rpm	90 rpm
Max Rate of Fire, Automatic	150/200 rpm	150/200 rpm	N/A	N/A
Sustained Rate of Fire	12/15 rpm	12/15 rpm	12/15 rpm	12/15 rpm
Maximum Range	2,635 m	2,635 m	3,534 m	3,534 m
Maximum Effective Range (Individual/Point targets)	460 m	460 m	550 m	550 mm
Table compiled from: M16A2 Rifles and Carbines, CM101, 2nd Edition, 1988 Colt Industries. TM05538C-23&P/2A, Organizational and Intermediate Maintenance Technical Manual, Rifle 5.56-MM, M16A2 W/E NSN 1005-01-128-9936, HQ, USMC and Dept. of the Army August 1987				

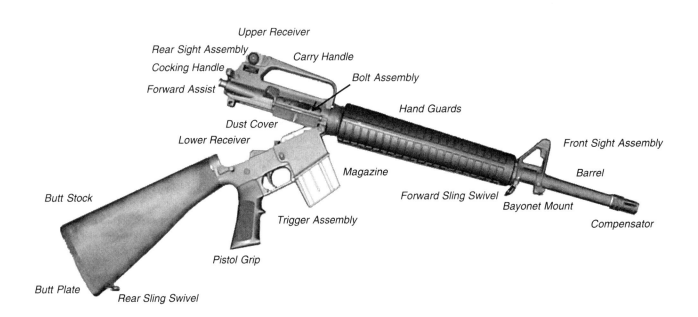

Fig. 1-4. The M16/AR15 rifle and its features.

2. THE M16 RIFLE IN MILITARY SERVICE

The adoption by the U.S. Army of a new class of light-weight combat rifle followed the usual torturous path of any military rifle adopted into the civilian service since the Declaration of Independence.

In the mid-1790s, the argument was between proponents of the French Charleville and the British Brown Bess. In 1855, the fight was over which was more serviceable, the breech loader or the muzzle-loader/Minié ball system. In 1865, the proponents of the repeating rifle and the single shot breech loader went head-to-head. In 1892, the battle between supporters of one magazine-loader over another culminated in

goal number four, the box magazine, proved an unqualified success.

As early as 1942, John C. Garand had begun working on a select fire modification for his M1 rifle, followed later by a box magazine feed. A series of prototype rifles were developed and tested — including the T-48 version of the Fabrique Nationale Fusil Leger Automatique (FAL) rifle — before the M14 was adopted in 1957. Production problems delayed manufacture until mid-1959.

Seven years later, in 1964, the M14 was replaced with the new M16, making it one of the shortest-lived first-line

Fig. 2-1. The M14 rifle in 7.62 mm NATO was adopted in 1957 by the U.S. military. North Cape Publications Collection.

the adoption of the Krag-Jorgenson system, although the Mauser adherents won their rematch in 1903. In 1939, the military and the civilian shooting world was divided over the question of replacing the bolt-action Model 1903 with a semi-automatic rifle, the M1 Garand. In 1957, powerful elements in the Ordnance Department bested those in the combat branches favoring light weight and small caliber by selecting the heavy .30 caliber M14 select fire rifle. But not for long.

The M14 Rifle

The M14 rifle was basically an improved, somewhat lighter M1 Garand, the first successful semiautomatic combat rifle to be developed and used by a major military power, see Figure 2-1. Four major design goals for the M14 over the M1 Garand had been: 1) lighter weight, 2) lighter cartridge, 3) selective fire capability and 4) removable box magazine.

Goal number one was met, but only by a few ounces. The adoption of the 7.62 x 51 mm NATO cartridge (the civilian version is known as the .308 Winchester) satisfied goal number two. Goal number three, selective fire capability, proved a mixed blessing as recoil and muzzle jump of the powerful 7.62 mm cartridge was so severe that the rifle was virtually uncontrollable in automatic fire after the third round. Only

combat rifles in U.S. history. It was removed from service before it had even reached full distribution in the military.

To understand how this happened, it is necessary to take a brief look at the development of the modern battlefield and its weapons over the past 150 years.

Infantry Tactics, A Short History

The Smooth Bore Musket — The smooth bore musket was little more than a hollow iron tube down which a charge of powder and one or more lead balls were crammed, see Figure 2-2. In an attempt to damn up as much gas as possible behind the ball to increase its speed and accuracy, the paper cartridge was wrapped around the ball and stuffed down the barrel to serve as a "wad." To make up for the smooth bore musket's deficiency in accuracy and range, soldiers were rigorously trained — and disciplined — to stand shoulder-to-shoulder in long lines facing the enemy. The lieutenant and sergeant, standing at either end of the line, called the cadence for loading, aiming and firing at the enemy line standing between 75 to 150 yards distant, firing back at them. A steady soldier could hit a man-sized target at 100 yards most of the time, but steadiness in combat was a rare commodity.

Discipline and the bayonet told. After each volley, the

Fig. 2-2. The tail of the paper cartridge was torn open, the powder poured down the musket barrel, the bullet and paper wadding pushed in after it and all driven down against the breech face with the iron ramrod.

could be trained to stand against the murderous sleet of lead and follow orders without question, see Figure 2-3.

In an attempt to increase the efficiency of the smooth bore musket, the multiball cartridge was widely used by the world's armies in the late 18th and early-to-mid-19th centuries. In U.S. Army service, it was known as the "buck and ball" load. The buck and ball service cartridge consisted of a paper wrapping containing the powder charge and three or more balls, usually one of .69 caliber and the other two of .36 or .41 caliber, see Figure 2-4)

But infantry tacticians had long recognized that if the enemy line of infantry could be brought under fire at greater ranges — say 600 or more yards — the number of friendly infantrymen struck by bullets before the two lines rushed together in hand-to-hand fighting would be increased by several times. But that required far greater accuracy than the smooth bore musket could provide. Rifling and close-fitting balls could provide that accuracy but were far slower and more cumbersome to

lines would advance again until they were so close that there was no more time to load and fire. At that point, one or both lines would charge with bayonets fixed. It was bloody, deadly work, and a premium was put on soldiers who

load — it could take up to two minutes to load rifled long arms — and so any advantage was lost.

The British had experimented with companies of flintlock riflemen during the campaigns in Spain against Napoleon. The riflemen made great skirmishers, snipers and light assault troops, but they could not sustain the volume of fire to match that of a regiment of soldiers armed with smooth bore muskets.

Rifled Musket — with the French invention of the hollow-base, thin-skirted conical bullet, the infantry soldier could now carry a "rifled" musket. Called the "Minié" ball after its inventor, a French Army officer, it was conical instead of round and had a hollow base and long, thin skirt. When the powder charge ignited, the burning gases expanded against the skirt, pressing it outward to conform to the lands and groove of the rifling. As the conical ball shot up the barrel, it turned with the rifling and emerged spinning about its own axis – acting as a gyroscope to gain stability in flight, see Figure 2-5.

During the Crimean War, new infantry tactics were devised by British and French troops armed with rifled muskets. Attacking Russian infantry were brought under accurate fire at ranges of up to 600 yards. Once again, the face of warfare had changed, and soldiers

Fig. 2-3. American troops, newly trained in the use of the bayonet, defeated British forces at Saratoga, making it a turning point in the War of Indpendence.

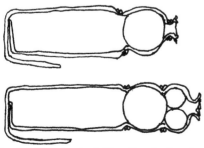

Fig. 2-4. The standard .69 caliber (top) and buck and ball paper cartridges compared.

trained in the previous school were slow to adapt. When war broke out in the United States between the federal government and the new confederacy of slave-owning states just six years later, the effect of the Minié ball was quickly felt. Opposing groups of soldiers still lined up shoulder-to-shoulder and the rifled muskets used by both sides mowed them down in hor-

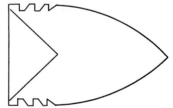

Fig. 2-5. The Minié ball made the rifled musket a practical reality. The powder gases forced the hollow skirt of the ball to expand against the rifling.

Fig. 2-6. "The Last Inspection." Members of Company A, 11th Virginia (Kemper's Brigade) undergo a final arms inspection before moving into position to attack Union troops dug in along the west side of Seminary Ridge during the Battle of Gettysburg. Their division commander was General George E. Pickett (mounted, second from right). Nearly 75% of the attacking troops were killed or wounded. Original oil painting by Dale Gallon, commissioned by the National Rifle Association.

rible massacres. It wasn't until the last year of the war that tactics began to change and soldiers began to dig trenches. The day of the bayonet was coming to a close, but many lives would be expended before the lesson was absorbed.

For instance, on July 3rd, 1863, Confederate General George Picket led 13,000 soldiers in a massed charge against Union lines dug in along Cemetery Ridge near the town of Gettysburg, Pennsylvania. Between artillery fire and accurate rifle musket fire from the Yankees, Picket lost over 9,900 troops killed or wounded, nearly 75% of his force, see Figure 2-6. Picket himself was also killed.

And another new change was about to take place. On the last day of the Battle of Gettysburg, brevet Major General George Custer led his Michigan 5th Cavalry Regiment armed with repeating Spencer rifles against Jeb Stuart's belated cavalry attack and smashed it, See Figure 2-7. Now rapidity of fire had been added to accuracy and range.

Fig. 2-7. Christopher Spencer's seven-shot rifle was the first repeating arm adopted by the U.S. Army. Custer's Michigan 5th Cavalry broke Confederate Cavalry General J.E.B. Stuart's desperate charge at Gettysburg on the last day. Roy Marcot Collection.

Technical Developments

In 1867, Emory Upton published "*Infantry Tactics*," the first in a series of tactical manuals for the U.S. Army that emphasized individual marksmanship. By the late 1870s, rapid reloading and long range shooting had become the rage. Several types of cartridges that made this possible had been developed in the century's middle decades. The first was the pinfire cartridge in which a thin steel shaft was mounted through the side of the cartridge case. When struck by the hammer the shaft, or pin, in turn struck and ignited a priming compound on the opposite side of the case. The rimfire cartridge was the next step, see Figure 2-8. The case was formed in one piece with only a single opening to hold the bullet. The priming material was contained in a rim formed by folding the case above the base. The rim also served to hold the cartridge in the chamber.

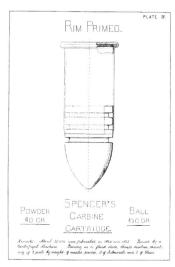

Fig. 2-8. Spencer rimfire cartridge patent drawing. (Ordnance Memorandum No. 14, 1873, Plate IV)

The Centerfire Cartridge

By the early 1880s, the centerfire, reloadable metallic cartridge had been perfected, and it quickly replaced the weaker rimfire. The centerfire cartridge was formed with two openings; the mouth which held the bullet, and a smaller hole opposite into which a separate smaller tube, closed at one end, was pressed, see Figure 2-9. This small tube, called the primer, held the priming compound. When the primer was struck by the hammer or a firing pin, the priming compound exploded and flashed into the cartridge case, igniting the main powder charge. The cartridge case could now be formed from a single slug of brass. without the need to fold in the rim that weakened the case. In fact, the centerfire case could be manufactured with additional wall thickness at the head of the case.

Two rimfire repeating rifles had seen service during the Civil War, the Henry and the Spencer. But the Henry with its open, spring-driven magazine was considered too delicate for military service and was never officially adopted although private militia units acquired a number of the rifles. The Spencer, in carbine form, became the standard Union cavalry arm during the last two years of the war, see Figure 2-10. It fired a .50 caliber rimfire cartridge containing a relatively small powder charge. The Spencer's cast-iron, one-piece receiver could not handle a more powerful cartridge to provide the range needed on the Western Frontier, as the Modoc War and the Forsythe battles demonstrated. But Forsythe's engagement at Beecher's Island on the Republican River did demonstrate the utility of disciplined fire from repeating rifles when they repulsed between 600 and 700 Oglala and Cheyenne warriors, even if they lacked the range to drive them from the battlefield.

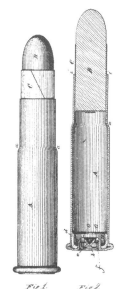

Fig. 2-9. Patent drawings for Hiram Berdan's centerfire, reloadable cartridges. Berdan's cartridge priming system has two flash holes rather than one. The Berdan system is widely used in Europe and Asia.

Fig. 2-10. Cavalry small arms, 1863-1872: Sharps Carbine (top), Spencer Carbine (below), Colt M1860 revolver. North Cape Publications Collection.

With a long Civil War just over, however, and the problems and costs of reconstruction ahead, Congress was in no mood to vote large sums for the development of new army rifles after having just paid for over 3 million rifle muskets.

The .45-70 Springfield

Instead, in 1865, the Ordnance Department was ordered to convert 5,000 of the Army's vast stock of muzzle-loading rifle-muskets into single-shot rifles, see Figure 2-11. The conversion was accomplished by cutting off the top of the barrel's breech and bolting a "trap-door" to it. To use, the soldier placed the side-mounted hammer on half cock, raised the trap — top half of the breech —and inserted a .58 caliber rimfire cartridge.

Fig. 2-11. The Allin system converted obsolete muzzleloading rifles into cartridge rifles. North Cape Publications Collection.

In 1866, a new .50-70 centerfire cartridge replaced the .58 rimfire cartridge. The .50-70 cartridge was used in the Models of 1866, 1869 and 1870 Springfield rifles with the "trapdoor system" and the cartridge conversions of the percussion Sharps cavalry carbines (refer to Figure 2-10). By

1873, the system had been improved to the point whereby the trap door had become an integral part of the Model 1873 receiver and the caliber had been reduced to .454 inches backed by 70 grains of black powder. In the 1882, a new reloadable .45-70 cartridge using a Boxer primer was introduced. The Model 1873 .45-70 Springfield Rifle served the army throughout the late Indian War period and should properly be called the "gun that won the west, see Figure 2-12.

rifle at ranges to 1,000 yards and target practice had become a religion for everyone, from enlisted man to commander-in-chief.

This "passion" for military marksmanship developed quickly on the frontier during the later Indian Wars. By the mid-1870s, Native American irregular soldiers were well equipped with a wide variety of firearms including repeating rifles. And while their marksmanship was not up to Army

Fig. 2-12. The Model 1873 .45-70 Springfield Rifle and its variations was in use by the regular Army until the adoption of the .30 caliber Krag-Jorgenson bolt action rifle in 1892. In actuality, the .45-70 Springfield served with the regulars into the mid-1890s before all were replaced. National Guard units were issued the rifle into the first decade of the 20th century. North Cape Publications Collection.

The .45-70 rifle with its powerful, large caliber cartridge provided the necessary range — up to a thousand yards — needed on the plains and prairies of the West. During the twenty-one years that it was in service, the Army tested a wide range of repeating rifles but alone among the major military powers of the world, chose to stay with the long range, accurate single shot rifle.

standards only because they lacked a surplus of ammunition for target practice, they had mastered the art of massed fire,

The European Experience

The story was much different in Europe. A series of wars from the 1840s through the 1870s had seen European armies progress rapidly from the single shot, large caliber breechloader to the repeating rifle using a small caliber cartridge. On Austrian and French battlefields, greater volumes of firepower at ever increasing ranges were needed as huge armies maneuvered across far larger spaces courtesy of the railroad.

The first repeating rifle was adopted in Austria in 1870 and in Switzerland the following year, see Table 2-1. The great rush came in the 1880s, however, when the technology had improved greatly. The United States, safe behind two oceans and with two weak nations on its borders, continued to use the single shot rifle until the Krag-Jorgensen began to replace it in 1894, see Figure 2-13, overleaf. National Guard and Militia units remained equipped with the single-shot .45-70 Springfield until after the turn of the century.

Tactical Developments

As early as 1864, infantry tactics began to evolve the small unit leader as responsible for spotting targets and directing the aimed fire of his troops. Upton's manual called for target practice to distances as great as 800 yards. By the turn of the century, the soldier was expected to be proficient with his

Table 2-1 Countries Adopting Repeating Rifles Before 1895 (Year and Model)		
Argentina	1891	Mauser
Austria	1870	Früwirth
	1886	Mannlicher-Schonauer
Belgium	1889	Mauser
Bolivia	1891	Mauser
Brazil	1894	Mauser
	1895	Mauser
China	1884	Mauser (M1871/84)
Columbia	1891	Mauser
Denmark	1889	Krag-Jorgensen
France	1878	Kropatschek
	1886	Lebel
	1890	Berthier
Germany	1884	Mauser (M1871/84)
Great Britain	1888	Lee

Table 2-1, con't. Countries Adopting Repeating Rifles Before 1895 (Year and Model)		
Italy	1887	Vettererli (M1871/87)
	1891	Mannlicher-Carcano
Japan	1887	Murata (M1880/87)
Netherlands	1888	Beaumont (M1871/88)
	1895	Mannlicher
Norway	1887	Jarman (M1881/87)
Russia	1891	Mosin-Nagant
Spain	1893	Mauser
Sweden	1894	Mauser
Switzerland	1871	Vetterli
	1889	Schmidt-Rubin
Turkey	1887	Mauser
	1890	Mauser
	1893	Mauser
United States	1892	Krag-Jorgensen

at a high angle. Hand-to-hand fighting finished the survivors.

The Army and Congressional hearings that followed provided support for increased marksmanship training among other things. But any implication that massed fire was still effective was studiously ignored. Custer was castigated for charging into battle without having conducted a thorough reconnaissance, and his

Fig. 2-14. Young Cheyenne warriors, circa 1880.

impetuousness was blamed for the massacre. But he became a public icon for his bravery and "heroic demise" anyway.

Into the New Century

By the end of the 1880s, U.S. Ordnance officials realized that America's enemies were no longer as distant as they once were. As the nation grew it acquired responsibilities and duties beyond the continental shores in the Carribean, Latin America and in the Pacific, see Figure 2-15. We also acquired, if not allies, then friendly nations who could call upon us for assistance if attacked. And our national interest — defined as trade agreements, mutual interests and a common heritage — dictated that we provide assistance, no matter how much we wished to remain isolated behind our ocean barriers.

Germany was beginning to prove itself an international competitor for markets and colonies, and crowded Japan was eyeing its neighbors in the Pacific and their

Fig. 2-15. The U.S.S. Olympia became the symbol of America's imperialist ambitions when Admiral Dewey defeated the Spanish flotilla at the Battle of Manilla Bay in 1898. Photo courtesy of the National Archives and Research Administration.

natural resources. Already, war gaming (invented a few years earlier at the U.S. Naval War College in Rhode Island) was directing attention to Japan's future moves in the Pacific and

Fig. 2-13. Infantry soldier with M1892 Krag rifle. Note the ramrod.

followed by a charge and hand-to-hand combat at which they were often very much more adept than the "blue coats, see Figure 2-14."

As recent excavations and studies at the Custer Battlefield National Memorial have revealed, the Native American contingents cut the troopers of Companies E and F, 7th Cavalry Regiment into several discrete groups, then overwhelmed them with massed rifle and pistol fire, much of it fired

Fig. 2-16. U.S. Army Private Albert Card, 24th Infantry, Company F, taken at Manila, P.I. in 1901. He is holding a M1898 Krag Rifle. Photo courtesy of Louis Card.

Germany's in Europe, Africa and the Atlantic. Far-sighted military officers and politicians began demanding that the U.S. reequip its fighting men with modern small arms.

Following years of testing a wide range of designs, the Ordnance Department adopted the Norwegian-designed Krag-Jorgensen as the Model 1892 Springfield Rifle, see Figure 2-16. Its unbridged breech limited the power of the smokeless cartridge it fired, but the Army recognized that it was only

Fig. 2-18. A U.S. Army sharpshooter on the range firing his Model 1903 Springfield. The sight appears to be set for 900 to 1,100 yards.

a stop-gap until the design they were really interested in, that of Paul Mauser, was "perfected." In the meantime, the Krag served in the Spanish-American War and the Philippine Insurrection to mixed reviews. In 1903, it was replaced by the American Mauser, the Springfield Model 1903 rifle, see Figure 2-17.

The Model 1903 was the first truly modern, general issue rifle that the U.S. Army had ever adopted. Firing a powerful .30 caliber cartridge, modified and adopted in 1906, it and its cousin the Model 1917 Enfield, enabled American troops to stand against experienced German storm troopers in the trenches of the Western Front. Rifle engagements were fought at ranges varying from 50 to 1,200 yards, and skill, accuracy and courage determined the outcome.

The Springfield Model 1903 was designed for accurate and rapid fire. Marksmanship training emphasized

Fig. 2-17. A U.S. Army private, identified only as "Jack" is shown holding a new Model 1903 Springfield.

long range rifle fire to 1,000 yards and beyond, and volley fire to 2,000 yards, see Figure 2-18. But the rifle's small magazine capacity of 5 rounds plus one in the chamber defeated this purpose. And in any event, the machine gun proved far more effective in that role.

Combat on the Western Front in 1917 and 1918 proved a real eye-opener for Army tacticians. It became increasingly apparent to them that while large volumes of rifle fire were needed, combat ranges had declined to between 300 and 600 yards — the maximum distance between opposing trenches. Trench warfare demanded vast quantities of men and rifle and machine fire to halt enemy attacks once supporting artillery fire ended, See Figure 2-19.

In 1917, Irwin Pedersen developed a device which fitted into the breech of the standard Model 1903 rifle. It fired a pistol-sized cartridge semiautomatically – as fast as a soldier could pull the trigger. A magazine extending from the left side of the rifle at an acute angle held twenty rounds, see Figure 2-20.

General John J. Pershing and his staff saw this device as the tool that would enable them to finally smash through the German lines, force them to fall back and convert the war from one of static defense to one of maneuver and movement. More than 60,000 Pedersen Devices were ordered for use

Fig. 2-19. New recruits of Company I, 8th Training Regiment drilling with Springfield Model 1903 rifles in early 1918.

in the spring offensives of 1919. The Army's tacticians in France envisioned entire divisions of doughboys rising out of their trenches and marching across No-Man's Land firing their rifles from the hip to lay down withering sheets of jacketed lead projectiles that would glue the Germans to the bottom of their trenches until the doughboys got in among them with bayonets and pistols.

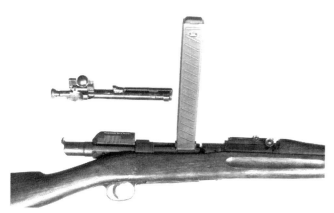

Fig. 2-20. The mysterious and highly classified Pedersen Device allowed a bolt action rifle to be fired as a semiautomatic. It used an anemic .30 caliber pistol round but the magazine held 32 cartridges. After World War I, almost all Pedersen devices were destroyed. Photo courtesy of Old Fort Lowell Press.

But a naval mutiny at Kiel in the autumn of 1918 threw the German military machine into crisis. The German government panicked and the Army, after horrible losses in previous offensives that year, and subjected to wave after wave of tank-led Allied offensives, collapsed. World War I was suddenly over.

Maneuver Warfare

For the next twenty-two years, the concept of maneuver warfare backed by massive firepower in the hands of the infantryman, occupied the thoughts and actions of many of the Army's more forward thinking planners.

For once the U.S. government found itself struggling into the forefront of arms design – at least as far as the infantryman's rifle was concerned. During the 1920s and 1930s, the Army tested and developed a variety self-loading rifle concepts. The clear winner was a design by John C. Garand. His semiautomatic, gas-operated rifle firing the standard .30-06 cartridge from 8-round en-bloc clips became the most famous military rifle in American history and gave the infantryman an edge when he met his better-trained and often-better motivated opposite number on the Axis side. The M1 Garand rifle, and its smaller cousin, the M1 carbine, emerged as the most effective small arms of the war, see Figure 2-21. Although the Germans had developed the "assault rifle" — the STG44 — it came to late and in quantities too limited to have a significant effect.

Fig. 2-21. The M1 Garand (above) and the M1 Carbine (below) were two of the most advanced semiautomatic rifles of World War II. North Cape Publications Collection.

On the opposite side of the European theater, the Soviet Red Army had issued millions of submachine guns to their troops to carry out exactly the kind of tactics that had been proposed by Pershing's staff in 1918. Russian infantrymen advancing at widely spaced intervals over open ground and firing massive amounts of ammunition at German defenders were a dire threat that could only be stopped by artillery and machine gun fire.

The Soviets had recognized as early as the Winter War with Finland that firepower was the key to winning infantry battles. But their submachine gun/pistol cartridge combination turned out to be less effective than hoped. The range of the 7.62 x 18 mm pistol cartridge was limited as was its penetrating power at ranges beyond a hundred or so meters. At the other end of the spectrum, their 10-round, semiautomatic SVT38 and SVT40 battle rifles were burdened with a too-powerful cartridge, the standard 7.62 x 54R mm rifle round. The Russians were never able to solve the parts breakage problem, and manufacture was stopped in 1943, see Figure 2-22.

Soviet ordnance personnel had instituted a crash program early in the war to develop a cartridge more powerful than the 7.62 x 18 mm pistol round but not as powerful as the 7.62 x 54 mmR rifle round. The result was the famous 7.62 X 39 mm cartridge (adopted as the Model 1943) chambered first in the SKS Carbine in 1944 (Figure 2-23) and then the Kalashnikov-designed AK-47 assault rifle in 1949.

Fig. 2-22. Russian troops on the Volkhov Front, south of Lake Ilmen, shoot at Nazi troops. The soldier in the foreground fires a Tokarev Model 1940 semiautomatic rifle while the solider to his right is firing a PPSh M1941 submachine gun. Courtesy Sovphoto.

The SKS and the AK-47 gave the Red Army exactly the firepower it needed for its massed infantry tactics in a war of maneuver. Nearly sixty years later, the M1943 remains a major world class military cartridge. And it heavily influenced the design of the current Russian 5.45 x 39 mm army cartridge.

Fig. 2-23. The SKS Carbine was the first firearm to be chambered for the M1943 7.62 x 39 mm cartridge. North Cape Publications Collection.

Post World War II

The lessons were there but had the U.S. Ordnance Department learned from them? Apparently not. In years following War II, Ordnance insisted on replacing the M1 Garand with a modified M1 Garand, the M-14, see Figure 2-24. The 8-round en-bloc clip gave way to a twenty-round detachable magazine

Fig. 2-24. The M14 semiautomatic battle rifle followed the M1 Garand. While a fine and accurate rifle, it was quickly superceded by the smaller, lighter M16. Photo courtesy Jim Gronning.

and the gas system and stock were shortened to lighten the rifle's weight. The M14 was chambered for a new cartridge, a shorter version of the .30-06 designated the 7.62 x 51 mm NATO (the civilian version was known as the .308 Winchester). The round, while shorter and lighter than the .30-06, had almost identical ballistics. The Ordnance Department having learned the lessons of range and fire power in two wars were determined to provide it to the maximum — 600 to 900 meters — even though studies of actual battle field conditions by S.L.A. Marshall, R. E. Moore and others had shown that few rifles were fired effectively beyond 350 meters.

The new M14 rifle was adopted in 1957, but production was delayed to 1959 by the need to develop new machinery and tooling. The new rifle was built at the National Armory at Springfield, at Winchester and at Harrington & Richardson, both old line firearms manufacturers with their roots in the 19th century, and by Tompson, Ramo, Woolridge (TRW), a new aerospace corporation.

Conflict Within the U.S. Army

The M14 was the end product of 100 years of development and marksmanship training in the United States. It was born at a time when the military was only just beginning to recognize the value of aimed, long range fire over massed, short range fire and ended when statistical studies of combat operations in World War II and Korea showed that in modern warfare, aimed fire was less effective than huge volumes of fire poured at the enemy, see Figure 2-25.

Fig. 2-25. American troops patrol the Korean Dimilitarized Zone in 1964, armed with M14 rifles. Photo courtesy U.S. Army.

The studies showed that the wheel had turned full circle and that in spite of the huge amounts of money spent by the military services in training combat infantrymen to be marksman, few were capable of firing effectively beyond ranges of 200 to 300 meters in the heat of battle. "Spray and pray" would come to be the practice on the future battlefields of Vietnam.

But just as the proponents of long range marksmanship had fought the Army establishment in the 1860s and '70s to adopt an accurate, long range rifle, so now did the proponents of light caliber, shorter range rifles and massed infantry fire struggle against an establishment held by proponents of heavy caliber, long-range rifles. This internecine quarrel at times took on the fervor of a religious crusade, on both sides. In 1951, the official position of the U.S. Army regarding the adoption of a smaller caliber cartridge was as follows:

"The Army is firmly opposed to the adoption of any less effective smaller caliber cartridge for use in either its present rifle or in any new weapons being developed. Any new rifle cartridge must have wounding power, penetration performance, and ballistics at least equal to that in use today. Battle experience has proven beyond question the effectiveness of the present rifle and ammunition, and there have been no changes in combat tactics that would justify a reduction of rifle caliber and power."

Reluctantly, and only at the repeated urging of Congress, did the U.S. Army begin development of a new battle rifle in the mid-1950s, even before the M14 entered production. It was clear to critics of the various departments and bureaus responsible for small arms development and procurement that the M14 was too heavy and bulky for the modern battlefield. And when fired in the full automatic mode, the rifle became uncontrollable beyond the third round. A single 7.62 X 51 mm cartridge weighed more than twice as much as the new 5.56 X 45 mm cartridge which the Remington Arms Company had developed from their .222 cartridge and which was being pushed as the ideal medium power, small caliber cartridge for a future "assault rifle."

The Genesis of the Stoner/Sullivan Design

In 1954, a young ex-Marine named Eugene Stoner met George Sullivan at the Topanga Canyon Shooting Range near Los Angeles. George Sullivan, a patent attorney for Lockheed Aircraft, had recently founded a company called Armalite, with the backing of Fairchild Engine and Airplane Company president, Richard Boutelle. Sullivan wanted to develop new concepts in small arms, after which they would be sold or licensed to larger arms companies for production and distribution. Gene Stoner was testing one of his own rifle designs at the range, and it so impressed Sullivan that he hired him shortly afterward as his chief designer.

Stoner's rifle design became the Armalite AR-3, a conventional-enough looking rifle until you removed the hand guard and took the barreled action from the stock. A thin metal tube snaked back from a port in the barrel to a port in the receiver. When the rifle was fired, gas from the burning propellant was bled through the port and channeled up and back through the tube to strike the bolt carrier which con-

tained a light-weight bolt assembly. As the expanding gas drove the bolt carrier back, the bolt rotated on cams inside the carrier and unlocked. The bolt carrier continued rearward with the bolt, compressing a stiff recoil spring and cocking the hammer for the next shot.

The direct gas impingement concept — gas bled directly from the bore to strike the bolt — had been used before. Designer Erik Eklund used direct gas impingement against the bolt in the AG42 Ljungman Semiautomatic rifle adopted by the Swedish Army in 1942, see Figures 2-26 and 27. His bolt, however, was similar to the dropping bolt design used in the FAL and the Tokarev Model 1938 and 1940 rifles, and in the French MAS 49/56 rifle.

Fig. 2-26. The Swedish AG42B Ljungman was the first issue military rifle to use a direct gas impingment system. A similar system was later used in the Stoner-designed M16 rifle. North Cape Publications Collection.

Fig. 2-27. This photo of the open breech of the AG42B shows the gas tube (1) leading from the gas port in the barrel and the closed tube (2) in the bolt carrier. Gas flowing through the gas tube into the bolt carrier, drove it back. A similar system was used by E. Stoner in the M16/AR15 rifle.

Melvin Johnson had developed the rotating bolt concept for his Johnson semiautomatic rifle, a contender against the M1 Garand in 1940-41, see Figure 2-28. Stoner's unique contribution was to combine the two concepts — direct gas impingement and the rotating bolt — and to add an unique means for venting excess gas. This last was extremely important. A certain amount of expanding propellant gas was needed to operate the action, but too much imposed strain on the operating parts, resulting in premature failure. In the Stoner system, as soon as the bolt carrier began to move rearward, the closed

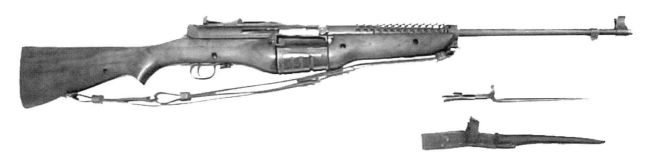

Fig. 2-28. The Johnson semiautomatic rifle was a contender with the M1 Garand as the U.S. military rifle. It employed a rotating bolt concept similar to that later used in the M16/AR15 rifle. Michael Metzger Collection.

tube in the bolt face which received the gas was pulled away from the gas tube and excess gas was vented immediately to the atmosphere. This meant a lighter-weight receiver could be used.

Working to further refine his system, Stoner next produced the AR-10, a full-scale military rifle, see Figure 2-29. His first prototype was chambered in .30-06 because the only magazine he had to work with was a Browning Automatic Rifle magazine. Intended from the start as a military rifle, the

pattern. The third prototype had a raised carrying handle which gave all subsequent the Stoner-designs their unique appearance. The carrying handle not only made it easier for the soldier to carry the rifle at trail, but provided a high mount for the rear sight. A compensator was threaded onto the muzzle to further reduce muzzle jump and it became a mounting location for the front sight. In later prototypes, the front sight was moved behind the compensator to the barrel.

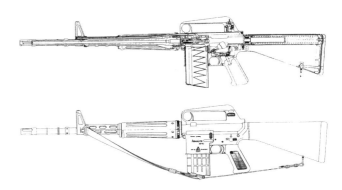

Fig. 2-30. Early engineering drawings of the Armalite AR-10 rifle. Courtesy of the late Eugene Stoner.

Fig. 2-29. The AR-10 was Eugene Stoner's first production military rifle. Its straight line stock, recoil reducer and high sight line make it an easy rifle to shoot. Tim Wikle Collection.

AR-10 was a distinct departure from his previous designs. To the unique gas system and rotating bolt, Stoner added a straight line stock made of plastic that allowed the barrel, receiver, bolt and bolt carrier and recoil spring to operate in a straight line from the muzzle to the shooter's shoulder to produce less muzzle jump and felt recoil. But the straight line stock required that the sights had to be raised to allow the shooter to get his head far enough down to aim the rifle comfortably, see Figure 2-30.

The second prototype was chambered for the 7.62 mm NATO cartridge. For this rifle, Stoner developed the AR-10's signature 20 round magazine with its distinctive "waffle"

The next step was to build a select fire version. An auxiliary — trip — sear was mounted above the selector switch to engage a spur on the back of the hammer. The auxiliary sear held the hammer until the bolt carrier ran all the way forward and the bolt was locked into the breech. At that point, the auxiliary sear released the hammer to strike the firing pin.

To reduce felt recoil as much as possible, Stoner designed a buffer and spring mechanism in a tube attached to the rear of the receiver. The butt stock was fitted over and secured to the tube. A strong spring in the tube was compressed when the bolt carrier struck the buffer which absorbed a sizeable amount of the recoil force generated.

At the same time, George Sullivan designed a unique barrel that provided additional weight reduction. The rear of the barrel was enlarged in diameter, and lugs were cut that engaged similar lugs on the bolt face. This moved the breech from the receiver to the barrel. The receiver could now be made of a lighter material as the "barrel extension" contained the 45,000 psi pressure developed by the 7.62 mm NATO cartridge. The AR10 — and all subsequent Armalite designs were manufactured with aircraft-grade aluminum receivers — 7075 T-6 aluminum forgings in the case of the AR-10 — at a distinct weight savings.

The aluminum AR-10 receiver was manufactured in two parts, upper and lower, a feature copied from the Fabrique Nationale FAL. The barrel was attached to the upper receiver and the trigger assembly and magazine well were part of the lower receiver. The two were hinged at the front and pinned togther at the back to form a rigid structure, yet one that opened easily to allow the soldier to clean the barrel and trigger mechanism, see Figure 2-31.

Fig. 2-32. The AK47, like its predecessor, the SKS Carbine, was designed to be easy to clean and maintain on the battle field. The rifle is almost indestructible.

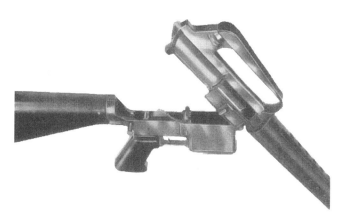

Fig 2-31. AR-10 receiver open. Adopted from an Artillerie-Inrichtingen brochure photo.

The AR-10 stock and hand guards were made of a foam-filled phenolic resin. The heavy steel Browning magazine was discarded and a twenty-round magazine made of light-weight aluminum was substituted.

While the AR-10 never did find its market, the design features it incorporated so withstood the test of time and hard usage that today, nearly fifty years later, they are still the cornerstone of the AR15/M16 rifle family.

The Vietnam War

Combat studies from World War II and Korea had shown that the number of rounds needed to kill one opposing soldier was growing almost exponentially. In World War II it had been quantified at 15,000 rounds of rifle fire. It nearly doubled during the Korean War and exceeded 50,000 rounds in Vietnam.

By the time United States troops entered the war in 1965, most Viet Cong Main Force (VCMF) and all North Vietnamese Army (NVA) units were armed with either the semiautomatic SKS Carbine or the Kalashnikov AK-47 assault rifle,

see Figure 2-32. In November 1965, elements of the 1st Air Cavalry battled NVA units in the Ia Drang Valley deep in the Central Highlands. The 1st Air Cav, which had served as a test unit for the M16, had rearmed completely with the new rifle only two months before leaving the United States. One battalion commander gave the M16 rifle a great deal of credit for the 1st Air Cav's success in the Ia Drang, but its initial introduction *throughout* the Army and Marine Corps could hardly be called a success, see Figure 2-33. As usual there was a great deal of resistance to replacing the M14 with the the new M16 rifle.

Fig. 2-33. Marines charge an NVA-fortified position on Hill 881 North during the battle for Khe Sanh Valley in May 1967. Photo by Catherine Leroy.

In addition to the usual skepticism and outright hostility which has traditionally greeted a new rifle in the U.S. military the Department of Defense insisted that the M16 be sent to the combat zone so quickly that the Ordnance Department was not able to follow its usual lengthy testing procedures to eliminate bugs as well as develop soldier-acceptable training, cleaning and maintenance techniques.

The 5.56 x 45 mm cartridge had been developed using IMR powder. But theArmy wanted to standardize on ball powder which would slow down the rifle's cyclic rate in full automatic mode. The ball new powder accomplished this but it did not burn as cleanly as the original IMR powder and left a sticky residue in the bore and gas tube. The ultra-humid climate of Southeast Asia hastened the fouling buildup which, if left uncleaned, hardened into a varnish-like substance that caused fired cartridge cases to stick in the chamber.

Those Army and Marine Corps units who brought their M16s from the States had received proper cleaning and maintenance training and experienced no significant problems. But units receiving their M16s in-country did not receive the same thorough training and had a high rate of failure due to fouling. Word of the rifle's problem was reported —inaccurately —by several journalists and it caused headlines around the world followed by Congressional hearings and denunciations of the rifle from every quarter.

A crash program was started to determine the cause of the fouling and eliminate it. As it turned out, ball powder as formulated then had a relatively high concentration (1.0%) of calcium carbonate ($CaCO_3$) which was included to neutralize the acid in the powder and extend its shelf life. It was the calcium carbonate reacting with water in the humid air that caused the problem. The powder was reformulated using only 0.25% calcium carbonate and the problem was solved. But the media circus that had been generated so obscured the real problem with rumor and innuendo that thirty-five years later, misinformation about the M16's unreliability is still rife.

As an example, in December, 1991 during the buildup to Operation Desert Storm, the author was asked by the executive news producer of a major Southern California television station to deliver an on-air report on the potential failure rate

Fig. 2-34. A radio operator makes contact during the armored thrust into Iraq in February 1991. Photo courtesy U.S. Army.

of the M16 rifle in the Arabian Desert. Only with difficulty was the producer convinced that the M16 had withstood the rigors of more than ten years of annual Bright Star joint exercises with the Egyptian Army in the North African desert and twenty-some years of similar exercises in the Mojave desert by Army and Marine Corps personnel and that desert sand would not be a problem, see Figure 2-34.

Even a cursory examination of ordnance records shows that the M16 is the most reliable and trouble-free rifle ever adopted by the United States military — more reliable and rugged than the M14 which it replaced.

Lessons Learned

The M16 rifle is a gas-operated, rotary bolt, self-loading rifle with a box magazine holding 20 rounds — a 30 round magazine became available to the troops late in the Vietnam war, see Figure 2-35. Above the receiver is a handle that doubles as the sight base. A three-position switch on the left side of the receiver controls the rate of fire and serves as the safety. When the switch is turned toward the muzzle, the rifle is on "SAFE"; straight up provides semiautomatic fire and when turned toward the butt stock, automatic fire.

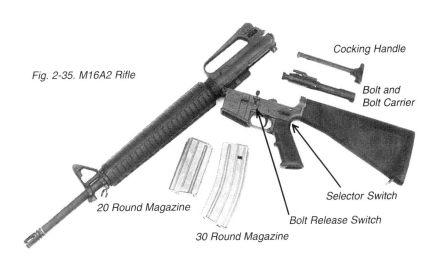

Fig. 2-35. M16A2 Rifle

Cocking Handle

Bolt and Bolt Carrier

Selector Switch

Bolt Release Switch

20 Round Magazine

30 Round Magazine

To fire the M16, a loaded magazine is inserted into the magazine well located beneath the receiver. The charging handle is pulled to the rear and released to load a round from the magazine into the chamber. The shooter turns the safety switch to the semiautomatic or automatic mode, sights and pulls the trigger.

While the M16's 5.56 (.223 caliber) bullet was smaller and lighter than the 7.62(.30 caliber) bullet used in the AK-47, it was nearly its equal in "mean energy," which is one measure of a bullet's effectiveness. The 5.56 bullet (55 grains) at 200 yards impacts with nearly the same force as the bullet from the Soviet 7.62 mm bullet (123 grains) in the M1943 7.62 X 39 mm cartridge used in the SKS Carbine and AK-47. At 300 yards and beyond, the 5.56 has a slight edge and a much flatter trajectory.

The M16A1 rifle served with distinction during the War in Vietnam and helped to prove the theory that massive amounts of firepower at ranges of up to 300 meters were more effective than aimed fire at the same distances — the thick rain forest and high grass of Vietnam often prevented soldiers from

Fig. 2-36. 1st Cavalry troopers fire on an NVA bunker during Operation Masher in the An Lao Valley in early 1966. Photo courtesy U.S. Army.

identifying targets at distances beyond 100 to 200 meters. Artillery, mortar fire and air support proved far more effective than long-distance rifle fire in suppressing enemy activity beyond a hundred or so hundred meters, see Figure 2-36.

Like every war, Vietnam provided new lessons to be learned. One important lesson was that too much fire power was as bad as not enough. Soldiers under fire had tendency to flick their selector switches to full automatic and spray an area, often with little or no effect. Even the mild recoil of the M16 provided sufficient muzzle lift that many soldiers could not maintain their point of aim in full auto fire. The result was wasted ammunition and a massive logistical problem of resupply.

Studies suggested that a soldier's effectiveness and accuracy could be improved significantly if automatic fire was limited to three rounds per trigger pull. At the same time, ballistic and bullet-redesign studies at Fabrique Nationale with a heavier 62 grain bullet (SS109 cartridge) showed that the M16s effective range could be pushed out to 600 meters by using a heavier bullet and a slower rifling twist in a stiffer barrel.

The military, which had always led the way in accurizing the current service rifle for match shooting, virtually ignored the M16 and continued to field the M14 for match shooting until the M16A2 model was adopted. The 'A1 version's "thin" barrel and rather rudimentary rear sight provided many excuses for poor shooting — barrel overheating, bent barrels, sights not sufficiently adjustable, and so on. As a consequence, civilian shooters also shunned the M16A1. Any competitor that dared show up on the line with one usually had to endure far more razzing than it was worth.

The Marine Corps' Position

The Marine Corps has long been convinced that its troops should be able to shoot accurately at combat ranges with the current service rifle, see Figure 2-37. While many members of the Corps loudly lamented the demise of the M14, they nevertheless buckled down to see what could be done with the M16. The result was the M16A2 in 1983.

Fig. 2-37. This Marine Corps marksman demonstrates a modified kneeling position to new recruits at the Marine Corps Training Depot at San Diego in 1943.

A new fully adjustable and relatively stable rear sight was installed which permitted windage and elevation changes to be made easily. The tapered round front sight was discarded in favor of a square front sight post. The hand guard cross section was changed from triangular to round (an iffy fix), a brass deflector was added to protect left-handed shooters from being struck by hot ejected brass, a longer butt stock was installed and best of all, a heavier barrel with a slower 1:7 rifling twist (reduced from 1:12) to handle the new heavier 62 grain bullet in the recently adopted M855 cartridge. The new M16A2 provided the range and effectiveness of the M14 out to 600 meters and nearly twice the accuracy!

The Army's Position

In the late 1980s, the U.S. Army Marksmanship Unit (USAMU) also came to the conclusion that its shooters should darn well know how to use the current service rifle for accurate shooting. USAMU gunsmiths and ammunition technicians dug in, experimenting on their own and consulting with civilian gunsmiths to develop accurizing techniques for the new M16A2. The work paid off. In 1994, SFC Kenneth Gill won the National Service Rifle Championship competition at Camp Perry, Ohio using a USAMU-accurized M16A2.

It is interesting to note that even though the Marines had been firing the M16A2 in Divisional matches since 1984, it was not until 1998, that they left their M14s behind when they traveled to Camp Perry. That year, their trailers racked nothing but accurized M16A2s and the top finishers in the service rifle competition (of whatever branch) fired accurized M16A2s. The M14 had been replaced as "king of the hill," just as it had replaced the M1 Garand, which replaced the Model 1903, which had replaced the Krag.

Major Changes
XM16 to M16A1 to M16A2

*   Chamber, barrel and bolt carrier chromed to reduce fouling (M16A2).
*   New barrel configuration: increased diameter forward of the front sight assembly (M16A2).
*   Rifle twist rate reduced from 1:14 to 1:12 to stabilize 55 grain bullet in Arctic conditions (XM16 /M16A1); reduced again to 1:7 (M16A2) to stabilize the 62 grain bullet.
*   Cleaning kit compartment added to butt stock (XM16/M16A1).
*   Buttplate thickness increased and heavily checkered, redesigned butt compartment door (M16A2).
*   Rear sling swivel removed from pin through butt stock and held with lengthened butt pad screw as in the M1 Garand and M14 (M16A1).
*   New buffer to reduce rate of fire (M16A1).
*   Full automatic firing feature added (XM16), full automatic firing feature changed to three round burst firing positions remarked from SAFE, SEMI and FIRE to SAFE, SEMI and BURST (M16A2).
*   Forward assist added to assure complete seating of bolt/carrier (XM16), shape of thumbpiece altered from "L" to round (M16A2).
*   Flash suppressor changed from open prong to closed-cage type compensator (M16A1) to closed bottom cage-type compensator (M16A2)
*   Butt stock lengthened by 0.625 inches (M16A2).
*   Pistol grip redesigned with sharper checkering and swell below middle finger position, stronger nylon used (M16A2)
*   Hand guard shape changed from triangular to round (M16A2)
*   Cartridge deflector added for left handed shooters (M16A2)
*   New rear sight adjustable by dial for elevation (M16A2).
*   New front sight post changed from round to square (M16A2).
*   New conical hand guard slip ring (M16A2).

3. M16/AR15 MILITARY AND CIVILIAN MODELS

Colt Firearms is the original manufacturer of the M16 rifle, having licensed the design from the ArmaLite Corporation. Until the early 1980s, Colt was the primary manufacturer of the M16 rifle for the American military although during the Vietnam War, other manufacturers were used. Fabrique Nationale also began to produce the M16A2 for the US military from their FNMI production facilities in Maryland in the 1980s.

Manufacturers and Models

Table 3-1 provides a list of all manufacturers of the M16/AR15 rifle and carbine, military and civilian, around the world known to the author. A brief description of each company with contact information is given in the following paragraphs.

Lower Receiver Markings

Manufacturer's and military inspection markings used on the M16/AR15 are largely confined to the receiver, both upper and lower, and the barrel. Receiver markings for military weapons were dictated by the military MIL-SPEC Mil-W-13855. Civilian markings reflect the particular manufacturing company's marketing desires and legal requirements as well as those required by the Bureau of Alcohol, Tobacco and Firearms.

Upper receiver markings are usually limited to the initials of the manufacturer or initials plus a symbol cut into the die. Lower receiver markings are invariably found stamped into the left side of the receiver on the magazine housing and the flat area above the trigger. The former provides the manufacturer's name, model number and serial number and, in the case of military rifles, the legend, "Property of U.S. Government." The latter, when used, provides the manufacturer's full name and address. Figure 3-1 provides a sample marking and Table 3-2 lists all lower receiver markings known to the author.

Upper Receiver Markings

Most upper receivers are unmarked but a few manufacturers do mold in or stamp an identifying code, usually on the right side near or ahead of the rear sight assembly. Figure 3-2 shows a Fabrique Nationale marking, and Table 3-3 lists some other upper receiver codes known to the author, by manufacturer.

Colt first offered a civilian version of the M16, the AR15, in 1965. Based on the original model supplied to the U.S. Air

Fig. 3-1. Standard style of marking found on non-military Colt-made AR15 lower receivers.

Force, it sold slowly but steadily. In the 1970s, returning Vietnam veterans who had used the M16 under the worst possible conditions and knew its capabilities as well as limitations, increased sales to the point where Colt began to fall behind in its civilian production. Others saw the market that had developed and moved to fill it. Today, there are fourteen or more manufacturers actively producing the M16A2 in a host of variations. Most manufacture their own upper and

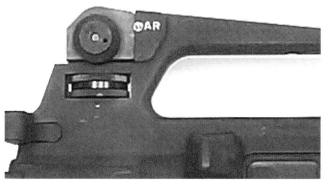

Fig. 3-2. Upper receiver marking found on FN-made in America upper receivers.

lower receivers. In addition to the manufacturers, there are innumerable suppliers of parts. Some actually manufacture the parts they sell, but most resell parts purchased from suppliers or from the military surplus market.

Table 3-1 M16/AR15 List of Models		AR-10(T) Carbine	.308 caliber, 1:11.25 twist, 16 inch barrel, floating hand guard, standard trigger, flat top upper, detachable carry handle and rear sight, compensator

Table 3-1 M16/AR15 List of Models	
American Spirit Arms Corporation	
ASA24" Bull Barrel	Semiautomatic, forged lower receiver, 1:8 twist bull barrel, flat top, free floated hand guard, A2 stock configuration
ASA 24" Bull Barrel A2	Semiautomatic, forged lower receiver, 1:8 twist bull barrel, free floated hand guard, fully adjustable rear sight, A2 stock configuration
ASA 16" Invader	Semiautomatic, forged lower receiver, 16 inch barrel, 1:8 or 1:9 twist, bull barrel, free floated hand guard, fully adjustable rear sight, A2 stock configuration
ASA 20"	Semiautomatic, forged lower receiver, 1:9 twist, 20 inch Wilson barrel, fully adjustable rear sight, A2 stock configuration
ASA 16" C.A.R	Semiautomatic, forged lower receiver, 1:9 twist 16 inch Wilson barrel, fully adjustable rear sight, non-collapsible stock
Armalite, Inc.	
M15A4(T)	.223 caliber, semiautomatic, heavy 1:8 twist, 24 inch barrel, flat top upper receiver, detachable carry handle, rear sight and front sight mount, floating hand guard, match trigger, no compensator
M15A4(T) Carbine	223 caliber, semiautomatic, 1:9 twist, 16 inch barrel, flat top upper receiver, detachable carry handle, rear sight and front sight mount, floating hand guard, match trigger, no compensator
M15A2	223 caliber, semiautomatic, heavy 1:9 twist, 20 inch barrel, A2 upper receiver, no compensator
M15A2 Carbine	223 caliber, semiautomatic, heavy 1:9 twist, 16 inch barrel, A2 upper receiver, no compensator
M15A4 Special Purpose Rifle	223 caliber, semiautomatic, heavy (HBAR-style) 1:9 twist, 20 inch barrel, flat top upper receiver, detachable carry handle and rear sight, compensator
M15A4 Carbine	223 caliber, semiautomatic, heavy (HBAR-Style) 1:9 twist, 16 inch barrel, flat top upper receiver, detachable carry handle and rear sight, compensator
M15A2 National Match	223 caliber, semiautomatic, National Match sleeved, 1:8 twist, 20 inch barrel, A2 upper receiver, no compensator
AR-10(T)	.308 caliber, heavy 1:11.25 twist, 24 inch barrel, floating hand guard, match trigger, flat top upper, detachable carry handle and rear sight, no compensator
AR-10(T) Carbine	.308 caliber, 1:11.25 twist, 16 inch barrel, floating hand guard, standard trigger, flat top upper, detachable carry handle and rear sight, compensator
AR-10A2	.308 caliber, heavy (HRAR-style) 1:12 twist, 20 inch barrel, standard trigger, A2 upper receiver, compensator
AR-10A2 Carbine	.308 caliber, heavy 1:12 twist, 20 inch barrel, standard trigger, flat top upper, detachable carry handle and rear sight, compensator
AR-10A2	.308 caliber, heavy (HRAR-style) 1:12 twist, 20 inch barrel, standard trigger, A2 upper receiver, compensator
AR-10A2 Carbine	.308 caliber, heavy 1:12 twist, 20 inch barrel, standard trigger, flat top upper, detachable carry handle and rear sight, compensator
AR-10A4 Special Purpose Rifle	.308 caliber, heavy 1:12 twist, 20 inch barrel, standard trigger, flat top upper, detachable carry handle and rear sight, compensator
AR-10A4 Carbine	.308 caliber, heavy 1:12 twist, 16 inch barrel, standard trigger, flat top upper, detachable carry handle and rear sight, compensator
Century International Arms	
C-15	223 caliber, semiautomatic, 1:12 twist, 20 inch barrel, A1 configuration built of surplus XM16 and M16A1part with Smith compensators and original Colt upper receivers and Olympic Arms lower receivers. Less than 2,000 in 1998
Colt Firearms	
Model 231 Port Firing Weapon	Select fire, no rear or front sight, no butt stock, round hand guard, 30 round magazine, no forward assist
Model 601 (AR15 Rifle)	Semiautomatic only, rear sight adjustable for windage only, 20 inch barrel, 6 groove, R.H. 1:12 rifling, no forward assist
Model 602 (AR15 Rifle)	Semiautomatic only, rear sight adjustable for windage only, 20 inch barrel, 6 groove, R.H. 1:12 rifling, no forward assist
Model 603 (M16A1 Rifle)	Select fire, rear sight adjustable for windage only, 20 inch barrel, 6 groove R.H. 1:12 rifling, with forward assist
Model 604 (M16 Rifle)	Select fire, rear sight adjustable for windage only, 20 inch barrel, 6 groove R.H. 1:12 rifling, no forward assist
Model 609 (XM177E1 Submachine Gun)	Select fire, rear sight adjustable for windage only, 10 inch barrel, 6 groove R.H. 1:12 rifling, with forward assist, 5.56 NATO

Model	Description	Model	Description
Model 610 (XM177 Submachine Gun)	Select fire, rear sight adjustable for windage only, 10 inch barrel, 6 groove R.H. 1:12 rifling, no forward assist, 5.56 NATO (US Air Force)	Model 6520 (AR1502 Government Carbine)	Semiautomatic, A2 receiver, A2 adjustable rear sight, 16.1 inch barrel, 6 groove RH 1:7 rifling, forward assist, collapsible butt stock, overall length 35 inches, butt stock extended, 32 inches, closed, chromeplated bore and chamber
Model 616 (Heavy Barrel Squad Automatic MG)	Select fire, rear sight adjustable for windage only, 20 inch heavy barrel, 6 groove, R.H. 1:12 rifling, no forward assist, attached heavy bipod, M16A1 configuration	Model 6530 (AR15 Government Carbine)	Semiautomatic, A2 receiver, A2 adjustable rear sight, 16.1 inch barrel, 6 groove RH 1:7 rifling, forward assist, fixed butt stock, overall length 35 inches, chromeplated bore and chamber
Model M621 (Heavy Barrel Squad Automatic MG)	Select fire, rear sight adjustable for windage only, 20 inch heavy barrel, 6 groove, R.H. 1:12 rifling, with forward assist, attached heavy bipod, M16A1 configuration	Model MT6530 Match Target Lightweight	Semiautomatic, A2 receiver, A2 adjustable rear sight, 16 inch barrel, 6 groove RH 1:7 rifling, forward assist, fixed butt stock, overall length 35 inches
Model 629 (M16A1 Submachine Gun)	Select fire, rear sight adjustable for windage only, 11.5 inch barrel, 6 groove R.H. 1:12 rifling, with forward assist, 5.56 NATO (US Air Force)	Model MT6551 Match Target	Semiautomatic, A2 receiver, A2 adjustable rear sight, 20 inch barrel, 6 groove RH 1:7 rifling, forward assist, fixed butt stock, overall length 39 inches
Model 630 (M16A1 Sub Machine Gun)	Select fire, rear sight adjustable for windage only, 11.5 inch barrel, 6 groove R.H. 1:12 rifling, with forward assist, 5.56 NATO (US Air Force)	Model MT6601 Target HBAR Rifle	Semiautomatic, A2 receiver, A2 adjustable rear sight, 20 inch HBAR heavy barrel, 6 groove RH 1:7 rifling, forward assist, fixed butt stock, overall length 39 inches
Model 633 Submachine Gun	Select fire, rear sight adjustable for windage only, 5.6 lbs empty, 9 inch barrel, 6 groove R.H. 1:12 rifling, 9 mm caliber	MT6700 Match Target Competition HBAR Rifle	Semiautomatic, flat top receiver, A2 adjustable rear sight, 20 inch heavy barrel, 6 groove RH 1:9 rifling, forward assist, fixed butt stock, overall length 39 inches, removable carry handle
Model 634 Submachine Gun	Semiautomatic only, A1 rear sight adjustable for windage only, 5.75 lbs empty, 10 inch barrel, 6 groove R.H. 1:10 rifling, 9 mm caliber, chromeplated bore and chamber	Model 6721 (AR15-A3 Tactical Carbine)	Semiautomatic, flat top receiver, A2 adjustable rear sight, 16.1 inch barrel, 6 groove RH 1:7 rifling, forward assist, collapsible butt stock, overall length 35 inches, butt stock extended, 32 inches, closed, chromeplated bore and chamber
Model 635 Submachine Gun	Select fire, rear sight A1 rear sight adjustable for windage only, 5.75 lbs empty, 10 inch barrel, 6 groove R.H. 1:10 rifling, 9 mm caliber, chromeplated bore and chamber	Model 6724 Colt's Accurized Rifle	Semiautomatic only, flat top receiver, telescopic sight and rings, 24 inch stainless heavy barrel, free floated hand guards, 43 inches overall, 6 groove, RH 1:9 rifling, 11 degree crown
Model 639 Submachine Gun	Three round burst, A1 rear sight adjustable for windage only, 5.75 lbs empty, 10 inch barrel, 6 groove R.H. 1:10 rifling, 9 mm caliber, chromeplated bore and chamber	Model 6731 Match Target Competition II HBAR Rifle	Semiautomatic, flat top receiver, A2 adjustable rear sight, 20 inch heavy barrel, 6 groove RH 1:9 rifling, forward assist, fixed butt stock, overall length 39 inches, removable carry handle
Model 6450 AR-15 Carbine	Semiautomatic only, A2 rear sight adjustable for elevation and windage, 16.1 inc barrel, collapsible butt stock, 35 inches overall extended, 32 inches closed, 6 groove, RH 1:10, 9 mm	Model 6920 (Law Enforcement Carbine)	Semiautomatic, flat top receiver, A2 adjustable rear sight, 16.1 inch barrel cut for M203 grenade launcher, 6 groove RH 1:7 rifling, forward assist, collapsible butt stock, overall length 34.6 inches, butt stock extended, 30.4 inches, closed, chromeplated bore and chamber
Model 649 (Submachine Gun)	Select fire, rear sight adjustable for windage only, 9.5 inch barrel, 6 groove R.H. 1:12 rifling, with forward assist, 5.56 NATO (US Air Force)	Model 6921 M4 LE	Semiautomatic, flat top receiver, A2 adjustable rear sight, 16.1 inch barrel cut for M203 grenade launcher, 6 groove RH 1:7 rifling, forward assist, collapsible butt stock, overall length 33 inches, butt stock extended, 29.8 inches, closed, chromeplated bore and chamber
Model 651 (M16A1 Carbine)	Select fire, rear sight adjustable for windage only, 14.5 inch barrel, 6 groove R.H. 1:12 rifling, with forward assist		
Model 652 (M16A1 Carbine)	Select fire, A2 rear sight, 14.5 inch barrel, 6 groove R.H. 1:12 rifling, no forward assist , 6 groove R.H. 1:12 rifling, with forward assist, collapsible butt stock		
Model 653 (M16A1 Carbine)	Select fire, rear sight adjustable for windage only, 14.5 inch barrel, 6 groove R.H. 1:12 rifling, with forward assist, collapsible butt stock		

Colt Model 701 (M16A2 Rifle)	Select fire, A2 adjustable rear sight, heavy contour barrel, 7.5 lbs empty, 39.63 inches overall, 20 inch barrel, 6 groove, R.H. 1:7 rifling, chromeplated bore and chamber	Colt Model 729 (M16A2 Carbine)	Three round burst, extendable butt stock, rear sight adjustable for windage only, 5.6 lbs empty, 33 inches overall (stock extended), 29.8 inches overall, (stock retracted), 14.5 inch barrel, 6 groove, R.H. 1:7 rifling, barrel groove for grenade launcher
Colt Model 702 (M16A2 Rifle)	Select fire, A2 adjustable rear sight, heavy contour barrel, 7.5 lbs empty, 39.63 inches overall, 20 inch barrel, 6 groove, R.H. 1:7 rifling	Colt Model 733 (M16A1 Commando)	Select fire, extendable butt stock, A2 adjustable rear sight, 5.38 lbs empty, 30 inches overall (stock extended), 26.8 inches overall (stock retracted), 11.5 inch barrel, 6 groove, R.H. 1:7 rifling, chromeplated bore and chamber
M16A2 (Colt Model 703) (M16A2 Rifle)	Select fire, A2 adjustable rear sight, light contour barrel, 7.24 lbs empty, 39.63 inches overall, 20 inch barrel, 6 groove, R.H. 1:7 rifling	Colt Model 735 (M16A2 Commando)	Three round burst, extendable butt stock, A2 adjustable rear sight, 5.38 lbs empty, 30 inches overall (stock extended), 26.8 inches overall (stock retracted), 11.5 inch barrel, 6 groove, R.H. 1:7 rifling, chromeplated bore and chamber
Colt Model 705 (M16A2 Rifle)	Three round burst, A2 adjustable rear sight, heavy contour barrel, 7.5 lbs empty, 39.63 inches overall, 20 inch barrel, 6 groove, R.H. 1:7 rifling, chromeplated bore and chamber	Colt Model 741 (M16A2 HBAR Rifle)	Select fire, heavy barrel, fully adjustable rear sight, heavy bipod, select fire, 10.5 lbs empty, 39.63 inches overall, 20 inch barrel, 6 groove, R.H. 1:7 rifling. Developed as squad automatic weapon
Colt Model 707 (M16A2 Rifle)	Three round burst, A2 adjustable rear sight, heavy contour barrel, 7.5 lbs empty, 39.63 inches overall, 20 inch barrel, 6 groove, R.H. 1:7 rifling	Colt Model 742 (M16A2 HBAR Rifle)	Select fire, heavy barrel, fully adjustable rear sight, without heavy bipod, select fire, 10.5 lbs empty, 39.63 inches overall, 20 inch barrel, 6 groove, R.H. 1:7 rifling
Colt Model 711 (M16A1 Rifle)	Select fire, rear sight adjustable only for windage, light contour barrel, 7.5 lbs empty, 39.63 inches overall, 20 inch barrel, 6 groove, R.H. 1:12 rifling	Colt Model 745 (M16A2 HBAR Rifle)	Three round burst, fully adjustable rear sight, with heavy bipod, select fire, 10.5 lbs empty, 39.63 inches overall, 20 inch barrel, 6 groove, R.H. 1:7 rifling. Developed as squad automatic weapon. Sold without bipod and select fire feature as "H-BAR" semiautomatic sporting rifle
Colt Model 713 (M16A2 Rifle)	Three round burst, rear sight adjustable only for windage, light contour barrel, 7.5 lbs empty, 39.63 inches overall, 20 inch barrel, 6 groove, R.H. 1:7 rifling		
Colt Model 715 (M16A2 Rifle)	Select fire, rear sight adjustable for windage only, heavy contour barrel, 7.34 lbs empty, 39.63 inches overall, 20 inch barrel, 6 groove, R.H. 1:7 rifling	Colt Model 746 (M16A2 HBAR Rifle)	Three round burst, heavy barrel, fully adjustable rear sight, heavy bipod, select fire, 10.5 lbs empty, 39.63 inches overall, 20 inch barrel, 6 groove, R.H. 1:7 rifling. Developed as squad automatic weapon
Colt Model 719 (M16A2 Rifle)	Three round burst, rear sight adjustable only for windage, light contour barrel, 7.5 lbs empty, 39.63 inches overall, 20 inch barrel, 6 groove, R.H. 1:7 rifling		
Colt Model 723 (M16A1 Carbine)	Select fire, extendable butt stock, rear sight adjustable for windage only, 5.6 lbs empty, 33 inches overall (stock extended), 29.8 inches overall, (stock retracted), 14.5 inch barrel, 6 groove, R.H. 1:7 rifling	Colt Model 777 (M16A4 Carbine)	Select fire, collapsible butt stock, 14.5 inch barrel, A2 adjustable rear sight, 5.65 lbs empty, 33 inches overall (stock extended) or 29.8 (stock retracted), 6 groove RH 1:7 rifling, equipped for M203 grenade launcher, chromeplated bore and chamber
Colt Model 725 (M16A2 Carbine)	Three round burst, extendable butt stock, rear sight adjustable for windage only, 5.6 lbs empty, 33 inches overall (stock extended), 29.8 inches overall, (stock retracted), 14.5 inch barrel, 6 groove, R.H. 1:7 rifling	Colt Model 779 (M16A4 Carbine)	Three round burst, collapsible butt stock, 14.5 inch barrel, A2 adjustable rear sight, 5.65 lbs empty, 33 inches overall (stock extended) or 29.8 (stock retracted), 6 groove RH 1:7 rifling, equipped for M203 grenade launcher, chromeplated bore and chamber
Colt Model 727 (M16A2 Carbine)	Select fire, extendable butt stock, rear sight adjustable for windage only, 5.6 lbs empty, 33 inches overall (stock extended), 29.8 inches overall, (stock retracted), 14.5 inch barrel, 6 groove, R.H. 1:7 rifling, barrel groove for grenade launcher		
Colt Model 728 (M16A2 Carbine)	Select fire, extendable butt stock, rear sight adjustable for windage only, 5.6 lbs empty, 33 inches overall (stock extended), 29.8 inches overall, (stock retracted), 14.5 inch barrel, 6 groove, R.H. 1:7 rifling, barrel groove for grenade launcher	Colt Model (M16A2 HBAR Rifle)	Semiautomatic, fully adjustable rear sight, without heavy bipod, select fire, 10.5 lbs empty, 39.63 inches overall, 20 inch barrel, 6 groove, R.H. 1:7 rifling as "H-BAR" semiautomatic sporting rifle

Colt Model 901 (M16A3 Rifle)	Select fire, removable carry handle, heavy contour barrel, 7.5 lbs empty, 39.63 inches overall, 20 inch barrel, 6 groove, R.H. 1:7 rifling, chromeplated bore and chamber
Colt Model 905 (M16A3 Rifle)	Three round burst, A2 adjustable rear sight, heavy contour barrel, 7.5 lbs empty, 39.63 inches overall, 20 inch barrel, 6 groove, R.H. 1:7 rifling, chromeplated bore and chamber
Colt Model 927 (M16A2 Carbine)	Select fire, extendable butt stock, removable carry handle, 5.6 lbs empty, 33 inches overall (stock extended), 29.8 inches overall, (stock retracted), 14.5 inch barrel, 6 groove, R.H. 1:7 rifling, barrel groove for grenade launcher
Colt Model 933 (M16A2 Commando)	Select fire, extendable butt stock, removable carry handle, 5.38 lbs empty, 30 inches overall (stock extended), 26.8 inches overall (stock retracted), 11.5 inch barrel, 6 groove, R.H. 1:7 rifling, chromeplated bore and chamber
Colt Model 935 M16A2 Commando	Three round burst, extendable butt stock, removable carry handle, 5.38 lbs empty, 30 inches overall (stock extended), 26.8 inches overall (stock retracted), 11.5 inch barrel, 6 groove, R.H. 1:7 rifling, chromeplated bore and chamber
Colt Model 977 (M16A4 Carbine)	Select fire, extendable butt stock, removable carry handle, 5.65 lbs empty, 33 inches overall (stock extended), 29.8 inches overall, (stock retracted), 14.5 inch barrel, 6 groove, R.H. 1:7 rifling, barrel groove for grenade launcher, chromeplated bore and chamber
Colt Model 979 (M16A4 Carbine)	Three round burst, extendable butt stock, removable carry handle, 5.6 lbs empty, 33 inches overall (stock extended), 29.8 inches overall, (stock retracted), 14.5 inch barrel, 6 groove, R.H. 1:7 rifling, barrel groove for grenade launcher, chromeplated bore and chamber

Defense Procurement Manufacturing Services (DPMS)

Arctic Panther	.223 caliber, 20 inch stainless, fluted bull barrel, 1:8, 1:9 or 1:10 twist, flat top upper receiver, free-floated hand guard, no rear or front sight, no compensator, white receiver/hand guard finish
Panther Deluxe Bull Twenty-Four Special	.223 caliber, 24 inch stainless fluted bull barrel, 1:8, 1:9 or 1:10 twist, flat top upper receiver, free-floated hand guard, no rear or front sight, no compensator
Panther Classic	.223 caliber, 20 inch stainless fluted bull barrel, 1:8, 1:9 or 1:10 twist, flat top upper receiver, free-floated hand guard, A2 rear, standard front sight, no compensator
DCM Panther	.223 caliber, 20 inch stainless heavy barrel, 1:8 or 1:9 A2 upper receiver, NM rear and standard front sight, free-floated hand guard, no compensator

Leightner-Wise Rifle Company

LW15.22	.22 or .22 WMR, 20 (A2 HBAR) or 16.5 (M4) RH 1:16 barrels, semiautomatic, 10 or 25 round magazines, fixed or detachable carry handle
LW15.499	12.5 x 40 mm, 6 groove, RH 1:14, flat top receiver, free floated barrel, 7-14 round magazine capacity
LW7.82S x 24	7.82S x 24 mm, 7.5 inch lightweight barrel, telescopic stock, flat top upper, free floated barrel

Olympic Arms

Model PCR-1	Semiautomatic, stainless steel 20 inch match barrel, 1:10 rifling, flat top upper, overall 39.5 inches, no rear or front sights, 10lbs, 3 oz, free floated hand guards, no compensator, .223 caliber
Model PCR-2	Semiautomatic, stainless steel 16 inch match barrel, 1:10 rifling, A2 upper receiver, A2 rear and front sights, 8 lbs, 2 oz, free floated hand guards, no compensator. .223 caliber
Model PCR-3	Semiautomatic, stainless steel 16 inch match barrel, 1:10 rifling, flat top upper receiver, A2 rear and front sights, 8 lbs, 2 oz, free floated hand guards, no compensator, .223 caliber
Model PCR-4	Semiautomatic, 20 inch barrel, 1:10 rifling, A2 upper receiver, A2 rear and front sights, 8 lbs, 5 oz, free floated hand guards, no compensator, .223 caliber
Model PCR-6	Semiautomatic, 16 inch barrel, 1:10 rifling, A2 upper receiver, A2 rear and front sights, 7 lbs free floated hand guards, no compensator, 7.62 x 39 mm
Model PCR-7	Semiautomatic, 16 inch barrel, 1:10 rifling, A2 upper receiver, A2 rear and front sights, 7 lbs, 10 oz, free floated hand guards, compensator
Model PCR-SM	Semiautomatic, 20 inch barrel, 1:10 rifling, A2 upper receiver, A2 rear and front sights, 8 lbs, 12 oz free floated hand guards, no compensator
Model CAR-97	Semiautomatic, 16 inch barrel, 1:10 rifling, A2 upper receiver, A2 rear and front sights, 7 lbs, compensator, 34 inches overall, non-collapsible telescoping or fixed butt stock. Available in 9 mm, .40 S&W, 45 ACP
Model 0A-96	Semiautomatic, 6 inch barrel, 1:10 rifling, flat top upper receiver, 4 lbs, 3 oz., compensator, 15.75 inches overall, no butt stock pistol configuration
Model 0A-93 TG	Semiautomatic, 7.5 inch stainless steel barrel, 1:10 rifling, flat top upper receiver, 5 lbs, compensator, 18.5 inches overall, no butt stock, pistol configuration, foregrip

Model 08-98	Semiautomatic, 6 inch barrel, 1:10 rifling, flat top upper receiver, 4 lbs, compensator, 15.75 inches overall, no butt stock, pistol configuration

Parker-Hale, Ltd.

SAR-15.22	.22 rim fire caliber, semiautomatic, 39.5 inches overall, 21 inch barrel A1-style barrel, compensator, 10 round box magazine insert, blow-back operating system, A2 features other than barrel.
SAR-15.22 CAR	.22 rim fire caliber, semiautomatic, 39.5 inches overall, 16 inch A1-style barrel, compensator, collapsible stock, 10 round box magazine insert, blow-back operating system, A2 features

Professional Ordnance, Inc.

Carbon 15 (Type 97)	.223 caliber, semiautomatic, 16 inch stainless steel match barrel, carbon fiber upper and lower receivers, flat top upper, 1:9 inch rifling, 35 inches overall length, weight 3.9 lbs, no sights
Carbon 15 Pistol (Type 97)	.223 caliber, semiautomatic, 7.25 inch stainless steel match barrel, carbon fiber upper and lower receivers, flat top upper, 1:9 inch rifling, 20 inches overall length, weight 3.9 lbs, ghost ring sights
Carbon 15I (Type 20)	.223 caliber, semiautomatic, 16 inch stainless steel match barrel, carbon fiber upper and lower receivers, flat top upper, 1:9 inch rifling, 34 inches overall length, weight 3.9 lbs, no sights
Carbon 15 Pistol (Type 20)	.223 caliber, semiautomatic, 7.25 inch stainless steel match barrel, carbon fiber upper and lower receivers, flat top upper, 1:9 inch rifling, 19.5 inches overall length, weight 2.5 lbs, ghost ring sights

Rock River Arms, Inc.

CAR A2	.223 caliber, A2-type semiautomatic, 16 inch chrome-moly barrel, 1:9 rifling, national match two-stage trigger, 7 lbs, fixed stock, options: muzzle, A2 style rear sights
CAR A4 Flattop	.223, A2-type semiautomatic, flat top receiver, 16 inch chrome-moly barrel, 1:9 rifling, fixed stock, national match two-stage trigger, 7 lbs, options: carry handle, compensator, detachable front sight, Weaver gas block front sight
LE Tactical Carbine	.223, A2-type semiautomatic, flat top receiver, 16 inch chrome-moly barrel, 1:9 rifling, 7 lbs, handle, collapsible stock, side swivel mount, options: detachable front sight, national match two-stage trigger, A4 upper, Weaver gas block front sight

Standard A2	.223 caliber, A2-type semiautomatic, 20 inch chrome-moly barrel, 1:9 rifling, national match two-stage trigger, 8.2 lbs, A2 style rear sights, fixed stock, options: muzzle
Standard A4 Flat Top	.223, A2-type semiautomatic, flat top receiver, 20 inch chrome-moly barrel, 1:9 rifling, fixed stock, national match two-stage trigger, 7 lbs, options: carry handle, compensator, detachable front sight, Weaver gas block front sight
NM A2 DCM LEGAL	.223, A2-type semiautomatic, A2 receiver, 20 inch stainless steel barrel, 1:8 rifling, fixed stock, national match two-stage trigger, 9 lbs, National Match 1/4 minute windage, ½ minute elevation, heat-resistant High Temp handguards

Quality/Bushmaster Parts Company

XM15 E2S Target Rifle	Semiautomatic, 20 or 24 inch heavy chrome-lined barrel, 1:9 twist, fully adjustable rear sight, A2 stock configuration
XM15 E2S Carbine	Semiautomatic, 16 inch heavy chrome-lined barrel, 1:9 twist, fully adjustable rear sight, A2 stock configuration
XM15 E2S Dissipator Carbine	Semiautomatic, 16 inch heavy chrome-lined barrel, 1:9 twist, fully adjustable rear sight, A2 stock configuration, full length hand guards for longer sight radius
Shorty AK Carbine	Semiautomatic, 14.5 inch heavy chrome-lined barrel with AK74-style compensator permanently attached, 1:9 twist, fully adjustable rear sight, A2 stock configuration
M17S Bullpup Rifle	Semiautomatic, 21.5 match chrome-lined barrel, RH 1:9 inch twist, iron sights, Picatinny Arsenal mount
XM15 E2S V Match Rifle	Semiautomatic, 20 or 24 inch heavy chrome-lined barrel, 1:9 twist, flat top receiver, free-floated hand guard, fully adjustable rear sight, A2 stock configuration
XM15E2S V Match Commando Carbine	Semiautomatic, 16 inch heavy chrome-lined barrel, 1:9 twist, flat top receiver, free-floated hand guard, fully adjustable rear sight, A2 stock configuration
DCM Competition Rifle	Semiautomatic, 20 inch barrel extra heavy (1 inch diameter) chrome-lined barrel, fully adjustable rear sight, DCM two-stage competition trigger, free-floated hand guard, balance weights, A2 stock configuration

Wilson Combat

Urban Tactical Model	Semiautomatic, 16.25 inch fluted match grade barrel, tactical compensator
Tactical Precision Model	Semiautomatic, 18 inch fluted matc grade barrel
Tactical Carbine Model	Semiautomatic, 16.25 inch match grade M4-style barrel, tactical compensator

Table 3-2 Some M16/AR15 Markings	
Receiver, Left, Magazine Well	Receiver, Left, Above Trigger
CENTURION 15 SPORTER CAL.223 ASSEM. BY. CIA ST. ALB. V.T. CAI XXXX	REC. MFD. BY OLYMPIC ARMS OLY WA USA
(Logo) COLT ARMALITE® AR15 PATENTS PENDING CAL. 223 MODEL 01 SERIAL XXX	COLT'S PATENT FIREARMS MFG, CO. HARTFORD. CONN USA
(Logo) COLT AR15 PROPERTY OF U.S. GOVT. CAL. 223 MODEL 02 SERIAL XXX	COLT'S PATENT FIREARMS MFG, CO. HARTFORD. CONN USA
(Colt Logo) PROPERTY OF U.S. GOVT. M-16 CAL. 5.56 M.M. (Serial no)	COLT'S FIREARMS DIVISION COLT INDUSTRIES HARTFORD. CONN U.S.A.
(Colt Logo) PROPERTY OF U.S. GOVT. M-16A1 CAL. 5.56 M.M. (Serial no)	COLT'S FIREARMS DIVISION COLT INDUSTRIES HARTFORD. CONN U.S.A.
(Logo) COLT AR-15 CAL. 223 MODEL SP1 SER. SP XXXXX	COLT'S FIREARMS DIVISION COLT INDUSTRIES HARTFORD. CONN U.S.A.
(Logo) Colt MATCH TARGET™ MATCH HBAR CAL. 223 SER. CHM XXXX	COLT'S MFG. CO. INC HARTFORD. CONN — U.S.A.—
(Logo) Colt AR-15 DELTA HBAR CAL. 223 SER. XXXXX	COLT'S FIREARMS DIVISION COLT INDUSTRIES HARTFORD. CONN U.S.A.
(Logo) COLT AR-15 CAL. 223 HBAR SPORTER SER. SP XXXXX	COLT'S FIREARMS DIVISION COLT INDUSTRIES HARTFORD. CONN U.S.A.

Table 3-2, con't (Some M16/AR15 Markings	
Receiver, Left, Magazine Well	**Receiver, Left, Above Trigger**
Colt (logo) AR-15 9 MM CARBINE Cal. 9 MM-NATO SER. XXXXXXX	COLT'S FIREARMS DIVISION COLT INDUSTRIES HARTFORD. CONN U.S.A.
(Colt Logo) PROPERTY OF U.S. GOVT M-16A2 CAL. 5.56 M.M. (Serial no)	COLT'S FIREARMS DIVISION COLT INDUSTRIES HARTFORD. CONN U.S.A.
(Colt Logo) M-16A2 CAL. 5.56 M.M. (Serial no)	COLT'S FIREARMS DIVISION COLT INDUSTRIES HARTFORD. CONN U.S.A.
(Colt Logo) PROPERTY OF U.S. GOVT M-231 (Serial no)	COLT'S FIREARMS DIVISION COLT INDUSTRIES HARTFORD. CONN U.S.A.
HYDRA-MATIC DIV. G.M. CORP. U.S.A. PROPERTY OF U.S. GOVT. M16A1 CAL. 5.56 MM (Serial no.)	(None)
(H&R Logo) PROPERTY OF U.S. GOVT. M16A1 CAL. 5.56MM (Serial no.)	HARRINGTON & RICHARDSON WORCESTER .MASS U.S.A.
(Left side) MADE BY ELISCO TOOL FOR THE REPUBLIC OF THE PHILIPPINES M16A1 (Serial No.) (Right Side) MADE IN THE PHILIPPINES UNDER LICENSE FROM COLT'S, HARTFORD, CT U.S.A	(None)

Table 3-2, con't. Some M16/AR15 Markings	
Receiver, Left, Magazine Well	**Receiver, Left, Above Trigger**
(Bushmaster Logo) SER. XXXX CAL .223 - 5.56 MM MOD. XM15	B.F.I WINDHAM, ME U.S.A.
(Logo) CAL. .223 5.56 MOD. P.C.R. 99 SA XXXX	OLYMPIC ARMS OLY WA USA
S.G.W. (In Octagon and Circle) CAL. 223 5.56 MOD. CAR-AR (Alphanumeric serial no.	OLYMPIC ARMS OLY WA USA
P.W.A (in oval) MILAN. IL CAL. 5.56 MM COMMANDO (Serial no.)	(None)
BREMMER ARMS COMPANY MODEL AR 5-22 SERIAL No. CAL. .22 RIM FIRE	(None)
PARKER-HALE, LTD MODEL AR 5-22 SERIAL No. CAL. .22 RIM FIRE	(None)
Rock River Arms Cleveland, IL CAL. 5.56MM LAR-15 (Alphanumic serial no.)	(None)
PROPERTY OF U.S. GOVT. (LOGO) CAL. 5.56MM SER. XXXX	FN MFG., INC. Columbia, SC MFG. CODE 3S679
(Knights Mfg. Co. Logo) STONER RIFLE SR-25 (Ser. No.) XXXX	(none)

Table 3-3 M16/AR15 Upper Receiver Markings	
Colt	CM
Fabrique Nationale	⊕ AR or F K
American Spirit Arms	Variable Forging Code
Armalite	None
Bushmaster	Variable Forging Code or None
DMPS	None
Olympic Arms	None

As always, the buyer must be careful here; many parts available are advertised as M16 parts, or as Mil-Spec standard parts when in fact they are neither. Inspect any M16 or AR15 part you purchase for quality of machining and finish —if you can detect machining marks, reject it. Also look for burrs, rounded corners and edges when they should be square. Always get the name and address of the seller and a money-back, no-hassle guarantee.

Note: If you are replacing trigger parts, barrels or bolt assemblies, they should be fitted and installed by an expert gunsmith familiar with the M16/AR15. Keep in mind that you are dealing with chamber pressures in excess of 52,000 psi. Don't be afraid to ask for credentials.

Finally, you should also be very careful about installing "M16" military parts in your AR15. Doing so could make it a machine gun in the eyes of the law. Never install military M16 bolt or trigger parts or an M16 safety/selector switch. Federal firearms law is quite specific about what constitutes a machine gun part and the Bureau of Alcohol, Tobacco and Firearms has ruled that ownership of "machine gun parts" and a non-machine gun firearm into which they can be fitted, in itself constitutes a machine gun. While this may not always stand up in court, who wants to spend tens of thousands of dollars fighting the Federal government? They have far more resources than you do.

A Survey of AR15 Manufacturers

The manufacturers of AR15 rifles and parts listed below are known to the author to manufacture or sell quality rifles and components. The products of the companies mentioned here have all been personally examined and most have been tested on the firing range. If you purchase a rifle or component from one of these companies, you can be assured of a quality product. The companies are listed in alphabetical order.

Fig. 3-3. American Spirit Arms ASA 24" Bull Barrel Rifle. Photo courtesy of American Spirit Arms Corp.

American Spirit Arms Corporation

American Spirit produces a series of high quality match rifles on forged lower receivers. Harris or Wilson chrome-moly barrels are standard, but they will custom fit any barrel of your choice, see Figure 3-3. ASAC uses many Colt subcontractors to build parts for their rifles. ASAC rifles and parts cost slightly more than some of their competitors, but company president, Randy Luth, says that he prefers to buy the best quality he can obtain.

Mark Hanish, IPSC distinguished grand master, has designed two match rifles for American Spirit which he also uses in competition. The first rifle is fitted with iron sights and has a 16 inch bull barrel, free-floated, full-length hand guard with a front sight mounted on the barrel to gain a full sight radius.

The second rifle has a telescopic sight, a 17 inch barrel of which 16 inches is rifled and the remaining one inch mounts a combined compensator/expansion chamber. Both rifles were designed to use the same handloaded cartridge which he developed. Mark said that using the same cartridge in both rifles reduces reloading time, storage space and eliminates the possibility of firing the wrong cartridge in the heat of competition.

American Spirit Arms Corporation, 15001 N. Hayden Rd. Suite# 112, Scottsdale, AZ 85242; Voice 888-486-5487, Fax 480-483-5301; Web Site: www.gunkits.com

ArmaLite®, Inc.

This company specializes in high quality AR15-type rifles (Figure 3-4) in both .223 and .308 calibers. Two lines are produced, Eagle Arms®, which are lower cost rifles with chrome-moly barrels and the ArmaLite® brand which include higher quality parts and finish. The Eagle Arms brand, while lower in cost and somewhat lower in quality is still a fine rifle for beginners, plinkers and hunters.

Fig. 3-4. Armalite M4C Carbine with stainless steel barrel. Photo courtesy of Armalite, Inc.

The ArmaLite AR-10 is a larger AR15-type rifle designed to fire the .308 (7.62 NATO) round. The AR-10B model is similar to the AR-10 produced by the original ArmaLite Corporation in the early 1960s and is aimed at the traditionalists. Other models in this line are similar to the M16A2 configuration except for their flattop upper with the Picatinny rail mountings for front and rear sights.

The AR15-type rifles in .223 include a wide range of models as listed in Table 3-1, from match to space guns. **Note**: There is no connection beyond the name between this ArmaLite company and the original ArmaLite company headquartered in Costa Mesa, California until the early 1960s.
ArmaLite® Inc., PO Box 299, Geneseo, IL 61254; Voice 309 944-6939, Fax 309 944-6949; Email armalite@geneseo.net; Website: www.armalite.com

Century International Arms

Century International Arms is probably the largest importer of surplus arms on the North American continent. What is not so well known is they also have a very respectable manufacturing facility and over the years have rebuilt thousands of surplus rifles and parts into inexpensive, well-made firearms for the hunter, target shooter, plinker and for law enforcement. In 1998, CIA rebuilt a little less than 2,000 AR15 rifles from XM16 and M16A1

Fig. 3-5. Century International C-15 rifle for law enforcement use. Photo courtesy of Century International Arms, Inc.

parts, see Figure 3-5. With due regard for federal laws regarding automatic weapons parts, these provided very serviceable AR15-type rifles for law enforcement and civilian use. Designated the C-15, they were built on lower receivers and trigger groups supplied by Olympic Arms. Uppers and all parts were manufactured by Colt and will be a mix of XM16 and M16 assemblies. Most were sold through distributors and can be identified by the Century International Arms markings.
Century International Arms, 48 Lower Newton, St. Albans, VT 05478; Voice, 802 527-1258, FAX, 802 524-4922, Website: www.centuryarms.com

Fig. 3-6. Colt Match Target HBAR rifle. Photo courtesy of Colt's Manufacturing Co. Inc.

Colt Firearms

Colt did not design the original M16/AR15 rifle but they did license its production from ArmaLite Corporation (Costa Mesa, CA) and produce it originally for the military and civilian market. Along the way, they developed and incorporated many of the design changes to the original model that have resulted in the today's M16A2 and M16A4 variations, see Figure 3-6.

The original production model, the XM16, underwent rigorous testing by the U.S. military and was the first variation to see military service in Vietnam. Today, over 61 different variations have been, or are in, manufacture at the Colt facility for the military, and for civilian shooters alike. Many shooters and collectors stand by Colt-manufactured M16/AR15s as the standard against which all others are measured. Colt production of the M16/AR15 encompasses a wide range of variations from the standard military rifle to carbines to match rifles to space guns. Colt's latest military version of the M16 is the M4 Carbine that has a 16 inch barrel, a collapsible stock and a flattop receiver with a Picatinny Arsenal mount system that will accept a wide range of optical and electronic sighting aids.
Colt's Manufacturing Company, Inc., PO Box 1868, Hartford, CT 06144; Voice 800 962-COLT; Website: www.colt.com

Defense Procurement Manufacturing Services (DPMS)

Established in 1986, DPMS has become a major supplier of AR15-type rifles and parts, many of which they have developed themselves, see Figure 3-7. All current production rifles are built on forged lower receivers but cast and stainless steel lowers are also offered. Cryogenic tempering is offered on any barrel in their inventory. Emphasis is on building fine production tactical and match rifles for law enforcement and civilian use. In addition to completed rifles, DPMS supplies virtually all AR15 parts and accessories. Because they sell their lower receivers to licensed federal firearms licensees for

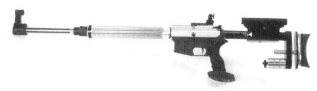

Fig. 3-7. DPMS RF-RG Race Gun. Photo courtesy of DPMS, Inc.

custom building, DPMS maintains a lower receiver serial number listing which may be consulted by anyone to determine whether or not a specific lower receiver was sold as part of complete rifle from DPMS or a lower receiver only.

DPMS, 13983 Industry Avenue, Becker, MN 55308; Voice 612 261-5600, FAX 612 261-5599; Email, dpmsinc@aol.com; Website: www.dpmsinc.com.

Knight's Manufacturing Company

The parent company, Knight's Armament Company, has been a Defense Department supplier of special weaponry since 1988. KMC builds both .223 and .308 AR15s for law enforcement and civilian shooters. The late Eugene Stoner helped design Knight's version of the .308 AR15-type rifle, christened the SR-25, see Figure 3-8. The .223 line is designated the SR-15. Both include numerous variations from rifle to carbines. Knight's also builds a .50 caliber BMG rifle, the SR-50, the last design from the great Eugene Stoner. All Knight's SR-15 and SR-25 rifles conform to the requirements of the 1994 Federal ban on "assault rifles."

Knight's Manufacturing Company, 7750 9th Street S.W., Vero Beach, FL 32968; Voice 561 778-3700, FAX 561 569-955.

The LW70.S™ pistol is built around the Government Model 1911 pistol design and is chambered for the 7.82S x 24 mm round. The LW7.82S x 24 and the LW70.S pistol are only available to military, police and government departments.

The other new system is the LW15.499™, a .50 caliber rifle for tactical situations needing heavy firepower. Using a new 12.5 x 40 mm cartridge and a 400 grain bullet, muzzle velocity is 1,600 fps. The cartridge uses a case with slightly curved walls but without a shoulder to improve feeding.

The rifle has forged upper and lower receivers, a 16 inch barrel and flat top. The hand guard is either standard or round and free floated. Magazine capacity is up to 14 rounds.

Leitner-Wise Rifle Company, 1033 North Fairfax Street, Suite 402, Alexandria VA 22314; Voice 703 837-9390, FAX 703 837-9686; Email, info@leitner-wise.com.

Les Baer Custom, Inc.

The Les Baer company is well known in the industry for their custom-built Model 1911s and accessories. They entered the AR15 market in 2000 with their "ultimate AR-.223 Rifle line, see Figure 3-9. They offer a variety of custom models for match, varmint and law enforcement needs. The varmint guns,

Figure 3-8. Knight's SR-25 Match Rifle.

Fig. 3-9. Baer.223 Match Rifle. Photograph courtesy Les Baer Custom, Inc.

Leitner-Wise Rifle Company

Leitner-Wise has produced both a .22 rimfire and .22 WMR version of the AR15 that resembles that rifle in virtually every respect except the action. Designed as a blow-back version, their LW15.22™ has been purchased in significant quantities by the U.S. military for training purposes. And that is its value to AR15 owners. Not only is the .22 version cheaper to shoot, but it allows short range and indoor range practice. L-W also produces a replacement upper receiver and barrel assembly that can be mounted on a standard AR15. Available in standard rifle and the M4 Carbine configuration.

L-W also produces two advanced AR15 rifle concepts and a new pistol based on new cartridges. The LW15.S™ Compact Assault Weapon uses the 7.82S x 24 mm with a 50 grain bullet in a short, necked case. The cartridge delivers low recoil with a flat trajectory to 200 yards at 2,400 fps. Available in a tactical carbine with a 7.5 inch barrel, this light weight weapon has forged upper and lower receivers and a telescoping stock, making it compatible in size and weight to existing submachine guns but packing far more punch.

for instance, are guaranteed to shoot 1/2 minute of angle. The company manufactures the critical AR15 parts to their own standard including bolts and bolt carriers, barrel extensions, extractors and titanium firing pins. All rifles are equipped with Jewell two-stage triggers. Upper and lower receivers are machined from 7075 T6 aluminum forgings. Matched uppers and lowers machined in special fixtures are also available. Uppers are available only in the flattop configuration with and without both forward assist and ejection port cover. A range of accessories are available including a newly designed pistol grip, free-floated handguard, new bipod, precision manufactured scope rings, stainless steel match barrels and an M4 or full-length 4-position free-floated handguard with the Picatinny Rail System.

Les Baer Custom, Inc., 29601 34th Ave, Hillsdale, IL 61257; Voice 309 658-2716; FAX 309 658-2610; Email lesbaer@netexpress.net; Website, www.lesbaer.com.

Parker-Hale, Ltd.

The well-known British firm of Parker-Hale introduced a very fine .22 caliber blow-back version of the M16/AR15 at the

Fig 3-10. Parker-Hale .22 AR15.

Fig. 3-11. Rock River Arms CAR A2.

1999 Shot Show, see Figure 3-10. A near copy of the original, it employs a blow-back rather than a gas-actuated operating system. Available in a full-length rifle and carbine model with a collapsible stock, you really have to look hard to determine that it is not a fully functioning AR15 — one point of identification is the combination of features, an A1-style barrel and a cosmetic, non-functioning forward assist plunger. It looks the same, field-strips the same and weighs the same. The rifle comes complete with a 10 round box magazine insert that fits inside a real M16/AR15 magazine, a barrel length of 21.5 inches (rifle) and 16 inches (carbine) and fully functioning, fully adjustable A2-style front and rear sights. The resemblance to the real thing is uncanny.

The Parker-Hale SAR-15.22 and the SAR 15.22 CAR were designed and built in Great Britain as British citizens are not trusted by the government to own any rifle larger than .22 caliber that will hold more than two cartridges. Any rifle in .22 caliber however is not plagued with such restrictions. The first 200-300 rifles and carbines sold carried the Bremmer Arms Corporation name, but later production was stamped Parker-Hale. Parker-Hale is a division of Bremmer. Unfortunately, at the time this was being written, Parker-Hale had no plans to introduce the rifle or carbine into the United States.

Parker-Hale, Ltd, Golden Hillock Road, Birmingham B11 2PZ, England; Voice 44 121 766 6996, FAX 44 121 772-0129.

Rock River Arms, Inc.

Better known for their fine line of National Match quality Government Model 1911 pistols, Rock River Arms entered the AR15 civilian market in 2000, introducing their rifles and carbines at the Shot Show that year, see Figure 3-11. Rock River Arms is known for attention to detail and the quality of

their products and though there was no opportunity to test their rifles before press time, an examination suggests that it has been carried over into the rifles. All rifles and carbines introduced to date are standard configuration rifles set up for match shooting. All have forged upper and lower receivers, two-stage national match quality triggers and chrome-moly barrels. Only the tactical carbine, limited to law enforcement sales, is equipped with a compensator. Also available are barreled upper receivers, upper receiver parts and bolt assemblies and parts.

Rock River Arms, Inc., 101 Noble Street, Cleveland, IL 61241; Voice 309 792-5780, FAX 309 792-5781; Email, rockriverarms@revealed.net; Website: www.rockriverarms.com

Olympic Arms

Located in Olympia, Washington, they are one of the largest manufacturers of AR15-type rifles. Their line is extensive and the quality uniformly excellent. Models range from carbines to space guns and include a line of AR15-derived pistols and other accessories. Olympic also manufactures a line of fine bolt action rifles and 1911 Government Model-style pistols. Their AR15 line includes a wide range of models. All barrels are manufactured by Olympic from either 4140 chrome-molydenum steel or 416 stainless steel and rifled by either the button or broach cutting methods. All barrels are air-gauged to ensure that they meet specifications. Also offered are a full line of accessories, tools and parts.

Fig. 3-12. Olympic Arms Model UM-1 Ultramatch.

Olympic Arms, Inc., 620-626 Old Pacific Highway SE, Olympia, WA 98513; Voice, 360 459-7940, FAX 360 491-3447; Website: www.olyarms.com.

Professional Ordnance

This company builds unique AR15-type rifles (Figure 3-12) with lightweight, carbon-composite upper and lower receivers, stocks and grips and fits them with stainless steel match barrels and a hard chromed bolt and carrier. As a result, they have achieved weights of 3.9 pounds for their full length rifles and their pistols weigh between 40 and 48 ounces. A line of accessories is also available.

Professional Ordnance, Inc., 1070 Metric Drive, Lake Havasu City, AZ 86403; Voice 520 505-2420, FAX 520 505-2141; Email, dlockett@professional-ordnance.com; Website, www.ProOrd.com.

Fig 3-12. The Professional Orndance C15-R97 carbine.

Quality/Bushmaster Firearms

Bushmaster is the division that manufactures AR15-type rifles and parts. Probably more AR-15 rifles are custom-built on Bushmaster lower receivers than those of any other company, including Colt, see Figure 3-13. Bushmaster rifles and lower receivers are seen at virtually every match and shooting range in the country. Lowers are made of 7075 T6 Aluminum alloy

Fig. 3-13. Quality/Bushmaster M4A3 PB

forgings and anodized to a hard military grey finish. Bushmaster provides a wide range of models from carbines to standard rifles to space guns. They also offer a full list of components and accessories.

Quality/Bushmaster Firearms, 999 Roosevelt Trail, Windham, NE 04062; Voice 800 883-6229; FAX 207 892-8068; Website: www.bushmaster.com.

Wilson Combat®

Wilson Combat is another company better known for the fine custom-built handguns than semiautomatic rifles. They have recently entered this market with a line of three AR15-style tactical rifles and carbines aimed at the law enforcement and match shooter markets. The U(rban) T(actical)-15 is a light, semiautomatic carbine with a 15 inch barrel (plus an attached muzzle brake that brings the length to 16.25 inches). The match-grade barrel is free-floated and an accuracy of 1 minute of angle at 100 yards is guaranteed. The M-4T Tactical Carbine was designed for Law Enforcement Tactical Response Entry Teams as well as home defense. It has a 16.25 inch M-4 style

Fig. 3-14. Wilson TYP-15 Tactical Precision Rifle.

heavy barrel with muzzle brake to reduce recoil and muzzle rise. A JP trigger/hammer group provides crisp 3 to 3.5 pound trigger pull. The M-4 shown here is equipped with an optional TTS Tactical Targeting System with a low power variable scope. The TPR-15 tactical precision rifle was designed as a law enforcement sniper rifle and has an 18 inch match grade, fluted barrel and free-floated aluminum handguard. All Wilson Combat AR15-type rifles have forged and matched upper and lower receivers, premium mil-spec bolts and carriers and hard anodized finishes.

Wilson Combat®, 2234 CR 719 Berryville, AR 72616; Voice 800-955-4856 or 870-545-3618; FAX 870-545-33; Website: www.wilsoncombat.com

4. M16/AR15 – PART BY PART DESCRIPTION

RECEIVER

The receiver is divided i nto two halves, upper and lower. The upper receiver carries the barrel, rear sight, gas, bolt and hand guard assemblies, while the lower carries the action mechanism, magazine, pistol grip and butt stock assemblies, see Figure 4-1.

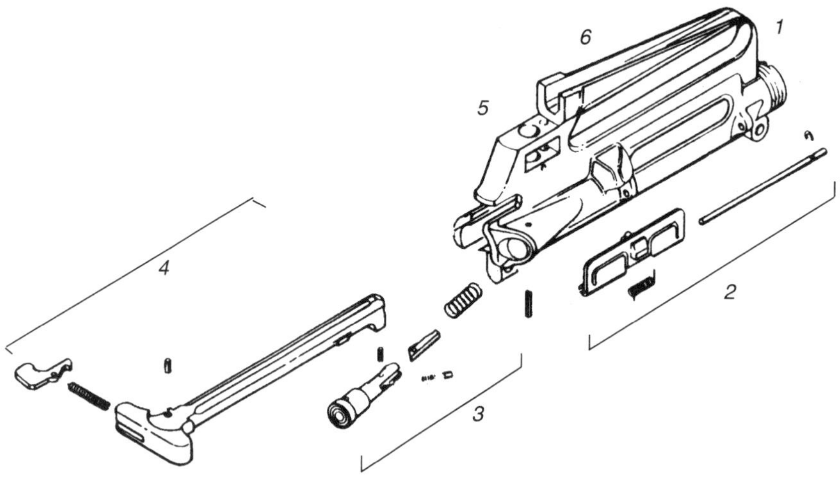

Upper Receiver

The upper receiver assembly consists of the bolt carrier assembly, forward assist assembly, charging handle, ejection port cover and the mounting system for the barrel assembly. In the standard A1 or A2 configuration, a carry handle forms the top of the lower receiver. In the flat top variation, a Picatinny rail mounting system forms the top of the upper receiver, see Figure 4-2.

The lower front of the upper receiver is machined into a square lug with a hole drilled through the center. This lug slides between two matching lugs on the lower receiver. A takedown pin is inserted through the three lugs to hold the front of the upper and lower receiver together. The takedown

Fig. 4-1. 1) M16/AR15 upper receiver, 2) ejection port assembly, 3) forward assist assembly, 4) cocking handle assembly, 5) rear sight mount, 6) carry handle.

pin serves as a pivot when the receiver is opened. In the military M16, the takedown pin is secured in place with a spring-loaded detent and is not normally removable. In the civilian AR15, the takedown pin is actually a two-piece screw which threads into one another and is removable.

A second square lug is machined at the bottom, rear of the upper receiver. It fits into a recess in the lower receiver, and the takedown pin secures the two halves of the receiver. This takedown pin is the same in both the military and civilian models.

The rear sight assembly is mounted at the end of the carry handle. The A1 rear sight is adjustable for windage only and the windage knob is mounted on the right side. In the A2 version, a square cut at the end of the carry handle provides a mount for the fully adjustable rear sight base. Below the cut is a rectangular slot that houses the elevation adjusting knob. Flat top versions are not equipped with integral rear sights.

On the right side of the upper receiver is the ejection port with its attached, spring-loaded cover. The A1 and A2 versions have a forward cartridge assist plunger and housing which enables the shooter to seat a cartridge in the breech if the bolt carrier short strokes, i.e., fails to complete its cycle and seat the cartridge. In the A2 version, ahead of the forward assist housing is a rhomboid-shaped cartridge deflector. When shooting the rifle left-handed, ejected cartridges occasionally are flung into the face of the shooter; the cartridge deflector prevents this from happening.

The gas tube penetrates the front half of the upper receiver. The barrel is a slip fit in the upper receiver and is secured by the barrel nut, which also contains the hand guard slip ring and spring. The hand guard retaining ring at the back of the assembly prevents rearward movement.

Fig. 4-2. The flat top receiver is used on the M4 Carbine and on other AR15-type rifles or carbines. A variety of optical and other sighting aids can be mounted quickly.

34

Carry Handle

A carry handle has been a feature of the Stoner-designed rifles since the second prototype of the AR-10. The carry handle does double duty by serving as a mount for a telescopic sight, night vision device or other accessories. A 0.270 by 0.390 oval mounting hole is cut into the channel of the carry handle for the mounting screw of the accessory or its base.

Cocking Handle

The cocking handle is located at the rear of the carry handle below the rear sight. It is drawn back to retract the bolt and cock the handle, see Figure 4-3. The cocking handle assembly consists of 1) the cocking handle, 2) latch, 3) latch spring and 4) latch pin.

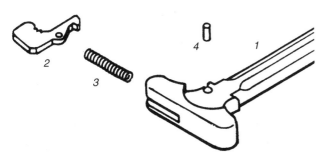

Fig. 4-3. Cocking handle.

The cocking handle is flared at the back to provide a hold for the index and middle finger. One inch behind the front end, metal is bent outward to form a tab on either side that enables the cocking handle to enter the cocking handle raceway (above the bolt tunnel) in the upper receiver. The forward length of the cocking handle is shaped into a semi-octagon, open on the bottom and closed at the front. The bolt's carrier key rests against the closed front end of the cocking handle when in battery and moves with it as the cocking handle is drawn back. The latch on the left side of the cocking handle seats in an oval detent cut into the left side of the upper receiver below the front sight. Depressing the latch allows the cocking handle to be drawn back.

To seat the cocking handle, insert it into the bolt tunnel and push forward along of the top side until the tabs drop into matching cuts in the top of the bolt tunnel and allow the cocking handle to enter the cocking handle raceway or tunnel.

Rear Sight Assembly

Two types of rear sight are used on the M16/AR15 rifle. The **Type 1** rear sight was installed first on the XM16 and on subsequent M16A1 models, as well as the following Colt A2 variations: the Models 711, 715, 723 and 730. This sight is adjustable for windage only. The **Type 2** rear sight was installed on all A2 models except those noted above and is adjustable for both elevation and windage.

No matter which rear sight is used, the basic zero is established by making adjustments to the front sight (see Adjusting the Basic Zero in Chapter 6). The A1 model was expected to be fired at ranges from 100 and 450 yards maximum. The relatively flat ballistic path produced by the 5.56 mm cartridge assured that the bullet would strike a man-sized target at those ranges when zeroed for 250 yards (battle sight).

The A2 model had a battle sight setting of 300 meters due to the heavier M855 bullet. The U.S. Army's practice was to set the sight index two clicks above the bottom, the USMC set their sight at the bottom.

Rear Sight, Windage Adjustable Only, Type 1

The original rear sight for the M16/AR15 is adjustable for windage only, see Figure 4-4. The aperture leaf is in the form of an "L" with apertures of two different diameters, 2 mm and 7 mm (0.079 inches and 0.275 inches). The large aperture in the long stroke of the "L" was intended to be used at ranges of 200 meters or less. The aperture in the short stroke of the "L" was intended to be used at ranges beyond 200 meters. Keep in mind that these are military battle and not target sights.

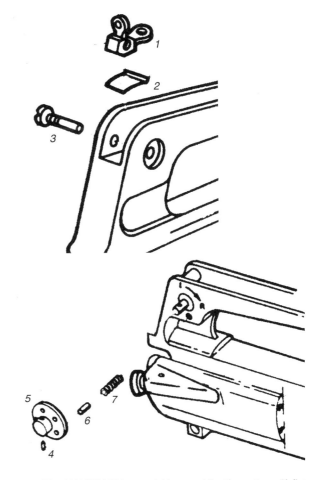

Fig. 4-4. The M16/AR15A1 rear sight assembly: 1) aperture, 2) flat spring, 3) windage screw, 4) spring pin, 5) windage drum, 6) rear sight detent and 7) helical spring.

To make it possible to adjust for windage, the aperture leaf threads onto the windage screw and moves horizontally as the windage knob is turned. A slightly curved flat spring beneath maintains pressure on the aperture leaf to hold it in the chosen position.

Rear Sight, Elevation and Windage Adjustable, Type 2

The A2 rear sight is rather more complicated than the original A1 rear sight, see Figure 4-5. It is composed of seventeen parts: 1) aperture, 2) windage screw, 3) flat spring, 4) rear sight base, 5) helical spring, 6) ball bearing, 7) ball bearing, 8) helical spring, 9) elevation knob, 10) spring pin, 11) elevation knob, 12) elevation index, 13) elevation index screw, 14) index screw, 15) ball bearing, 16) helical spring and 17) spring pin. Aperture diameters are 2 mm and 7 mm (0.079 and 0.275 inches), the same as for the A1 sight.

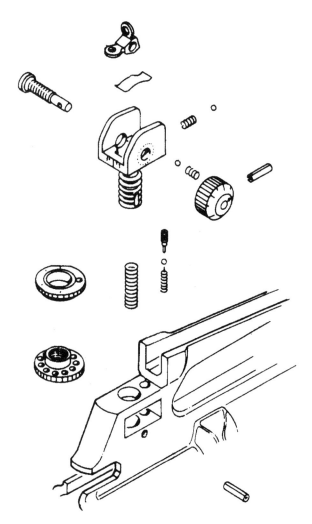

Fig. 4-5. M16/AR15A2 rear sight assembly.

The elevation knob separates into two parts; the upper (elevation knob) with a single threaded screw hole and a lower (elevation index) with twenty-four index holes. They are held together by the elevation index screw which threads into the hole in the elevation knob and slides into one of the holes in the elevation index. This allows the elevation knob assembly to be set to match the basic zero and provide the shooter with range guide markings.

Windage is adjusted on the A2 rear sight in much the same manner as with the A1, but it is easier to accomplish as a knob has been substituted for the flat disk. The sight aperture is threaded onto the windage screw and moves horizontally as the windage knob is turned. A slightly curved flat spring maintains pressure on the sight aperture to hold it in place.

The sight leaf is "L"-shaped and revolves on its axis to present one of two apertures. The long stroke of the "L" is 0.71 inches above the axis and has a 2 mm (0.079 inch) aperture; the short stroke is 0.306 above the axis and has a 7 mm (0.275 inch) aperture. The short stroke and large aperture is usually marked 0-200 and is normally used at ranges from 1 to 200 meters. The long stroke and small diameter aperture is unmarked and used for ranges from 200 to 800 meters. It can also be used when a smaller diameter aperture is desired at ranges below 200 meters.

Elevation and Windage Clicks

When either the elevation or windage knob is turned it stops at each of a series of detents, referred to as "click stops." Click stops are produced by a spring-driven ball bearing seated in the receiver under the knob assembly. On the standard military and civilian M16A2/AR15A2, elevation sight click detents drilled through the A2 elevation index provide 1 minute of angle adjustments. The 5 click detents in the right side of the A1 receiver beneath the windage knob provide 1 minute of angle windage adjustments while the 8 detents on the right side of the A2 receiver beneath the windage knob provide 1/2 minute of angle windage adjustments.

Forward Assist

The forward assist has been installed on all models since the XM16E1. It is housed in a projection on the right side of the upper receiver and is composed of the 1) plunger, 2) forward assist pawl, 3) spring pin, 4) helical spring, 5) detent, 6) helical spring and 7) spring pin.

If a dirty or slightly malformed cartridge is driven into the chamber by the bolt carrier, it may not seat and the bolt will not lock closed. It was the Army's requirement that the shooter be able to seat the cartridge rather than withdraw it and reinsert a new cartridge. When the shooter slaps the forward assist with the heel of his or her hand, the plunger strikes the pawl which engages the series of notches on the bolt carrier, forcing it far enough forward for the bolt to lock closed.

The coil spring between the pawl and plunger then forces the plunger back, pulling the pawl out of engagement with the bolt carrier. Disassemble the forward assist assembly only for cleaning. Drive out the spring pin and ease the plunger and spring out. Clean, relubricate and reassemble.

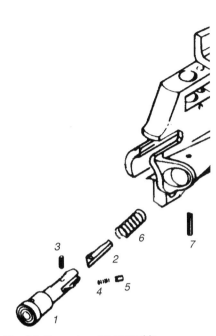

Fig. 4-6. Foward assist assembly.

port pin out to the rear, controlling the spring so that it isn't lost. If the pin binds, tap it out with a hammer and flat-faced punch of the proper size. If the forward assist housing interferes, depress the free end of the pin to slide it past. To avoid scratching the finish, apply a piece of electrician's PVC tape to the underside of the forward assist housing before removing the pin.

Check the cover and pin for bends or cracks and the pin for flat spots. Replace either or both if necessary. Position the cover and spring over the ejection port. The long leg of the spring bears against the cover and the short end against the upper receiver. Insert the ejection port pin with the recessed groove end first, tapping it into place with the punch if necessary to clear the forward assist housing. Position the retaining ring over the recessed groove and press into place. Needle nose pliers are helpful here.

Detachable Carry Handle

Several variations of the M16/AR15A2 model have a "flat top" to which a detachable carry handle can be fitted, see Figure 4-8. The "flat top" is milled into a "Picatinny Arsenal"-designed mounting surface which employes a series of parallel ridges milled at right angles to engage two or more cross bolts on the underside of the detachable carry handle. Various devices, including iron sights, telescopic scopes in low mounts, night vision devices, visible light sources and infrared vision or other heat sensing devices, can be mounted on the rifle. A side-mounted clamp on the carry handle or mounting device secures the unit on the receiver.

Ejection Port Cover

The ejection port cover is a four piece assembly consisting of: 1) ejection port cover, 2) ejection port cover spring, 3) ejection port cover pin and 4) retaining ring, see Figure 4-7. The ejection port cover flips up over the ejection port to prevent the entry of dust and dirt into the action and breech. The ejection port cover must be closed manually but is automatically opened when the cocking handle it pulled to the rear. It is good practice to close the cover when the rifle is being stored. But when on the range or when transporting the rifle, leave the cover open, the safety on, an open bolt indicator flag in the chamber and the magazine removed to indicate that the rifle is empty and on safe.

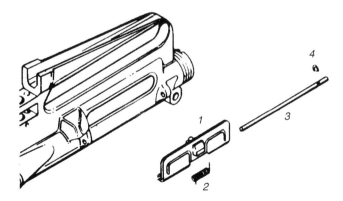

Fig. 4-7. Ejection port cover.

The ejection port cover should not be removed unless repair or replacement is needed. To do so, use two flat-bladed screw drivers to turn the retaining ring until the open ends of the pin are visible, then pry open and off. Slide the ejection

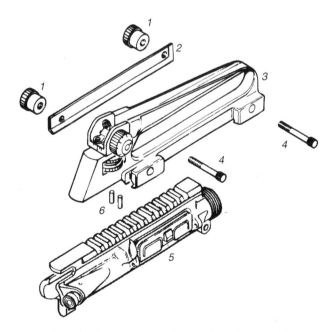

Fig. 4-8. Detachable carry handle with Picatinny Arsenal-style mount: 1) Handle nuts (2), 2) bar clamp, 3) carry handle base, 4) clamp screws (2), 5) flat top upper receiver, 6) dowel pins (2).

The rear sight assembly is mounted on the detachable carry handle and the standard 0.270 by 0.390 oval mounting hole is also cut into the trough of the carry handle.

Lower Receiver

According to the provisions of the 1968 Gun Control Law, the lower receiver is the "gun" as it contains the firing mechanism in the form of the trigger assembly. It also contains the magazine assembly, the pistol grip and the butt stock assembly including the recoil spring assembly, see Figure 4-9.

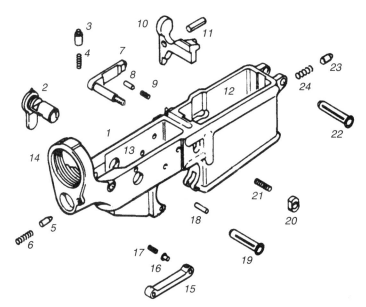

Fig. 4-9. M16/AR15 lower receiver assembly: 1) lower receiver, 2) selector, 3) buffer retainer, 4) buffer retainer spring, 5) takedown detent, 6) takedown detent spring, 7) magzine release, 8) magazine release plunger, 9) plunger spring, 10) bolt release, 11) bolt release pin , 12) magazine well, 13) trigger well, 14) receiver extension housing, 15) trigger guard, 16) trigger guard plunger, 17) plunger spring, 18) trigger guard pivot pin,19) rear receiver pin, 20) magazine release button, 21, button spring, 22) forward receiver pin, 22) takedown pin detent, 23) detent, 24) detent spring.

The lower receiver of both models is forged or cast aluminum alloy. Military models are forged as are many commercial lower receivers. A casting, if properly done and heat-treated, is neither stronger nor weaker than a properly executed and heat-treated forging.

The front of the lower receiver has two ears or lugs. The front lug fits between the two lugs on the lower receiver and is held by a two-piece takedown pin in civilian models or a captive single-piece retaining pin. A recess milled into the lower receiver at the back, just ahead of the recoil spring housing, provides room for the upper receiver's rear lug which is secured by a takedown pin. The takedown pin is held in the lower receiver by a spring-loaded detent.

At the front of the lower receiver is the magazine well. Immediately to the rear on the right side is the magazine release button housing. Below and behind are the two ears for the trigger guard which is held in place with the spring-loaded plunger at the front and a roll pin at the rear. The rear roll pin should only be removed and reinstalled using a 1/8 inch flat-faced punch. Be careful not to let the punch slip or you will deform the ears. The front pin can be depressed on the right side with the point of a cartridge to lower the trigger guard for use when wearing heavy gloves.

Receiver Extension

At the rear of the lower receiver is the threaded ring to which the receiver extension is mounted and which contains the buffer

assembly. The butt stock (fixed or collapsible) slides over the receiver extension and is secured by the receiver extension nut.

The original buffer was a hollow tube containing five "Edgewater" ring springs. The ring springs had alternating male and female ends and were shaped to act like wedges when compressed, a clever idea that worked in the laboratory and on the range but not in the field. Oil, dust and debris affected their performance, and they were replaced in December 1966 by a new buffer design from Colt. The Colt-designed buffer assembly replaced the "Edgewater ring springs" with a polyurethane "bumper" or shock absorber. The bumper impacted five sliding weights in the body that were separated by butyl rubber disks to prevent the bolt carrier from rebounding at the end of the stroke.

The new Colt buffer was three times heavier than the old and so acted to reduce the cyclic rate in full auto fire. A very fast cyclic rate had caused excessive jamming and parts breakage. Military cartridges loaded with the original Olin WC846 ball powder had been found to raise cyclic rates as high as 850 to 900 rounds per minute with the old buffer.

The buffer assembly is held in the receiver extension by the buffer retainer driven by a coil spring. When removing the buffer assembly always make certain you hold the buffer piston in place as you depress the buffer retainer. The buffer is under heavy spring pressure and could cause injury if allowed to fly loose.

The spring that drives the buffer is referred to as the "action spring." It is formed from steel wire 0.070 inches in diameter. The spring is 0.940 inches in diameter and has 38 coils. Military specifications require the spring to be between 11.75 and 13.5 inches long.

The buffer is piston-shaped with three flats around the circumference of its head (0.980 inches), and the tubular portion is 0.695 inches in diameter and 2.86 inches long. The polyurethane shock absorber is shaped like a truncated cone and pinned into the open end of the buffer.

Solid Butt Stock Receiver Extension — The solid butt stock receiver extension screws into the rear of the receiver. It is a smooth, round tube 1.25 inches in diameter and 10 inches long. The end of this receiver extension is rebated into a cap 7.25 inches in diameter flattened on two sides and drilled and tapped for the upper butt stock screw, see Figure 4-10.

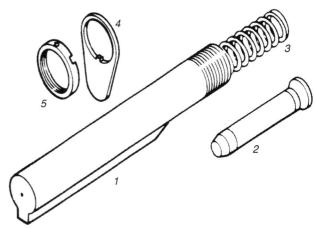

Fig. 4-11. Collapsible stock buffer assembly: 1) receiver extension tube, 2) buffer assembly, 3) action spring, 4) receiver end plate, 5) receiver extension nut.

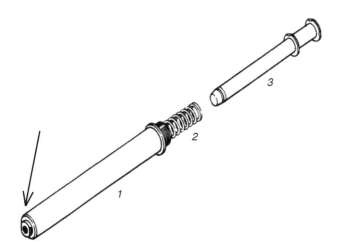

Fig. 4-10. Solid butt stock receiver extension: 1) receiver extension tube, 2) action spring and 3) buffer assembly.

The solid butt stock model uses a separate stepped spacer at the end of the receiver extension. It is 1.20 inches in diameter and 0.820 inches long. The stepped end is 0.720 inches in diameter and 0.210 inches high. A recess on the opposite end is 0.755 inches in diameter and 0.210 inches high. The butt stock screw (upper screw in butt plate) threads into a hole drilled into the end of the extension tube (arrow).

Collapsing Butt Stock Receiver Extension — Rifles or carbines equipped with the collapsing butt stock use a tube 1.45 inches in diameter and 7.25 inches long with raised channel along the bottom for the sliding butt stock catch, see Figure 4-11. A steel collar or "end plate" fits between the receiver and the receiver extension nut. The hole through its center has a key with a channel cut along the threaded end of the receiver extension tube. The plate holds the rear takedown pin spring and detent in place, provides support to the receiver extension and serves as a washer for the receiver extension nut to be torqued against. The after end of the receiver extension has a small, 0.085 inch diameter hole drilled through it to allow air to escape when the buffer is being compressed by the bolt carrier.

Note: If for any reason you remove the solid butt stock rifle receiver extension, it must be tightened when replaced to between 35 to 39 ft-lbs using a torque wrench and the combination wrench. If a carbine receiver extension, the correct torque setting is 38 to 42 ft-lbs. Since the lower receiver must be gripped in a vise is such a way that it is not deformed, this is

an operation best left to an experienced gunsmith with the proper torque wrench and vise jaw inserts.

Trigger Assembly

Three trigger assemblies have been developed for the M16/AR15. The first was semiautomatic only in function with two positions, "SAFE" and "SEMIAUTOMATIC." The second was select fire in function with three positions, "SAFE," "SEMIAUTOMATIC" and "AUTOMATIC." The third was developed for the A2 military rifle and also had three positions, "SAFE," "SEMIAUTOMATIC," and "BURST."

The **semiautomatic trigger mechanism** has eight parts: 1) trigger, 2) trigger spring, 3) hammer, 4) hammer spring, 5) disconnector, 6) disconnector spring, 7) hammer pin and 8) trigger pin, see Figure 4-12.

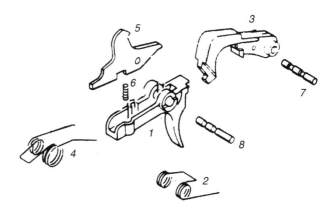

Fig. 4-12. Semiautomatic trigger assembly.

The trigger, disconnector and hammer are pinned into the receiver by and pivot on two cross pins. The same pin passes through the trigger, trigger spring and disconnector.

If the hammer is pivoted back far enough, the trigger nose — the squared forward end of the trigger — engages a slot in the bottom of the hammer and holds it in the cocked position.

When the trigger is depressed, either the trigger nose or the disconnector releases the hammer and it flies forward to strike the firing pin at the rear of the bolt. The trigger return spring forces the trigger back into its normal position when it is released by the shooter.

The rearward movement of the bolt carrier pushes the hammer back where it is once again engaged by the trigger nose and held until the trigger is again depressed.

The **full automatic trigger** mechanism has four more parts that the semiautomatic trigger. It consists of: 1) hammer, 2) hammer pin, 3) hammer spring, 4) disconnector, 5) disconnector spring, 6) trigger, 7) trigger pin, 8) trigger spring, 9) automatic sear pin, 10) automatic sear spring bushing, 11) automatic sear spring and 12) the automatic sear.

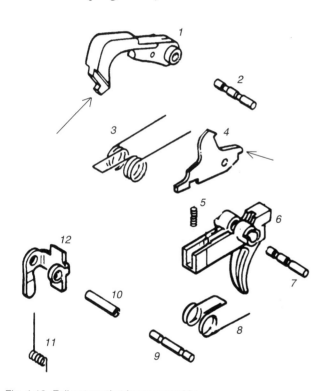

Fig. 4-13. Full automatic trigger assembly.

The full automatic trigger mechanism differs from the semiautomatic trigger mechanism in that the trigger bar is forced lower by a cam on the selector lever, thus moving the trigger nose out of possible alignment with the hammer slot. The automatic hammer has an additional "automatic sear hook" on the top *rear* of the hammer (arrow), and the automatic disconnector has a vertical nose that rises at a sharp angle (arrow), see Figure 4-13.

When the automatic mode is selected, a cam on the selector lever forces the trigger bar and disconnector down. When

the rifle is cocked, the hammer is tipped back far enough for the vertical nose on the disconnector to engage the "automatic sear hook" on the top rear of the hammer. When the trigger is pulled to the rear, the disconnector nose releases the automatic sear hook and the hammer revolves forward and strikes the firing pin. As long as the trigger is held back, the hammer will continue to be released on each cycle as both the trigger nose and disconnector nose are to low to catch the lower hammer slot or automatic sear hook.

The full automatic trigger and selector switch is found in the M16, M16A1 and A1-style carbines and AR15A1 models sold in conformance to National Firearms Act rules. It is also found in some A2 models as well, refer to Table 3-1.

The **three-round burst mechanism** adds four parts to the automatic trigger assembly: 1) *burst disconnector*, 2) *burst disconnector spring*, 3) *burst cam* and 4) *the clutch spring*, see Figure 4-14. The other parts include: 5) hammer, 6) hammer spring, 7) hammer pin, 8) semiauto disconnector, 9) disconnector spring, 10) trigger, 11) trigger pin, 12) trigger spring, 13) automatic sear, 14) automatic sear bushing, 15) automatic sear pin and 16) automatic sear spring. The hammer has an additional sear notch at the rear and an automatic sear hook. The auto sear has one stop; the burst disconnector has two hooks — one at the front offset to the right to engage the burst disconnector and a second at the rear to engage the rear hammer notch.

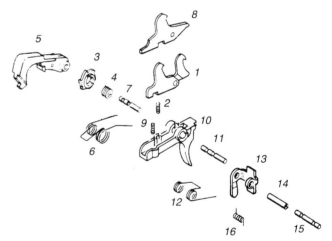

Fig. 4-14. Three-round burst trigger assembly.

How the three-round burst mechanism functions is quite simple but explaining it is not easy. When the hammer is cocked, the front hook on the burst disconnector rests in one of the two stop notches on the burst cam. The burst cam also has two pair of shallow notches opposite of one another.

When the trigger is pulled, it releases the hammer to fire the first round. As the hammer falls forward, the clutch spring releases the burst cam, but the front hook on the burst disconnector prevents the cam from turning.

As the bolt carrier moves rearward, it forces the hammer back which now allows the clutch spring to engage the burst cam and rotate it one notch counter clockwise. When the hammer reaches its full rearward position, the auto sear tips forward and engages the hammer stop at the top of the hammer. At the same time, the front hook on the burst disconnector drops into the first notch on the burst cam.

As the bolt carrier is pushed forward by the buffer assembly, the rear hook on the auto sear releases the hammer stop and it flies forward to strike the firing pin and ignite the second cartridge. This again forces the bolt carrier to the rear, moving the hammer back with it to be caught by the auto sear and the front hook on the burst disconnector to engage the second notch on the burst cam.

The cycle is repeated once more but this time the front hook on the disconnector drops into the deeper "stop" notch on the burst cam. This causes the burst disconnector to tip forward far enough for the rear hook to engage the rear hammer notch and prevent it from firing a fourth cartridge, even if the shooter holds the trigger back.

Only by releasing the trigger and allowing the hammer to rise far enough to be caught by the trigger nose does the burst cam reset itself, ready to fire three rounds again.

Trigger and Hammer Pins

Both the trigger and hammer pins are 0.17 inches in diameter and 0.90 inches long. They penetrate the walls of the lower receiver to serve as an axis for both pieces. The trigger pin has a circular slot at each end into which the legs of the hammer spring fit to hold it in place. The hammer spring legs go over the top of the trigger pin.

The hammer pin has a single circular slot in its center. The hammer has an internal spring which projects into the hammer axis hole and engages the circular slot in the hammer pin to hold it in place.

Selector Lever

The selector lever is mounted in the lower receiver in alignment with the trigger mechanism. Envision an "L" shaped object with the short side of the "L" flattened into a thumb piece and the long side formed into a cylinder. The selector lever is held in place by a spring-loaded detent and rotates to select the mode of operation: SAFE (9 o'clock) AUTO (12 o'clock) and SEMI (3 o'clock) in the M16 and SAFE (9 o'clock) and SEMI (12 o'clock) in the AR15. In the M16A2, BURST replaces AUTO.

The semiautomatic selector lever has a shallow flat (cam) milled on one side of the cylinder only that prevents the trigger bar and disconnector from being depressed far enough to catch the lower hammer slot, see Figure 4-15.

The automatic selector has a second, deeper cam that when turned into the proper position, allows the trigger bar and disconnector to be depressed far enough that neither the trigger nose will catch the lower hammer slot nor the disconnector nose will engage the automatic sear hook on the top rear of the

Fig. 4-15. Semiautomatic selector lever.

hammer, see Figure 4-16.

When turned to the SAFE position, the diameter of the selector lever immobilizes the trigger bar and prevents it from being moved to release the hammer.

The selector lever is held in position by a pointed detent driven by a coil spring. The detent rides into a vertical hole drilled into the right lower side of the receiver and the spring is captured in a hole drilled into the right side top of the pistol grip. When removing the pistol grip be careful not to lose the spring, refer to Figure 4-9, parts 5 and 6.

Trigger Guard

The M16/AR15's "winter" trigger guard can be lowered for use while wearing gloves. The right

Fig. 4-16. Automatic selector lever.

side front of the trigger guard has a spring-loaded pin that can be depressed with a bullet point, allowing the trigger guard to pivot down against the pistol grip. The after end of the trigger guard (1) is held in place with a 1/8 inch split pin (2) at the rear and a plunger (3) at the front, Figure 4-17.

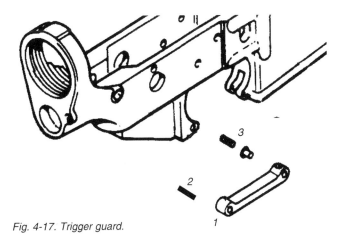

Fig. 4-17. Trigger guard.

Takedown Pin

The takedown pin is at the rear of the lower receiver. It is 1.15 inches long and 0.25 inches in diameter. The pin has a rounded, rivet head 0.375 inches in diameter. The pin penetrates both sides of the lower receiver from the right and the rear lug on the upper receiver. It is held in place by a spring-driven detent that penetrates the rear of the lower receiver under the stock ferrule. The pin has a channel milled along one side in which the detent rides. Use caution when removing the butt stock, see Figure 4-18.

Fig. 4-18. Rear takedown pin (1). The detent and spring are under the receiver end plate (2).

Magazine Release

The magazine release assembly consists of the 1) magazine button, 2) magazine button coil spring, 3) magazine release, 4) magazine release plunger and 5) plunger spring, see Figure 4-19.

Essentially, the magazine release is a bar with rectangular detent on its forward end that fits into a rectangular hole in the right side of the magazine. The release bar has a threaded tail at right angles that fits into a hole through the lower receiver at the rear of the magazine well. A coil spring fits over the tail, and the magazine button screws onto the threaded end to hold the assembly in place. Pushing in on the magazine button pushes the bar away from the left side of the receiver, withdrawing the plunger from the hole in the magazine and allowing it to drop free.

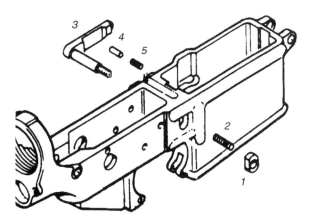

Fig. 4-19. Magazine release assembly.

The magazine release can be disassembled by using a punch to push the magazine button in as far as it will go and then unscrewing the protruding magazine catch.

Bolt Release

The bolt release consists of the 1) bolt catch, 2) bolt catch pin and 3) bolt catch spring, see Figure 4-20. The bolt release holds the bolt in the rear position when the last cartridge is fired as a warning to the shooter that the magazine is empty. It functions by allowing the magazine floor plate to rise high enough to lift the bolt release into the path of the bolt, blocking it from moving forward. The bolt release can also be activated by drawing the bolt back with a magazine in place, or when the magazine is absent, by depressing the bolt release.

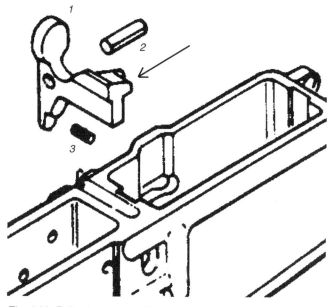

Fig. 4-20. Bolt release assembly.

The bolt release fits into a slot in the left side of the lower receiver behind the magazine well and above the magazine release bar. A spring forces the end of the bolt stop (arrow) to remain below the path of the bolt until the magazine floor plate raises it into the path of the bolt when the magazine is empty. A split pin holds the assembly in place. Be careful when removing the split pin that you do not allow the plunger and spring to escape.

Bolt Assembly

The bolt assembly consists of six major components: 1) bolt carrier, 2) key, 3) bolt, 4) bolt cam pin, 5) firing pin and 6) firing pin retaining pin, see Figure 4-21, overleaf.

Bolt Carrier

The bolt carrier for the 5.56 NATO caliber rifle and carbine has two gas relief ports on the right side, beneath the key. Behind the gas ports on the bolt carrier are a series of notches which the bolt assist engages when pushing a cartridge into the chamber. Only the very earliest XM16 bolts did not have these notches.

The key is mounted on top of the bolt carrier with two socket head screws which are staked to prevent backing out. The key is a hollow tube which captures the propellant gas from the gas tube and drives the bolt carrier to the rear.

The bolt itself is inserted into the front of the bolt carrier and is retained

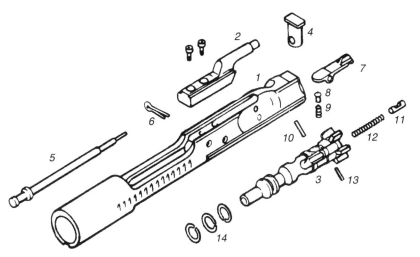

Fig. 4-21. Bolt and carrier assembly.

by the bolt cam pin. The bolt cam pin fits into a hole in the top of the bolt carrier, beneath the key. It rotates 1/2 turn to allow the bolt to lock and unlock.

The firing pin is inserted through the bolt carrier and into the bolt's firing pin tunnel. It is retained by a firing pin retaining pin which is similar to a split pin. Do not attempt to substitute a common split pin for the proper firing pin retaining pin as it may not hold.

The 9 mm NATO submachine gun bolt differs considerably as it is powered by the recoil of the cartridge and not gas pressure from the bore. Therefore, it does not have a carrier but is solid. It also lacks the bolt carrier key, bolt cam pin and has a spring-loaded firing pin and a smaller, different extractor. See Figure 4-22. The rifle bolt weighs 11 ounces; the submachine gun bolt weighs 15.9 ounces.

Fig. 4-22. 5.56 mm bolt and carrier (R), 9 mm bolt and carrier (L).

Bolt

The rifle bolt (refer to Figure 4-21) consists of ten parts: 7) extractor, 8) rubber insert or second spring, 9) extractor spring, 10) extractor pin, 11) ejector, 12) ejector spring, 13) ejector pin 14) rings (three).

The bolt head has seven locking lugs around its circumference with the eighth locking lug being supplied by the extractor. These lugs rotate into and out of matching receptacles in the receiver extension to lock or unlock the bolt. The ejec-

tor protrudes through the bolt face beneath the lug at the 12 o'clock position. The opening for the firing pin nose is centered in the bolt face. The extractor lip overlaps the bolt face at the 6 o'clock position.

Extractor

The extractor is a curved plate with a lip that fits into a channel cut for it on the right side of the bolt. The extractor spring is captured between the extractor and the bolt in a depression in the rear of the channel.

The extractor is pinned at about mid-length which allows it to pivot in and out. A short coil spring at the rear supplies pressure to keep it closed. When assembling, the flared base of the spring must be seated in the extractor and the rubber insert seated in the narrow end that fits inside the bolt. Later bolts substitute a second spring. Failing to seat the spring(s) and/or rubber insert properly may cause malfunctions

Ejector

The ejector is a steel dowel rounded at the forward end. The top of the ejector has an arc cut out for the ejector pin to hold it in place. The ejector spring is at the rear of the pin and is contained in a tunnel in the bolt.

Firing Pin

The M16/AR15 firing pin looks something like a duplex or scaffold nail. The firing pin is 3.277 inches long and may be made of chrome-moly, stainless steel or titanium. This last is a new material for AR15 firing pins. It is intended to produce a lighter and stronger firing pin that will fall faster when struck by the hammer.

The firing pin should not protrude excessively past the face of the bolt. Check with firing pin gage (Colt part #62679) whenever a new firing pin is installed.

Gas Seal Rings

The three gas seal split rings are contained in a groove cut into an expanded area along the firing pin tunnel. The rings press against the walls of the bolt tunnel just behind the gas ports to contain any gas that might escape from the breech if a cartridge or primer ruptures. This prevents the hot gases from flowing back through the bolt carrier and out and up into the shooter's face.

The gas seal rings should be checked periodically to make certain that they have not cracked, twisted or bent. If they must be replaced, it is best to do all three at the same time.

Note: Do not remove the rings (or a ring) unless you have replacements on hand. Once removed, do not reinstall the same ring. Lubricate and use gentle but steady pressure when installing. New rings will be slightly oversized and must wear in.

Key

The key is an angled tube closed at the after end and mounted on plate that attaches to the bolt carrier with two socket head screws. The key fills with hot gases bled from the bore when a cartridge is fired. The force of the gas acting on the key drives the bolt carrier back, causing the bolt to rotate along its cam and unlock from the receiver extension. When the bolt carrier returns to battery, the key slides over the gas vent in the upper receiver.

It is not a good idea to remove the key and its screws from the bolt carrier unless it has been damaged. The screws are staked in by deforming the metal of the key around the circumference of the screw heads. For this reason, do not attempt to tighten or loosen the screws.

If you do replace the key, new screws must be used. Tighten with a torque wrench to between 35 to 40 inch pounds and restake securely.

Bolt Cam Pin

The bolt cam pin has a flat, rectangular head with rounded corners and a hole through its shaft for the firing pin. The pin slides through a cam way cut into the top of the bolt carrier and passes through a hole drilled in the bolt. When the bolt carrier moves forward or back, the bolt cam pin moves in the bolt carrier cam way. Because the cam way is angled, a rotary motion is imparted to the bolt to cause the locking lugs to unlock or lock.

Firing Pin Retaining Pin

The firing pin retaining pin passes through the side wall of the

bolt to prevent the firing pin from backing out. The pin passes between two flanges on the afterend of the firing pin.

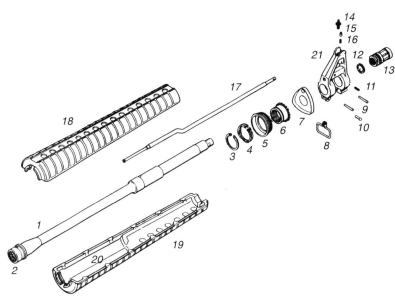

Fig. 4-23. M16/AR15 barrel assembly: 1) barrel, 2) barrel extension, 3) handguard retaining ring, 4) slip ring springs (4), 5) handguard slip ring, 6) barrel nut, 7) handguard cap, 8) sling swivel, 9) front sight taper pins, 10) swivel rivet, 11) gas tube pin, 12) compensator spacer or washer, 13) compensator, 14) front sight post, 15) front sight detent, 16) detent spring, 17) gas tube, 18) upper handguard, 19) lower handguard, 20) handguard heat shield, 21) front sight.

Barrel Assembly

The barrel assembly consists of five sub-assemblies: barrel, retaining assembly, front sight assembly, compensator, gas system and handguards, see Figure 4-23.

Barrel

The M16/AR15 barrel is made in many lengths, diameters and rifling types. Two common barrel types, the M16A1 and the AR15 Sporter II barrels are shown in Figure 4-24. Custom barrels can be and are cut in a variety of diameters and lengths as well as shapes. Those used in service rifles tend to follow the contour, size and weight pattern of military rifles, see Figure 4-25. Those used in non-service match shooting are limited only by the gunsmith's imagination and experience. See Table 4-1 and Figure 5-1 (page 67) for types and dimensions.

The barrel's after end contains the chamber and is threaded for the barrel extension. The muzzle end is threaded for the

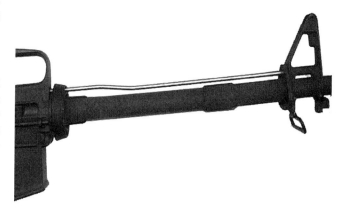

Fig. 4-24. AR15A1 sporter barrel configuration (top), AR15A2 HBAR configuration (bottom).

Fig. 4-25. M16A2 military barrel configuration.

compensator if intended for military use, or if manufactured before late 1994 as a civilian sporting rifle in the United States, see Figure 4-26. Barrels manufactured for civilian sale after late 1994 may have an unthreaded rebated end to which a muzzle extension in the form of a muzzle brake may be permanently affixed. Custom-made barrels rarely use a compensator nor are they threaded or rebated, see Figure 4-27. An alignment pin is fixed at the top dead center position 0.07 inches from the end. The ring 0.135 inches wide and 1.165 inches in diameter encircles the barrel and butts against the upper receiver wall. The alignment pin indexes the barrel in the correct vertical position. The barrel nut (described below) slides over the barrel and screws to the front of the upper receiver. It bottoms against the ring and holds the barrel, retaining ring, slip ring spring and slip ring in position.

Fig. 4-26. Military and pre-1994 barrel and compensator.

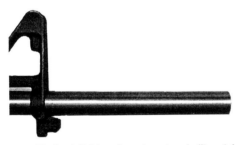
Fig. 4-27. Post-1994 and most custom-built match AR15s lack a compensator.

The barrel extension is 0.82 inches long and 1 inch in diameter. It is screws onto the barrel (160 foot-pounds) and provides the locking lugs for the bolt. The barrel extension fits over the chamber end of the barrel and has eight machined lugs into which the bolt locks when in battery, see Figure 4-28. The barrel extension penetrates the upper receiver.

Barrel Nut Assembly

The barrel slips into the front of the upper receiver and is

Table 4-1 Barrel Configurations, Lengths and Rifling Rates*	
Configuration	Light Machine Gun, heavy barrel, 20", 1:7
	A2 Heavy Barrel Rifle, squad automatic, 20", 1:7
	A2 Heavy match, straight, no reductions, 20", 1:7
	A2 HBAR, three step reduction, 20", 1:7
	A2 Service, enlarged diameter forward, 20", 1:7
	A1 Service, reduced diameter forward, 20", 1:12
	A2 Carbine, two step reduction, 16", 1:7
	A1 Carbine, reduced diameter forward, no groove for grenade launcher, 16", 1:12
	A1 Carbine, reduced diameter, groove for grenade launcher, 16", 1:12
	A2 Carbine, two step reduction, no groove for grenade launcher, 20" 1:7
	A2 Carbine, two step reduction, groove for grenade, 16", 1:7
Calibers	.223 (5.56 NATO)
* This table includes current and past Colt and U.S. military model configurations. See Table 3-1, M16/AR15, List of Models for specific models and manufacturers	

indexed by the alignment pin. The barrel is secured to the receiver with a barrel nut which threads onto the front of the upper receiver, see Figure 4-29,1.

Retaining Ring — The retaining ring is a slip or snap ring which is fitted with snap ring pliers having straight 0.045 inch tips. The ring must be compressed to fit inside the slip ring. To do so, the tips of the snap ring pliers are inserted into the holes in the retaining ring on either side or the split and squeezed together, refer to Figure 4-29, 2.

Fig. 4-28. M16/AR15 barrel extension.

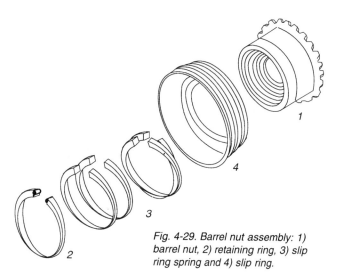

Fig. 4-29. Barrel nut assembly: 1) barrel nut, 2) retaining ring, 3) slip ring spring and 4) slip ring.

Fig. 4-30. Types of compensators used on the M16/AR15: top, early prong and bottom, closed cage types.

Slip Ring Spring — The slip ring spring is actually composed of four split rings made of spring steel. Each ring is slightly kinked so that when the ring is compressed horizontally, outward force is exerted against both the receiver face and the rim of the slip ring, refer to Figure 4-29, 3.

Slip Ring — The slip ring is shaped like a truncated cone (A1) or a cylinder (A2) with a rim around the interior of its forward end. It is large enough to hold the barrel nut, slip ring and retaining ring, refer to Figure 4-29, 4.

Assembling the Barrel to the Upper Receiver

Doing so is not difficult with the proper tools and an understanding of the process. But unless you are an experienced gunsmith, do not attempt to fit a custom barrel that has not been machined to final shape with the shoulder and indexing stud properly located. The barrel extension also should be fully machined and the barrel already headspaced.

You will need an M16/AR15 combination wrench, a torque wrench capable of exerting and measuring accurately at least 60 foot pounds and a set of barrel remover fixtures. See Appendix A, Item 34 for assembly/disassembly details.

Compensator

The compensator functions to reduce muzzle climb when the rifle is fired and also the amount of heat emitted as light at the muzzle, thus preserving the soldier's night vision. The compensator on the M16/AR15 is variously known as a muzzle brake, flash hider and flash suppressor. The compensator works by both venting gas to the side and upward to drive the muzzle down and by absorbing heat from the hot gases leaving the muzzle to reduce the amount of illumination. Original compensators for the M16/AR15 series of rifles will have flats milled on either side so that the combination wrench can be used to mount or dismount them.

The original AR15 compensator (see Figure 4-30, top) was really a flash suppressor with three prongs. The prongs

were narrower than the body of the flash suppressor. The XM16 and M16/AR15 also employed a three-pronged flash suppressor of a slightly different design. The pronged (or open) flash suppressor worked well but had a tendency to catch in vegetation and to kick up dirt when fired from the prone position.

It was replaced by the *caged* compensator installed on latter M16A1/AR15A1 models. Starting with the A2, a *closed* compensator was installed on it and subsequent models which had five narrow elongated ovals cut through the top circumference but had a closed bottom. This design reduced the amount of dust and debris kicked up by propellant gases from the muzzle when the rifle was fired from the prone position, see Figure 4-30.

The XM177 series of submachine guns and carbines were equipped with an elongated version of the cage compensator which not only reduced muzzle jump and served as a flash suppressor but also acted to reduce the excessive muzzle blast from the shortened barrel. The front end of the compensator had six elongated oval cutouts which extended around the circumference, see Figure 4-31.

Fig. 4-31. Extended compensators like those installed on the XM77 and later carbine models may also act as sound suppressors.

Numerous variations of this type of compensator produced for nonmilitary use have been observed. The reader is cautioned that the Bureau of Alcohol, Tobacco and Firearms has classified some of these elongated compensators as "sound suppressors." It is best to check with the Technical branch of the BATF before acquiring or installing one (phone 202 927-7777).

Other elongated types of compensators have been used to make short barrels legal. For instance, compensators 5 inches long have been permanently attached to 11.5 inch barrels to make them legal for civilian sale. Before purchasing a barrel shorter than the legal 16 inch minimum, make certain that the compensator not only brings it to the legal length of 16 inches but that it is permanently attached to the barrel. These types of compensators can usually be identified by the lack of flats on either side of the mount for the combination wrench. A close inspection will also reveal brazing at the barrel/compensator join with the barrel.

No matter which type of cage compensator is used, it must be installed so that the middle slot is at top dead center (TDC).

Note: It will have not escaped notice that antigun elitist politicians have fastened onto the compensator or "flash suppressor" as one characteristic of the so-called "assault rifle." One California state senator responsible for that state's 1999 Assault Rifle law believes that the flash suppressor eliminates the muzzle flash at night and is therefore an aid to criminals since the weapon cannot be seen by the police when it is fired. Since antigun elitist politicians cannot possibly seek advice from those knowledgeable about firearms, they and their brethren will probably continue in their ignorance until removed from office by the voters — as were his two predecessors responsible for the 1989 California assault rifle law.

Compensator Lock Washer

The compensator lock washer exerts pressure between the rebated end of the barrel and the compensator to prevent the latter from unscrewing. All A1 and early A2 models used a thick, split ring washer. Newer A2 civilian models use a thin washer and military A2s use a "peel" washer. The peel washer consists of a series of steel laminates. When the cage-type compensator is installed, the middle slot must be at top dead center (TDC) or within 10 degree's of TDC. To bring the compensator to this position, laminates can be "peeled" off the washer. As each laminate is 0.0002 inches thick, the angular position of the compensator will move 10 degrees clockwise for each lamination removed.

Gas System

The gas system drives the M16/AR15 rifle. Propellant gases bled from the bore flow through a port drilled in the barrel. The gases flow back through a stainless steel tube into the hollow key attached to the bolt carrier. The energy imparted by the propellant gases to the bolt carrier via the key drives the bolt carrier backward, causing the bolt to unlock from the lugs in the barrel extension. The bolt carrier continues back in its track in the upper receiver, cocking the hammer as it goes, until the spring-loaded buffer overcomes its rearward motion and drives it forward again, stripping a new round from the magazine and loading it into the chamber. The final step of the forward motion causes the bolt to turn as it moves along the cam way and lock into the barrel extension again.

The gas system consists of the 1) barrel port, 2) front sight base and 3) gas tube, see Figure 4-32.

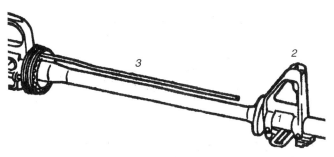

Fig. 4-32. M16/AR15 gas system assembly, shown separated.

The diameter of the barrel's gas port is critical to proper functioning. The gas port in the standard configuration 20 inch rifle barrel is 0.82 inches in diameter. In the 16 inch barreled carbine it is 0.62 inches in diameter and 0.92 inches in diameter in the 11 inch Commando model.

The gas system includes the front sight assembly and gas tube. The rear front sight assembly is drilled to provide a vent for the propellant gases leaving the barrel through the port. The gas tube fits into the rear of the front sight assembly and leads back through a hole in the front wall of the upper receiver. It projects 1.0 inch into the upper receiver. When the bolt is in battery, the hollow key fits over the gas tube projection.

Front Sight Assembly

The front sight assembly is mounted on a triangular tower through which the barrel passes, refer to Figure 4-32. The front sight mount also serves as channel for propellant gases vented from the barrel. The muzzle end of the gas tube fits into a hole drilled into the rear lower section (above the barrel) of the front sight. The front sight post screws into a threaded socket at the top of the front sight assembly. The front sight post is mounted on a disk with notches cut around its perimeter. A spring loaded detent beneath the front sight post keeps it from moving under recoil.

The front sight post used with the XM16 and M16A1/AR15A1 is round with a flat top. To improve visibility, the front sight post installed on the M16A2/AR15A2 has four flat sides. Turning the latter sight one click at a time moves the front post up or down 1/4 minute of angle.

To prevent the front sight from moving once the rifle is zeroed, you can coat the front sight post threads with "Loctite." Or you can have a gunsmith drill and tap a hole beneath the front sight post and insert a set screw. The set screw is turned in until it presses against the bottom of the front sight post. Using the set screw rather than Loctite allows you to make changes to the front sight post easily. With Loctite, you have to heat the front post to break the bond and remove it completely to re-coat it before reinstalling and readjusting.

Stock Assembly

The stock assembly consists of the following subassemblies: 1) butt stock, 2) butt plate, 2) hand guards and 3) pistol grip. Three types of hand guard were used and three styles of butt stocks. All are made from reinforced polymers. The butt stocks are foam-filled for reinforcement.

Butt Stocks

Three types of butt stocks are used, two solid and one sliding. which are used primarily on carbines.

Solid Butt stocks — The first type of buttstock installed on the XM16 and M16A1/AR15A1 rifles were 9.5 inches long. The second type installed on the M16A2/AR15A2 are 10.1 inches long. Both are 5.20 inches high at the butt plate, see Figure 4-33

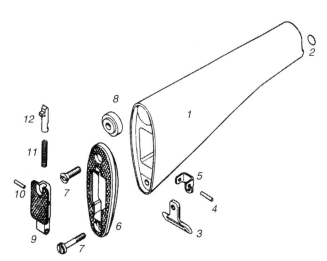

Fig. 4-33. M16/AR15 fixed butt stock: 1) butt stock, 2) O-ring, 3) sling swivel, 4) hinge pin, 5) hinge, 6) butt plate, 7) butt plate screws (2), 8) butt plate spacer, 9) butt plate door, 10) retaining pin, 11) plunger spring and 12) plunger.

The rifle butt has two holes. The upper hole is 1.13 inches in diameter and slides over the receiver extension tube. The lower hole is 1.1 wide x 1.85 inches high and 7/8 inches deep and is used to store the rifle cleaning kit. Competition shooters often use the lower hole to hold lead weights to improve the balance of the rifle.

Note: When removing the butt stock, do so slowly and carefully so that the rear retaining pin detent spring, which is compressed in a tunnel between the receiver and butt stock, is not lost.

Sliding Butt stocks — The sliding, or collapsible, butt stock was developed for use on the carbine versions of the M16/AR15, see Figure 4-34. When closed, this butt stock is 6.8 inches long; when open, it is 10.1 inches long, the same as the solid butt stock.

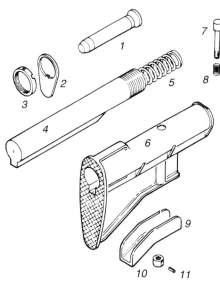

The sliding butt stock consists of a replacement receiver extension with its own buffer and spring assembly, receiver end plate and receiver extension nut. The receiver extension has an inverted channel for the polymer butt stock which slides over the receiver extension. A spring-loaded release lever controls the position of the butt stock on the receiver extension. It has three positions, closed, half extended and fully extended.

Fig. 4-34. M16/AR15 carbine sliding buttstock: 1) buffer, 2) end plate, 3) receiver extension nut, 4) receiver extension tube, 5) action spring, 6) sliding butt stock, 7) release lever locking pin, 8) spring, 9) release lever, 10) lock nut and 12) pin.

The top of the sliding butt stock has a mounting slot that allows the use of a sling over the top of the rifle. The front of the sling attaches to the front sight with a clip that slips around the rear of the front sight and under the gas tube.

The rear of the sliding butt stock is formed into a flat, oval butt pad. Those manufactured by Colt are 1.765 inches in diameter and 4.25 inches high. A nonslip diamond pattern with eight diamonds to an inch is molded into the butt pad. The butt pad is cut out for the receiver extension end.

The lever is a wide "V" shaped trigger which bears against the bottom of the stock. When depressed, it pulls a spring-loaded steel pin out of a hole cut in the bottom of the inverted channel on the receiver extension so that the sliding butt stock can be moved to a new position.

Hand Guards

All hand guards are made in two pieces (left and right in the XM16 and M16A1/AR15A1, and upper and lower in the M16A2 and M4A1) and clamped in place around the barrel by the barrel slip ring at the receiver end and a hand guard cap at the muzzle end, directly behind the front sight assembly.

The original hand guards installed on the XM16 and M16A1/AR15A1 were triangular in cross section and wider at the receiver end (2.6 inches) than the muzzle end (1.7 inches) and 12.25 inches long. They had ten oblong cooling holes across the top and five along the bottom for heat dissipation, see Figure 4-35.

Fig. 4-35. M16/AR15 handguards: A1-type below and A2-type above.

Hand guards on the M16A2/AR15A2 were round in cross-section with a slight taper from rear to front. At the rear, the hand guards are 2.5 inches in diameter and at the front, 2.05 inches. Length is 12.25. They have fifteen round cooling holes, top and bottom.

Hand guards installed on carbines are shorter at 7 inches long. They are 2.8 inches in diameter at the rear and 2.5 inches in diameter at the muzzle end. They have six round cooling holes top and bottom.

All hand guards have metal liners riveted to the interiors to provide heat protection for the shooter's off hand.

Pistol Grip

The pistol grip on the M16/AR15 is four inches long and angled to the rear 60 degrees to help the shooter position his or her hand so that the trigger finger is more in line with the trigger than if the hand were grasping a straight stock. It is most

Fig. 4-36. Right, M16A1 pistol grip; left, M16A2 pistol grip.

effective when the rifle is fired on full automatic.

The pistol grip assembly consists of the pistol grip, pistol grip screw, and pistol grip screw lock washer. In addition, the pistol grip holds the buffer detent and its spring in place.

Two types of pistol grip were used, see Figure 4-36. The M16A1/AR15A1 pistol grip has a checkered panel on either side and a smooth front and rear surface. The M16A2/AR15A2 pistol grip has vertical ridges at the rear and finger grips.

A machine screw and split ring lock washer are inserted through the bottom of the pistol grip to thread into a lug behind and below the trigger assembly. Immediately ahead of the pistol grip is the lug mounting for the front rear of the trigger guard which is held in place by the rear trigger guard pin.

Finish

The standard finish for the military M16 rifle steel parts of whatever configuration is a matt gray-black parkerizing. Parkerizing is the trade name for a process by which a coat of manganese phosphate is applied to the metal to slow down the rusting and corrosion process. Notice, I said slow down, not prevent. Aluminum parts are anodized. Both finishes are applied to matt polished metal to produce a non-reflective surface that will not reflect light.

Parkerizing is applied to all steel surfaces on military rifles, including bolt carriers. The U.S. Army *does* allow non-parkerized bolts to be installed in rifles used within the borders of the Continental United States (CONUS), but only parkerized bolts can be used overseas.

Aluminum parts such as upper and lower receivers are hard anodized to Military A8625, Type III, Class II finish which provides a dull gray-black coating. A finish coat of nickel acetate is applied as a sealant.

The plastic used to make stock and hand guards is colored a nonreflective matt gray-black. The coloring material is embedded in the plastic.

On most commercial AR15 rifles steel parts are parkerized to something approaching the military Mil-Spec standard. Aluminum parts are hard anodized to a variety of standards. In earlier years, some manufacturing companies painted upper and lower receivers and other aluminum parts with various types of enamel paint. Obviously, this will not be as long-wearing a finish as anodizing.

After use or cleaning, the surface of your M16/AR15 should be wiped down with a clean cloth. Dirt can be removed with a mild solvent or soap and water. The surface should then be wiped with an oily rag to leave a coat of lubricant on the surface to retard rust and corrosion. Do not apply so much oil that the rifle becomes slippery and hard to hold.

For long term storage, oil lightly with a silicone-based lubricant and store the rifle or parts in airtight bags with a desiccant. Silicone lubricants are also rust preventatives.

Accessories

The M16 accessories issued to the soldier include the following: 1) magazines, 2) cleaning kit, 3) sling, 4) bipods, 5) bayonet and 6) protective muzzle cap.

Magazines

The M16/AR15 uses a box magazine holding either twenty or thirty rounds. While magazines for the M16/AR15 are manufactured by a variety of companies in many countries, the basic Colt M16/AR15-manufactured magazine will be described. The same magazine fits all models and variations within a specific caliber, see Figure 4-37.

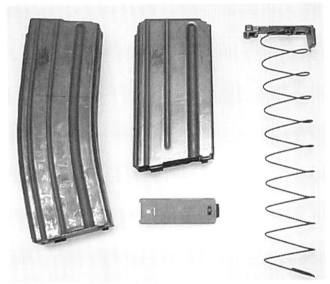

Fig. 4-37. M16/AR15 magazines: left, 30 round; right, 20 round, disassembled showing floorplate (below) and follower and spring (far right).

Standard magazine bodies and floor plates are made from sheet aluminum while the follower is made of cast aluminum. The Z-shaped spring is steel. A steel "spine" or stiffener reinforces the front of the magazine and is riveted to the inside. The end of the stiffener is folded into a catch to engage the floor plate.

The magazine body is stamped and folded to shape and spot welded along the rear seam where the sides overlap. A rectangular hole is cut in the left side of the magazine for the magazine release catch.

A variation on the thirty round M16/AR15 magazine is manufactured by Orolite Engineering Company, Inc. and was developed for the Israeli Defense Forces. The magazine body, floor plate and follower are made of carbon fiber polymer while the spring is, of course, made of steel, see Figure 4-38.

Aftermarket Magazines — Aftermarket magazines may be made entirely of aluminum without the steel spine. Floor plates and followers may be made of plastic.

9 mm Magazines — Magazines for the Colt 9 mm NATO Carbine (Models 643, 653, 639 and 649 as well as the AR15 9 mm Carbine) resemble a long 9 mm pistol magazine with a protruding spine, see Figure 4-39. A plate is secured with folded clips to the bottom of the spring. All parts are steel. An aluminum spacer block is pinned into the magazine well of the lower receiver to hold the narrow magazine in place. A rectangular hole is cut in the left side, well to the back of the magazine, to engage the magazine release.

7.62 x 39 mm Magazines — Dimensions of the 7.62 x 39 mm magazine are identical to the 5.56 mm magazine. The only difference lies in the shape of the follower which has a pointed, rather than a bottle-necked separator.

Fig. 4-38. Plastic 30 round magazine manufactured by Orolite.

The standard 5.56 mm NATO magazine can be disassembled by using a bullet tip to depress a catch near the bottom front of the magazine. Slide the floor plate to the rear, controlling the magazine spring as you do so. The follower and spring can be removed through the bottom.

The Orolite magazines have a round button on a plate attached to the bottom of the spring. The button protrudes through the floor plate. To remove, depress the button and slide the floor plate off to the rear.

The 9 mm NATO magazines have a hollow rimmed hole in the plate secured to the spring. The rim engages the floor plate to hold the magazine spring in place. The magazine can be disassembled by inserting a bullet tip in the hole and pushing in until the floor plate can slide out to the rear.

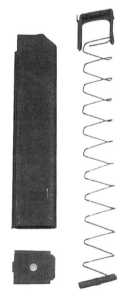

Fig. 4-39. 9 mm Magazine for the Colt Submachine Gun Models 633, 634, 635 and 639.

When reinserting the follower and spring in the standard magazine, make certain the spring and follower are clipped together. Insert the front of the follower first, rolling it slightly to one side to clear the inward curve on the magazine walls. Holding the spring and follower in alignment, roll the rear of the follower to one side to clear the folded metal tabs then push all the way in, working the spring around the tabs as needed. Push the spring below the tabs and start the floor plate onto the magazine body. Depress the catch and apply a slight bit of downward pressure on the front of the floor plate until it clicks in to place.

The Orolite magazines are easier to reassemble. Slide the follower and spring into place and slip the floor plate along the guide ribs molded into the bottom of the magazine body until the tab on the plate protrudes through the hole in the floor plate.

The 9 mm NATO magazines assemble just like the Orolite magazines.

Magazines should be disassembled, inspected and cleaned periodically. While they should be lubricated lightly, a dry powder lubricant is preferred as it will not attract dirt and form muddy deposits that could interfere with the workings of the spring and follower.

Magazine Cover

A rubber gasket-type cover is used to cover the open end of M16/AR15 magazines to keep out dirt and moisture. The cover is made of soft- rubber and fits tightly over the top of the maga- zine, see Figure 4-40.

Fig. 4-40. Magazine cover.

Muzzle Cap

The M16/AR15 is shipped from Colt and many other manufacturers with the protective cap in place and a desiccator tube in the bore. The muzzle cap is a simple plastic tube closed at one end which slips over the muzzle to keep out moisture and dirt when in the field, Figure 4-41. The muzzle cap is made of polyethylene and is thin enough that if the rifle is fired when the cap is in place, the bullet will pen- etrate without being de- flected.

The muz-

Fig. 4-41. Muzzle cover.

zle cap should not be used when the rifle is stored. If the protective cap is kept on the muzzle without the desiccator tube, moisture will condense in the bore.

Cleaning Kit

The cleaning kit issued with the rifle consists a 1) four piece steel cleaning rod, 2) bore and 3) chamber brushes and 4)

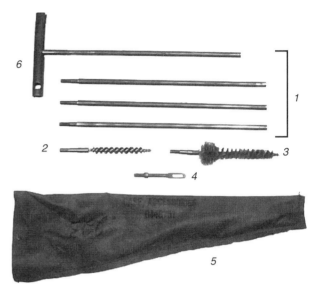

Fig. 4-42. M16/AR15 cleaning kit.

patch holder, called a "swab" holder by Colt. The cleaning kit is carried in a 5) conical-shaped rubberized fabric pouch and stowed in the butt stock compartment, see Figure 4-42.

Two types of cleaning rods have been issued. The earlier version had a T-shaped handle (6) attached to the last section. The last section had a ball-shaped end. The handle — a tube with the bottom cutaway for one-half its length — fitted over the ball. A depression stamped in the center prevented it from sliding off. The other end was crimped. The handle section had a 2 inch long flat milled on either side 1 inch from the end.

The later version does not have a cleaning handle section. Instead, the last section is knurled for easier grasping.

Two types of brushes were issued. The first (2) is for cleaning the bore only. It is 3.2 inches long overall and screws into the cleaning rod. The second brush (3) is a combination bore and chamber brush. The end of the brush has a ruff of brass or stainless steel bristles that fits into the chamber.

To clean the bore using the T-handle cleaning rod, pull the handle as far to the left as it will go and press down so that it forms a "T." Screw in the other three sections and either the patch holder or brush.

To clean the chamber, leave the handle clipped around the rear cleaning rod section. Attach the bore brush and insert a cleaning rod section through the hole in the "T" handle.

Note: The bore and chamber should always be cleaned from the rear. Open the receiver and remove the bolt carrier and charging handle. Insert the cleaning rod with the bore and chamber brushes attached. To prevent wear against the rifling, always use a chamber rod guide. See Appendix B, Cleaning and Maintenance. If you must clean from the muzzle end, it should always be done using a cleaning rod guide. The lands and grooves at the muzzle are extremely sensitive. Wear or denting will cause a loss in accuracy.

Slings

The standard issue sling is referred to as the "silent sling" and is made of woven nylon 1.3 inches wide by 52.25 inches long in green or black for rifles and carbines, see Figure 4-43. Two steel buckles, called sling loops, are used to secure and adjust the sling at the front and back. A longer 72 inch tactical

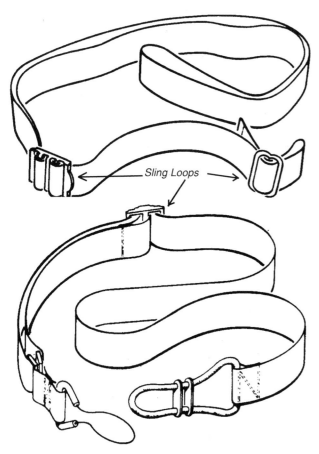

Sling Loops

Fig. 4-43 and 4-44. Top, standard 52.5 inch M16 "silent" sling; below, 72 inch "tactical" sling.

sling is also issued for all rifles and carbines, see Figure 4-44. The tactical sling permits the rifle or carbine to be carried across the chest with the sling looped around the neck.

The U.S. military sling for the M1 Garand/M14 rifle made of woven canvas or nylon can also be installed on the M16/

AR15. It is easier to adjust, and many shooters prefer it over the issue sling. The Model 1907 leather sling first issued for the Model 1903 Springfield is often used by competitive shooters for its ease of adjustment when changes are required during a match. Several companies manufacture a variety of other slings for the M16/AR15 for match, sporting and tactical use. The author's favorite "sporting" sling is from Uncle Mikes and has a padded shoulder section.

Any military sling of 50 inches or more can be installed on the M16/AR15 rifles with or without clips. To do so, run one end of the sling through a sling loop then through the sling swivel, then back through the sling loop. Repeat the process with the other end then adjust to the proper length.

Note: Rigging the sling for support while shooting may cause the barrel to bend if drawn tightly. A compromise should be struck between utility and the shift in grouping caused by a tight sling. Experimentation is required here.

For tactical carry, slings can be installed across the top of the rifle or carbine with fixed or collapsible stocks — the 72 inch sling for the rifle or the 52.25 inch sling for the carbines.

Original military sling adaptors can be obtained from SARCO or the front clip can be formed from steel wire. Form the clip by bending the wire around nails driven into a board in a rectangle approximately 1.25 wide by 2 inches long. Overlap the wire ends at the narrow end by at least 2/3 thirds. Bend each end into a ring. The bight on the front end of the sling is slipped between the overlapping ends.

To mount on a rifle or carbine with a fixed stock, run one end of the sling through the rear sling swivel, then through both sides of the sling loop. Run the loose end back through the buckle to form a loop. Pull the loop over the top of the butt stock and cinch it tightly. The sling swivel will hold it in place. Place the sling swivel clip through the space between the barrel and the bar on the front sight carrying the gas port. Run the other end of the sling through both sides of the second buckle, through the clip and back again through both sides of the buckle. Adjust to fit.

To mount a tactical sling on a carbine with a collapsible stock, run one end of the sling through both sides of the buckle, then through the slit in the top of the collapsible stock, just ahead of the butt. Run the loose end back through both sides of the buckle. Mount the forward end of the sling using the clip as described above. The standard 52.25 inch sling can also be secured to the front sight with the sling loop.

Bipod

Three bipods are manufactured specifically for the M16/AR15, two light and one heavy. The heavy bipod is used on only the M16A2 HBAR Light Machine Gun. The light bipods have two different jaw diameters, the smaller (5/8 inches) for the XM16 and M16A1 and the larger (3/4 inches) for the M16A2, see Figure 4-45.

The light bipods are made of aluminum and are not adjustable. They are attached to the barrel below the front sight. Insert the jaws around the barrel between the legs of the front sight and spread the legs.

Fig. 4-45. M16/AR15 bipod.

The heavy bipod is factory installed only on the light machine gun version of the M16 (Models R0750 and R0950), see Figure 4-46. It is mounted on a collar behind the compensator. The legs can be extended and adjusted for use on rough ground and can be folded back beneath the barrel by pulling them down and rotating them backward until they lock into place.

Fig. 4-46. M16 Light Machine Gun with attached bipod.

Bayonets and Scabbards

Bayonets — Two bayonets are issued for the M16/AR15. The most common is the US Model M7 in either the M8, M8A1 or M10 scabbards. It is used on all variations of the rifle and carbine except the M16A1/A2 Commando. The M7 bayonet is a direct descendent of the World War II M3 Fighting Knife and M4 bayonet developed for the M1 Carbine at the end of World War II, as are the scabbards, see Figure 4-47.

Fig. 4-47. M7 bayonet and M8A1 scabbard.

The M7 bayonet is 11 15/16 inches long overall. The blade is 13/16 inches wide at the ricasso and 6 11/16 inches long. Two plastic grips are attached with two bolts, two lock washers and two nuts embedded in one grip. The grips are heavily checkered and can be removed for cleaning. The blade and tang are forged in one piece. The cross guard contains the bore at the top which slides over the compensator. The bayonet's catch is in the pommel and slides over and locks around the bayonet mount on the bottom front of the front sight.

The release consists of two pivoting release bars driven by a single coil spring. The release bars are held in place with two roll pins on which they pivot. The coil spring presses them apart. When the bayonet is mounted on the rifle, the bore on the cross guard slides over the compensator and the two release bars pivot outward as they pass over the bayonet mount and lock. To release the bayonet, squeeze the release bar tabs so that the release bars pivot outward from the channel and lift off the rifle.

The M9 bayonet uses an identical release system but has a spear-point blade 7.15 inches long and is 1.3 inches wide at the cross guard, see Figure 4-48. The left side, top of the blade is serrated 2.7 inches to form a saw. Overall, the bayonet is 12.2 inches long. The handle is cast plastic, round with five segments.

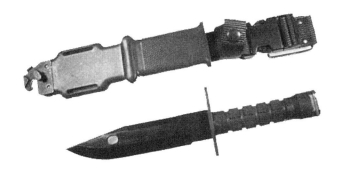

Fig. 4-48. M9 Bayonet and scabbard.

The original Colt-designed bayonet for the Air Force AR15 rifles had a one piece molded grip which simulated the turned leather grip of the M4 Bayonet. A scabbard similar to the M8 was manufactured for these bayonets and can be distinguished from the World War II period M8 scabbards by the fact that they are unmarked.

Scabbards — The M8 and M8A1 scabbards are made of polymer-reinforced cloth and have a steel throat on which is stamped the model number and manufacturer, see Figure 4-49. A vertical web strap is attached to the scabbard throat with two steel rivets, and the cross strap near the top is attached with a single steel rivet. The cross strap holds the bayonet securely in the scabbard. The belt attachment is steel wire and designed to fit into the grommet-lined holes in the standard rifle or pistol cartridge belt. All M8 scabbard web straps are cotton duck while M8A1 web straps can be either cotton duck or nylon, depending on the period of manufacture. The M8 scabbard is pierced at the tip for strap or lace to hold it to the leg. The M8A1 scabbard has a steel reinforcing plate over the hole at the tip to keep the lace from cutting through the plastic, see Figure 4-50.

Only a few WWII production M8 scabbards were issued with the standard military M7 bayonet and they are considered quite rare. They are marked "USM8/B.M. Co" on the throat and VP/XX on the back of the scabbard proper where XX is a changing two digit number.

The M10 scabbard was very similar to the M8A1 scabbard except it was molded entirely of polymer without the reinforcing cloth, see Figure 4-51.

The scabbard for the M9 bayonet has a sharpening stone glued to the back and a quick detachable belt loop for the standard cartridge belt. The scabbard was also designed to be used as a wire cutter. A metal plate bolted to the scabbard tip has a protruding post that serves as an axle for the bayone, refer to Figure 4-48. To use, hold the scabbard in the left hand with the axle up. Hold the bayonet in the right hand, sharp edge of the blade to your left and slide the oblong hole over the axle. Insert the wire to be cut in the notch in the plate and pull the bayonet and scabbard toward one another to close the jaws and clip the wire.

Front Sight Adjusting Tool

This rebated cylinder with five or four prongs on the narrow end is slipped over the front sight post, see Figure 4-52. Pushing down on the tool depresses the front sight detent and allows the front sight post to be turned to adjust elevation. The front sight post can be adjusted with the point of a bullet, but the tool makes it easier to do.

There are two variations of the front sight adjusting tool. Those with five prongs were for use with the A1 round sight post; those with four prongs were used on the square cross-section A2 sight post.

Fig. 4-49. M8 scabbard (WWII origin) above, M8A1 scabbard below.

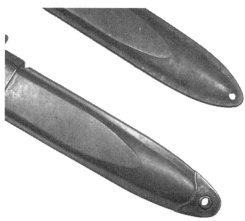

Fig. 4-50. M8 scabbard, above; reinforced M8A1 scabbard, below.

Fig. 4-51. M10 scabbard.

Fig. 4-52. Front sight adjusting tool.

5. THE M16/AR15 AS A MATCH RIFLE – CONSIDERATIONS

The M16A2 was introduced in 1985. Its heavier 62 grain bullet, three-round burst mechanism, redesigned hand guard and heavier barrel renewed its lease on the number 1 spot as the U.S. military's rifle. And it is destined to remain so well into the 21st Century. It also prompted Colt Firearms to issue a civilian version (HBAR) with a heavy barrel extending from the receiver wall forward, rather than from the front sight assembly forward as in the military model. This, coupled with a 1986 rules change by the National Board for the Promotion of Rifle Practice (paragraph 4-15, c., AR 920-30) allowing the use of the Colt AR15A2 HBAR Sporter in service rifle match competition, sparked a revolution in match rifle design and use.

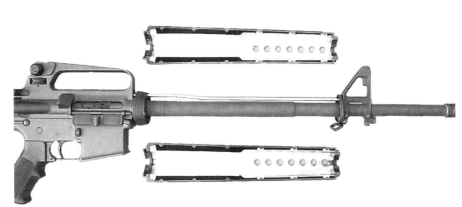

Fig. 5-1. The Colt AR15A2 HBAR Sporter with its full-length heavy barrel was the first commercial production model to really demonstrate the inherent accuracy of the M16/AR15 rifle.

Note: The military M16A2 barrel is "heavy" forward of the front sight post only so that the M232 30 mm grenade launcher could still be mounted.

The M16A2/AR15A2

When civilians competing in service matches around the country in the mid-1980s noticed that military shooters with their M16A2 were achieving excellent scores they began to ask questions.

This led a few custom gunsmiths to start duplicating the accurizing techniques worked out by military gunsmiths. The M14 was still undisputed king of the civilian-military National Match service rifle competition and took up most of the energy and interest of military and civilian gunsmiths alike, see Figure 5-2. As a result, few AR15A2s or M16A2s were seen in serious National Match competition in civilian hands until the early 1990s.

The military sea change began in 1984 when the word was passed down from Quantico that only M16A2s would be used in Divisional Matches. But every one knew that the Marines were obsessed with marksmanship, and the Army resisted. In the early 1990s, Colonel Lory "Mac" Johnson assumed command of the Army Marksmanship Unit. One of his early questions concerned why the Army was not using its service rifle in competition, see Figure 5-3. He was told that while the rifle was used in interservice competition, neither the 62 grain M855 service ammunition nor the new 68 grain competition bullet could buck the wind at 600 yards as successfully as the heavy M80 match ammunition used in the M14. As a consequence, the M14 was still the Army's preferred national match rifle.

Colonel Johnson quickly gave the required orders and the Army used the M16A2 in national match competition for the

Fig. 5-2. ATC Mike Evertt (L) and LCDR Ted Janacek, both USN, firing Navy accurized M14s at the Service Rifle Match at Camp Perry in 1997. Photo by Journalist 1st Class Mark Overstreet, U.S. Navy Shooting Team

Fig. 5-3. This U.S. Army soldier fires an M16A1 at the 1987 Combat Rifle Competition — Small Arms Championships for Active, Reserve and National Guard. Photo courtesy of U.S. Army.

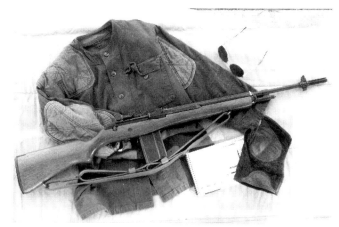

Fig. 5-4. The M14 National Match Rifle.

first time in 1993. While the Army shooters lost the precision rifle competition at Camp Perry at ranges beyond 600 yards that year, for the first time, an Army team member using an M16 made it into the President's 100.

If we step back ten years, a new 6 mm bullet had been developed in the early 1980s as an alternative to the .308 Winchester bullet for 300 yard international match rifle competition. Designated the VLD for Very Low Drag, it proved quite successful. The Sierra Corporation applied the design to a wide variety of bullets including the .223 for use in benchrest competition. But benchrest cartridges are very different from service ammunition. Their bullets are seated out to touch the lands to eliminate any tendency to yaw as they leave the case. To achieve a similar effect, Sierra redesigned their 80 grain bullet with a longer bearing surface to tolerate a greater degree of bullet jump without yawing. By the the early 1990s, VLD-style bullets were appearing in variety of calibers and weights, including .223 bullets up to 80 grains.

In 1994 the Army fielded a team with two squads at camp Perry. One squad fired the M14 and the other, the M16A2. SFC Kenneth Gill won the Service Rifle Championship and SP4 Christopher Hatcher took the President's 100, both firing M16A2s accurized by the USAMU. It was the beginning of the end for the M14 as the National Match Rifle, see Figure 5-4.

Fig. 5-5. An unmodified Colt AR15A2 HBAR fired this 0.94 inch group using Federal Gold Medal Match (68 grain boat tail bullet) at 100 yards from a rest.

The reason was simple enough. Right from the box, The AR15/M16 had been shown to be an exceptionally accurate rifle. In the hands of a competent shooter it demonstrated time after time its ability to produce group sizes nearly half those obtained from the M14, even when both were using GI ammo, see Figure 5-5. The precision match of bolt to breech — contained in the barrel and not the receiver — was the key. If a custom gunsmith slicks up the trigger system, fits a "proper match" barrel, free floats the hand guard and stabilizes the sights, the shooter has a light, compact rifle producing little recoil to disturb the point of aim and capable of minute or angle or less. And depending on the skill of the gunsmith, much less.

If the sight radius is shorter than the that of the M14 (a difference of 6.87 inches), its other advantages will go a long way toward making up the deficiency, as many match shooters were beginning to discover.

By 1997, civilian and military competitors alike were entering with M16/AR15 rifles in all long range service matches That year, Sgt. Tobie Tomlinson, firing an M16, in the Porter Cup (1,000 yards) placed second — one point behind the winner who used an M14. In 1998, the fate of the M14 was sealed when the U.S Marine Corps team arrived at Camp Perry with accurized M16s and not an M14 in sight.

One civilian competitor wandered over to the Marine's trailer to ask for some help in adjusting his M1A sights. The

Marine armorer looked at his rifle and shook his head. "I worked on one of them," he drawled, "some years back."

Needless to say, the 1999 National Matches were dominated by the M16 service rifle. And as a portent of even more startling changes to come, in 1999 at Camp Perry, Joe Bartoli, a California junior team member (see Figure 5-6) firing an accurized AR15A2 rifle built by custom gunsmith Jim Grunning of Grúning Precision, Riverside, California, scored high civilian in the service rifle match. He also placed 2nd in the Palma 1000 yard match, scoring only *one point* behind the winner. And she was firing a bolt action rifle.

Fig. 5-6. Joe Bartoli, then a member of the California Junior Rifle team, standing next to the Alice Bull Trophy, awarded to him at the National Matches at Camp Perry, Ohio in 1999. The Alice Bull Trophy is awarded to the civilian with the highest aggregate score in the National Trophy Individual Rifle Match and the President's Match. Mr. Bartoli was shooting an AR15 custom built by Grúning Precision of Riverside, California. California's 1999 "assault rifle law has now eliminated Junior teams in the state.

Building an Accurate Rifle

Custom Gunsmith Fred Johnson, formerly of The National Armorer, Phoenix, Arizona and now retired, put it succinctly when he said that "the M16 is an inherently accurate rifle. Combine one in good condition with good service ammunition, you have a match contender. Add custom-loaded or match grade ammunition and you have a potential match winner." The potential Fred referred to is the shooter's ability to hold on target, squeeze without disrupting sight picture, and read the wind.

This last is most important as wind does affect the range of ammunition used in the M16A2/AR15A2 — 55 or 62 grain

service, 68, 69, 75, 78 and 80 grain match bullets — to a greater degree than it does the range of heavier 7.62 mm bullet fired from the M14/M1A.

We will take our examination of a custom-built match rifle a step at a time, just as we did when we sat down to plan the two custom match rifles we wanted to build, one a service match AR15 and the other a long-range match gun, more commonly known as a "space gun."

You start by deciding what you want these rifles to do. Ask yourself, will my rifle be used for plinking, hunting, match shooting or self-defense? If for such recreational shooting pursuits as plinking and hunting, then you will probably find that any of the AR15s built by one of the major manufacturers (refer to Table 3-1) will be as accurate and reliable as you want it to be. And short of adding a telescopic sight, you won't need to spend extra money to improve it. There are not many rifles that will shoot near minute of angle right out of the box.

If you chose the M16/AR15 for self-defense purposes, again, there is very little you need do to the rifle to improve its accuracy. It was built for combat. As for reliability, after you have tested it with a range of ammunition from various makers, you will probably find that it eats just about anything (commercial or military) you can load into the chamber.

But if you are interested in target shooting, service rifle or tactical rifle competition, then the M16/AR15's accuracy can be improved at least an order of magnitude and this chapter is directed at achieving that improvement.

Selecting a Custom Gunsmith

While the M16/AR15 is a fairly simple rifle mechanically and much easier to accurize than the M1 Garand or the M14, it still requires an expert's touch. If you want a truly accurate M16/AR15, select your gunsmith with care.

Start by talking to other match shooters that you see on the range with customized M16/AR15s. Try and get a sense of not only what was done to the rifle but how much improvement they saw before and after. Then discuss the gunsmith who did the work. What are his credentials? How long has he been working? What other rifles has he accurized? What techniques does he use? Was the owner satisfied? Would he have the same gunsmith build another rifle?

The author has never run across any part of this wonderful country that does not have several custom gunsmiths that the locals swear by. So don't be afraid to make a list of candidates based on your discussions with match shooters, then go and interview them. Make a list of questions you want to ask and stick to the point. A custom gunsmith is usually good because he or she does all the work him or herself rather than handing it off to assistants. So, keep in mind that the longer you keep the gunsmith talking, the less time he or she will have for work. Hanging around the gunshop or gunsmith on Saturday afternoon shooting the breeze may be a fine old American tradition, but it can also rob the owner or gunsmith of his or her most precious commodity, time.

Do your homework before you talk to the gunsmith. You should have talked to enough match shooters and read sufficient magazine articles and books on the subject (See Appendix G, Bibliography and use it as a study guide) to ask intelligent questions. Make an appointment. Have your questions ready. Ask for the gunsmith's suggestions and when you are through, ask for an estimate for the costs. Repeat this procedure with everyone on your list. Then make your choice — not necessarily based on the lowest price.

A real professional will provide you with a written estimate of the work to be performed and the time to do it. The estimate should include the cost of new barrels, triggers, stocks and other parts as well as the labor costs involved in turning them into a fine precision rifle. Keep in mind that the final price may be as much as ten percent higher due to vagaries of price increases and shipping costs. Recognize also that if you phone the gunsmith several weeks into the project

---

Selecting M16/AR15 Parts

M16/AR15 parts, while not as plentiful as they once were, are still available on gun show tables and from mail-order houses. But the buyer should be careful when selecting parts. Many assume that the original GI parts are superior to newly manufactured parts offered by many companies. This may be true if the GI parts are in new condition, but if they have been re-finished to hide wear and defects, you may well wind up wasting your money. Examine parts you intend to buy very carefully. If the parkerizing is grainy or if wear marks, gouges or cracks are visible, reject the part. Conversely, when purchasing newly made parts, examine them carefully for mold or tool marks, rounded surfaces, edges that are not straight, burrs or uneven surfaces.

Improperly made, over- or undersized parts are worse than useless. If the mail order house is reputable you stand a chance of getting your money back. If the bad parts were bought at a gun show, you may never see your money again.

---

and change your mind about the barrel contour or the trigger assembly, that you will see that increase reflected in the price.

When the rifle is delivered, take it to range and break it in carefully as described in Chapter 6. Do not make any judgements about the rifle's accuracy and reliability until you have fired at least 200 rounds. If at that point, the accuracy or reliability is not what you expected, make another appointment with the gunsmith and discuss the matter with him. Bring your targets and be prepared to describe the steps you took to break in the rifle and fire the test shots. Do not be confrontational. Mechanical systems always take a bit of tweaking before they provide the service you expect. Any custom gunsmith who expects to stay in business will — within reason — rework the rifle until it is performing the way you expect.

Receivers

Little has been written about the different lower and upper receivers that are available for the M16/AR15, probably because there is very little to choose from between the various brands. If they are made to mil-spec standards, are of weapons grade material and all the holes are cut and drilled in the right places, then only the markings differentiate one from another. A survey of custom riflesmiths specializing in M16/

AR15 rifles reveals little hard criteria for preferring any particular brand over another. Most custom gunsmiths choose or recommend a receiver because they are familiar with it, have good relations with the manufacturing company or simply get a pretty good deal. Most will be just as willing to use the receiver you bring to them as long as it is of good quality.

The author has assembled dozens of AR15 receivers from different manufacturers and has rarely encountered a problem fitting either GI or well-made non-GI parts. See the Sidebar for more on the parts problem. About all that can be said is that some finishes are darker than others, some a little smoother, some a little lighter. Every aftermarket lower or upper receiver the author has examined has been well-made. Tracks are cut with sharp edges, holes are deburred, sliding surfaces well-machined and finish marks polished away.

There are a dozen different brands of M16/AR15 upper and lower receivers available for custom building. Colt, the leading and original manufacturer of the rifle, makes its receivers available to holders of Federal Firearms Licences through a number of distributors. Other well-known manufacturers are described in Chapter 3.

Recently, upper receivers from Fabrique Nationale have also been seen in the marketplace. FN has long manufactured M16 rifles for the military at their plant in Maryland. The author owns an FN upper receiver (they do not sell lower receivers) and has examined several others. Except for the slightly deeper sandblasting on the outer surface and the darker gray parkerizing, there do not seem to be any other differences from any of the other uppers examined. Most M16/AR15 upper receivers are unmarked, but a few do carry manufacturer's codes. Refer to Table 3-3 in Chapter 3.

Of course, you will find a great deal of argument among shooters over which is the best receiver to use, but in many cases, they come down to a matter of personal preference. The points to keep in mind are 1) quality of manufacturing and 2) do the upper and lower receiver mate properly. If the receiver does not meet, at a minimum, Mil Spec standards, or holes and slots are not drilled in exactly the right place, the gunsmith will have to do far more work to fit parts, thus incurring greater expense. It is also strongly suggested that you purchase upper and lower receivers from the same manufacturer to avoid fitting and mating problems.

The author has checked receivers from many of the manufacturers listed in Table 3-1 above. All were found to be of high-quality and all were represented as meeting military specifications. While most manufacturers advertised their upper and lower receivers as being "tight fitting," the phrase is subject to interpretation.

If you detect play between the upper and lower receivers in your rifle, test it on the range. Fire several five round groups at 200 yards and look for evidence of vertical stringing. If you see any, wedge slips of cardboard or thin plastic between the upper and lower receiver halves until the vertical stringing disappears. If it does, then a loose receiver fit is the culprit.

There are at least four things you can do about it, in order of difficulty. 1) Continue to insert cardboard or plastic shims until all play is eliminated. 2) Install the drop-in Accu-Wedge, a plastic shim manufactured by Z-M Performance (see Figure 5-7). 3) Obtain and use a tensioning rear take-down pin such as that manufactured by J.P. Enterprises. After installing it, turn the pin until all play is removed. Do not over tighten. 4) Glass bed your upper and lower receiver.

The problem with solution number one will be inconsistency. The pounding from the two receiver halves will thin the cardboard and you might not be able to achieve the same fit when you replace the cardboard shims.

Fig. 5-7. A Z-M Performance ACCU-Wedge behind the rear take-down pin is a quick way to tighten loose receiver halves.

Solution two: plastic ACCU-Wedge drops into the space behind the rear take down pin. A "wedge" of plastic juts upward so that when the two halves of the receiver are closed, the wedge is squeezed between them and removes excess play. It is a good idea to buy at least two of the inexpensive wedges. When you notice vertical stringing, discard the one in the rifle and insert the new one.

Solution three: a tensioning pin will reduce the consistency problem if your receiver is not too "loose." Scribe a line across the head of the pin and onto the receiver on either side to use as an index mark so you know where to turn the pin the next time you have to open the receiver.

Solution four: the Army's Marksmanship Unit gunsmiths and a significant number of custom gunsmiths and match shooters believe that only glass bedding will produce the most consistent and reproducible groups. If that is your choice after testing, see the Sidebar overleaf for instructions.

Barrel

The barrel is the heart and soul of the M16/AR15 rifle where accuracy is concerned. Certainly, the gas system and the bolt assembly as well as ammunition play an important role, but the "be all" and "end all" of M16/AR15 accuracy is the barrel. Anything else you do to the rifle is sweetening. Here are the eight main factors necessary for an accurate barrel.

1) The barrel must be straight and stiff enough to resist bending, 2) the stresses set up by machining must be relieved, 3) the barrel must vibrate without interference from any other part of the rifle, 4) the rifling must be matched to bullet weight, 5) the chamber must be cut to the proper depth so that it will head space properly, 6) the muzzle crown must be cut absolutely perpendicular to the bore and 8) the gas port must be of the proper diameter and located exactly. We will examine each factor in turn.

Barrel Material, Bore and Shape — Modern barrels are made in several ways but all have in common the fact that the hole for the bore is first drilled in the barrel blank and then the barrel is rifled. Finally, the barrel is turned to its final shape in a lathe.

Barrels are made from one of several alloys of steel. The two most commonly used alloys for the M16/AR15 barrel are SAE 4140 steel (an alloy of chrome and molybdenum) or 416 stainless steel. Both steels are high in tensile strength, resist corrosion and abrasion — 416 stainless steel more so than 4140 — and are machinable — 4140 more so than stainless steel.

The barrel is mounted in a fixture and drilled using a slightly undersize drill bit. The barrel is then reamed to final diameter, which is the nominal diameter of the bullet, i.e., 0.300 for .30 caliber bullets, 0.223 inches for .223 (5.56 mm) bullets, and then rifled.

Rifling is usually done in one of two ways, using either a broach or a button. Button rifling is done by inserting a tool shaped to the desired rifling and drawing and turning it through the bore to form the lands and grooves. The twist is controlled by how the button is turned as it is drawn. Broaching is done by pulling a cutter through the bore to cut the lands and grooves from the metal. Single point broaching uses a cutter that forms one land and groove at a time and multipoint broaching cuts

Glass Bedding an M16/AR15 Receiver

Glass bedding an M16/AR15 rifle is much easier than glass bedding a hunting rifle or an M14 or M1 Garand. The M16/AR15 is bedded by applying an epoxy compound to the front and rear lug areas and to the surfaces where the upper and lower receivers meet. Bedding compound in the lug areas prevents side-to-side movement. Vertical movement is also eliminated by the additional material along the joint. Keep in mind that you're applying plastic to make up for deficiencies in steel, and that it will eventually wear away and require rebedding.

The author has used both Brownell's Steel Bed stainless-steel filled epoxy rifle bedding compound and Devcon, and found either quite easy to work. Remove the front and rear receiver pins and separate the upper receiver from the lower. Clean the areas in the upper and lower receiver to receive the bedding compound thoroughly, repeat thoroughly! Use acetone to remove all traces of oil and grime. Use a good hard wax to coat the upper edges of the lower receiver to prevent the bedding compound from sticking where it is not wanted. Work the wax down into both the front and rear lug openings. Coat the pins as well.

Now mix the epoxy and use a flat stick to apply it to the upper receiver's lower edges where they touch the lower receiver. Work the epoxy up along the vertical edges of the upper receiver to increase the bond with the metal. Using a Q-tip or toothpick, coat the inside and outside of the upper receiver's front and rear lugs and work the material into the pin holes as well. Be careful not to let the epoxy run down into the magazine well but use enough material so that when the two halves are joined, all gaps will be filled and a slight excess will be squeezed out. If you have waxed all areas where you do not want the epoxy to stick, clean up will be quite easy.

Reassemble the lower and upper receiver and replace the pins so that the two halves are locked tightly together. Wipe off all excess epoxy that has been forced out with the solvent recommended in the directions for the material you are using. Stand the assembled rifle on its muzzle in a corner for twenty-four hours to allow the bedding compound to set.

When the epoxy compound has dried, remove both the front and rear pins. Work the lower receiver loose from the upper by pulling straight down. Use Swiss files to remove excess bedding compound, particularly from around the magazine well. Your glass bedding job will last longer if instead of breaking the receiver open for cleaning by removing only the rear pin, you remove both pins and separate the two receiver halves by pulling lower receiver down and away so that the two lugs slide out of their bedding.

all lands and grooves at the same time. The single point cutter must be indexed for each pass through the bore. *Broaching* is a cutting procedure while *button* rifling compresses the displaced metal into the walls of the bore. A third less common rifling procedure is called hammer forging. A die is placed into the bore and hydraulic hammers form the outside and inside of the barrel at the same time. Most barrels supplied by manufacturers of complete rifles are button rifled or single point broach cut. Full broach cutting is considered to be superior.

The more expensive barrels are "honed" after rifling to provide an extremely smooth bore by eliminating chatter marks left by the drill bit. When purchasing a custom barrel, be certain to ask the supplier how the rifling was cut and if it was honed. When the rifling is completed satisfactorily, the barrel is threaded at the breech for the barrel insert.

No drilling machine has ever been invented, nor probably ever will be, that can drill a perfectly centered hole through a piece of steel round stock between 10 and 28 inches long. So, the custom gunsmith will mount the barrel on trued centers in a lathe and turn it along its length, both to provide the final external shape and to center the bore exactly in the barrel. Simply put, if the line of the bore wandered slightly to the right during the drilling process, centering the bore in a lathe will allow the cutting tool to strip away more metal on the opposite side so that the end result is a perfectly centered bore.

Jim Gronning of Grüning Precision demonstrated the process for us. Centers were gripped by two chucks, one in the head stock and the other in the tail stock. The centers were trued to 1/30,000 of an inch and the barrel placed between them. The tail stock was then tightened down, see Figure 5-8.

Fig. 5-8. An AR15 match barrel being turned between trued centers by custom rifle smith Jim Gronning.

The first cuts removed excess metal to the diameter of the barrel collar, truing the exterior surface to the bore's line of axis. The collar was next cut to a diameter of 0.998 inches starting 0.618 inches from the breech end, to a width of 2.60 inches. The first step was cut to 0.980 inches in diameter, the second step to 0.845 inches in diameter, the third step to .0749 inches in diameter to accept the front sight assembly bracket. The collar was cut to 0.752 inches in diameter. The remainder of the barrel was cut to 0.740 inches in diameter with an overall length of 19.250 inches from the receiver face to the muzzle which was recessed at an 11 degree slope. The collar was threaded 13/16-16 UN 3A.

The original XM16 and its immediate successor, the M16/AR15A1 configuration was criticized for its thin diameter barrel (0.575 inches ahead of the front sight assembly). It was felt in some quarters that there was not enough metal to radiate heat away quickly and therefore, the barrel had a tendency to soften.

Instead of barrel softening, what the early critics were observing was a barrel bending under the pull of a tight sling. Barrel bending first showed up in service match shooting where a sling is used. It was rarely reported to occur under combat conditions in Vietnam and other combat theaters because soldiers rarely use a sling in combat to steady their aim.

The author tested an AR15A1 using both a nylon and leather military sling. When wearing a leather shooting coat with the sling cinched tightly, deflections of between 1.5 and 2 MOA were recorded as against a sling drawn taut. Barrel temperature did not appear to make any difference.

The A2 configuration barrel is larger in diameter (0.740 ahead of the front sight assembly) and considerably "beefier" than the A1 barrel but is the same diameter behind the front sight assembly where the sling swivel is attached, refer to Figure 4-25 and see Figure 5-9. When the same test was repeated using a USMC M16A2, deflections of 0.75 to 1.5 MOA were still noted. This should not be surprising as the same type and degree of deflection has been recorded with the M1903 Springfield where the front sling swivel is mounted on the rear barrel band and can force the hand guard and stock against the barrel.

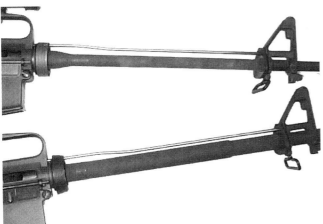

Fig. 5-9. Barrel configurations compared; above, AR15A1, below, AR15A2 Sporter II.

In an attempt to eliminate this phenomenon, Colt produced the HBAR, or heavy barrel, which has a thicker diameter from the receiver forward. The HBAR barrel has five steps, and from the receiver ring forward, the diameters are

0.985 inches, 0.946 inches, 0.861 inches, 0.751 inches, 0.715 inches and 0.700 inches. The author was unable to detect any deflection with HBAR barrels with a sling cinched tight. Partly for this reason, the HBAR configuration is quite popular with match shooters, particularly service rifle match shooters.

Stress Relief — If the barrel is being manufactured at the factory that will assemble the rifle, it is sent for straightening and final machining, and hopefully, stress relieving before being attached to the receiver. If the barrel is being marketed to custom gunsmiths, it is straightened and, hopefully, stress relieved. Always ask when ordering a barrel.

Why stress relieving? Any machining operation performed on a piece of steel that changes its form will disturb its crystalline structure and set up stresses in the metal. As a result, there is a tendency for the metal to return to its former shape. A common method of straightening barrels after drilling was to run a string attached to a taut bow through the bore and check the shadow it casts. If the barrel was crooked, the string's shadow bent at that point. The gunsmith tapped opposite that point with a hammer. Today is is done with lasers and automatic hammers. But even though the barrel has been made straight, it will retain a tendency to bend again at that point, particularly when heated. That is just one reason why the point of aim can move as a barrel heats up.

Stress relieving is accomplished by heating (or cooling) the barrel to a certain temperature and holding it there for a predetermined period of time, then allowing it to cool (or warm) slowly. This causes the crystalline structure to relax and adjust to the new shape.

Here is the tricky part. When the custom gunsmith obtains a new barrel blank, it comes to him usually as a rifled steel tube. He then machines it to its final shape, threads or otherwise machines the end and cuts the chamber for the bullet. All this work sets up a new series of stresses in the metal. To achieve the best accuracy, these stresses must be relieved. Again, the barrel can be heated, or cooled, allowed to "soak" at the desired temperature and then allowed to cool, or warm up, depending on the method used.

Heating something as long as a rifle barrel requires an expensive furnace. In the 1980s, the aerospace industry perfected a new method for stress relieving, and it has been applied to rifle barrels over the last eight to ten years — cryogenic stress relieving. The barrel is reduced to a very cold temperature, on the order of liquid nitrogen. The advantage is that the process uses less expensive equipment and is slightly faster but with the same results.

The author has had personal experience with this method. A custom-made precision .30 caliber match rifle was built that fired *three* shot groups averaging .50 inches at 100 yards. But when *five* shot groups were fired, the fifth shot was always several tenths of an inch toward the 2 o'clock position.

The barrel was sent for cryogenic treatment. When it was returned, the gunsmith had to relieve the right side of the forend at the muzzle about 0.32 inches to reseat the barrel. Five shot groups now averaged 0.40 inches and the "flyer" problem disappeared. The gunsmith in building the rifle had fluted it for two-thirds of its length to provide a lighter barrel but retain the stiffness of a 1.25 inch bull barrel. Cutting the flutes from the round barrel set up sufficient stress in the barrel that when heated, it shifted slightly to the right and up, which accounted for the 2 o'clock flyer. Stress relief of barrels can be very important and cryogenic treatment is so inexpensive — between $20 and $50 — that it seems silly not to have it done.

Yes I know that several "controlled" studies of cyrogenic tempering have been reported in the literature that suggest that little is achieved by the method. Without meaning to criticize the authors of those studies, my own experience suggests that there *is* benefit to be achieved. And as I said, with the cost of the process so low, why not have it done and eliminate one more variable.

Barrel Vibration — All gun barrels vibrate from the effects of burning propellant and the bullet passing along the bore at high velocity. If the barrel is cut and mounted so that it vibrates in the same amplitude every time and is not interrupted by touching another part of the gun, then the bullet will strike true every time, all other factors being equal.

John C. Garand, the inventor of the M1 Garand and the parent of the M14, had shown as early as 1944 that a gas system attached to the barrel did not hamper accuracy because both vibrated together as a single unit. But if the barrel was allowed to touch any other part of the firearm, such as the stock, then accuracy suffered.

Mr. Garand found that when several rounds were fired in rapid succession, the barrel could heat to 300 degrees Fahrenheit or higher, causing the barrel to expand. If it came in contact with the stock or the hand guards, then the barrel's natural harmonics were interrupted, and accuracy suffered. Relieving stock and/or hand guards allowed the point of aim to remain the same as when the barrel was only moderately warmed. This led to the practice of widening barrel channels, relieving hand guards and attaching ferrules solidly to the barrel — in other words, free floating the barrel.

Free-Floating — After installing the proper barrel with the proper rifling rate for the ammunition you intended to shoot, the most effective thing you can do to improve accuracy in the M16/AR15 is to free float the barrel.

Free floating a hand guard is a fairly simple procedure. A stiff aluminum or stainless steel tube is attached to the front of the upper receiver and the hand guards are then attached to it.

Two types of free-floated hand guards are commonly used. The first type is found on service match rifles. This is basically a long tube with the handguards and ferrule attached to it rather than the front sight assembly. The second type is most commonly found on "space guns," a nickname for ultra accu-

rate AR15 rifles used in bench rest, long range and Palma competition, see Figures 5-10 and 5-11. It is usually a steel or aluminum tube with a knurled or grooved surgave rather than separate handguards. It may or may not have mountings for a forward sling swivel and may also be equipped with a provision for attaching a hand stop.

Fig. 5-10. Lisa Gronning demonstrates a "space gun" built by her father. See the succeeding figure for an indication of its accuracy. Lisa was an up-and-coming match shooter until the 1999 California Assault Rifle law made it illegal for her to compete using a semiautomatic rifle.

In service rifles, steel tubes are to be preferred over aluminum tubes for strength and for the extra weight they provide which helps to steady the rifle while the reverse is true in the long range match or "space" gun.

Fig. 5-11. After only twenty rounds, this Grúning Precision space gun was producing five-shot groups at 200 yards measuring less than .90 inches.

When fitting a free-floated hand guard, some gunsmiths weld or otherwise attach the tube to the barrel nut, but in the author's opinion, this does not always provide enough strength.

When a sling is cinched up tight, the strain placed on the tube through the sling point 12 inches or so away from the tube's attaching point is very heavy. To prevent bending, the tube should be made of stainless steel with a wall thickness of at least 0.05 inches. Jim Gronning of Gruning Precision selected an extra long barrel nut designed and built by A. H. Merchant that provides greater attaching surface than does the standard AR15 barrel nut (see below).

In service rifles, the tube walls should be a minimum of 0.04 inches thick; thicker is better. You say you don't think such a heavy-walled tube is necessary? Frank White of Compass Lake Engineering was asked by the Marine Corps to design a free-floating hand guard assembly for their service rifle teams that would not break. It seems that the Marines had a tendency to hitch their slings so tight that they broke or bent every tube they tried. You might not be rigging your sling that tight, but a broken or bent hand guard tube in the middle of a match can prove mighty embarrassing.

The Compass Lake tube has a shorter slot cut into it for the gas tube which requires that you also add their gas tube, bent to accommodate the slot in the hand guard tube. Frank White's testing showed that the extra-long slot in most tubes was responsible for most of the problems the Marines were experiencing. He solved the problem with a shorter slot, heavier tube and a custom-bent gas tube.

Fig. 5-12. The A. H. Merchant hand guard tube attaches to the upper receiver by an extra long barrel nut to provide additional strength.

Another excellent floating hand guard assembly is available from A. H. Merchant. They replace the star barrel nut with an threaded tube 2.8 inches long, 1.345 inches in diameter. The tube attaches to the upper receiver, and the hand guard tube threads into the other end forming a very secure platform for the front ferrule to which the forward sling swivel is attached, see Figure 5-12. A special spanner nut with a 3/16 inch pin is used to install the hand guard tube. The forward sling swivel is welded to the front of the hand guard tube, see

Figure 5-13. The hand guard tube must be sized properly to leave a gap between the front of the ferrule and the back of the front sight assembly. The aluminum heat shields must be removed from the inside of the hand guards and the lower hand guard notched to fit around the swing swivel clevis.

Fig. 5-13. The ferrule is welded to the front of the hand guard tube and the sling swivel suspended from it, rather than from the front sight assembly. Notice the gap between the ferrule and front sight assembly.

Free floating the barrel with the proper hand guard tube assembly will eliminate barrel bending on the M16/AR15 due to sling pressure. We chose to install the A. H. Merchant system and when a sling was rigged as tight as we could stand it, there was no detectable bending of the hand guard tube or perceptible shift in point of impact.

Rifling — In 1964, the 5.56 x 45 mm, Ball M193 cartridge was adopted as the standard round for the new M16 rifle. It was a combination of a 55 grain bullet as used in the .222 Remington Magnum (a cartridge developed jointly by Springfield National Armory and Remington in the mid-1950s for military use but never adopted) coupled with the slightly longer case which was really a scaled-down version of the .30-06 cartridge case.

The business end was full metal jacket, boat-tailed 55 grain bullet propelled to a nominal velocity of 3,250 fps by the powder charge. To stabilize this light bullet, the Ordnance Department established the rifling twist rate at one turn in 14 inches (1:14) or one turn in 356 mm (1:356 mm). When it was discovered that rate would not stabilize the 55 grain bullet in very cold weather (Arctic conditions), the rifling rate was reduced to 1:12 (1:305 mm).

A major and continuing criticism of the M16/AR15 system after its adoption was the light weight of its bullet, 2.7 times lighter than the bullet used in the M14. The original 55 grain, semi-boat-tailed bullet used in the 5.56 mm M193 cartridge was certainly more sensitive to wind than the heavier

149 grain 7.62 mm Ball M80 for the M14 or the 173 grain M118 cartridge for the .30-06 M1 Garand. And it showed in wind drift patterns.

In a 10 mph crosswind, the rule of thumb for the 55 grain bullet was 4.4 inches of drift at 200 yards. Compare this to the M14's 149 grain bullet which would drift only 3.3 inches and the M1 Garand's 173 grain bullet which would only drift 3.0 inches under similar wind conditions. At 400 yards with a 10 mph crosswind, deflection for the 55 grain bullet opened to 20.1 inches and at 600 yards, to 53.3 inches, significantly higher than with either the M80 or M118 ball ammunition.

In 1980, NATO and the U.S. Army's Ordnance Department commissioned Fabrique Nationale of Liege, Belgium to develop an improved 5.56 x 45 mm cartridge that provided greater accuracy and retained velocity at longer ranges. The result was a heavier 62 grain spitzer, boat-tailed bullet with a mild-steel penetrator. Muzzle velocity was reduced slightly to a nominal 3,100 fps. The new bullet was designated the SS109 (FN's nomenclature) and the entire cartridge was adopted by both the U.S. and NATO as the M855. The rifling rate in the new M16A2 was changed to 1:7 (1:178 mm), a compromise that also allowed the heavier M865A1 Tracer bullet to be stabilized as well.

In non-NATO countries not restricted by collective rules, a 1:9 (1:228 mm) twist is commonly employed and provides slightly better accuracy with either weight bullet. Many match shooters have adopted this rifling rate and have been happy with it, particularly when using heavier bullets such as Sierra's or Hornady's 68 and 69 grain match grade bullets. In fact, Colt, Remington and Ruger, and other manufacturers of sporting rifles chambered for the .223 sporting round using the 62 to 69 grain bullet like chamber their AR15A2 or Ruger Mini14s to 1:9 (1:228).

Stabilizing the light bullet has always been an area of argument, and it is only in the past few years that rifle twist rates have been nailed down with a great deal of certainty — mostly through the efforts of match shooters.

While the heavier SS109 did offer improved range and accuracy, it was still not enough, as match shooters quickly discovered. The bullet remained light enough that it was unduly affected by wind over the longest ranges when compared to the heavier 7.62 mm bullets. Heavier .223 bullets weighing 75 and 80 grains compare quite well to heavier .30 caliber match bullets, see Figure 5-14. Extensive experimentation by the manufacturing companies and by hand loaders and match shooters have established a rifling rate of 1:77 as ideal for these heavy bullets. But for those who prefer to shoot a wide

Table 5-1 Preferred Rifling Twist Rates — Bullet Weight vs. Rifling Rate 5.56 x 45 mm Cartridge	
Bullet Weight in Grains	**Rifling Rate inches (millimeters)**
40 to 50	1:14 (1:356)
55	1:12 (1:305)
62-65	1:10 (1:254)
68-69-70	1:9 (1:228)
75-80	1:77 (195.58)*
62 grain (US military)	1.7 (177.8)
* also referred to as 1:8	

range of bullet weights and will accept less than "President's 100" accuracy in return for versatility, the 1:9 rifling weight remains preferred. Bullet weights and rifling twists are matched in Table 5-1, above.

Fig. 5-14. .223 caliber cartridges with — 55 grain (Lake City–U.S. Military), 62 grain (IVI), 69 grain (HSM), 75 grain (Black Hills) and 80 grain (U.S. Army Marksmanship Unit) — bullets.

Barrel Gas Port — The size and exact location of the gas port on the barrel is critical to the proper semi-automatic or automatic functioning of the M6/AR15 rifle. The proper amount of gas must be released through the port and gas tube to unlock or lock and drive the bolt carrier. Too little gas and the piston will short stroke; too much gas and the bolt carrier will batter the receiver. The gas port must be drilled in the top dead center of the barrel when installed. To do so, Colt recommends locking the barrel in a barrel vise and drilling the gas port directly in line with the locating pin in the top of the barrel extension, exactly 12.42 inches ahead of the barrel shoulder (Figure 5-15, overleaf). A No. 45 drill should be used to produce a hole 0.082 inches in diameter in a 20 inch standard diameter barrel. The gas ports in the 16 inch barrel and 11 inch barrel are 0.62 inches and 0.92 inches in diameter, respectively. Take care during drilling to locate the holes exactly and to use only the amount of pressure needed to move the drills through the metal.

Many custom rifle smiths encounter difficulties when installing heavy barrels on the M16/AR15 rifle. When a heavy barrel is installed, the depth, or length, of the gas port is increased, which reduces the flow of gas against the piston.

Fig. 5-15. The gas port location on a Colt AR15 barrel.

and addresses, consider another gunsmith.

The chamber is extremely important to accuracy. The chamber must be cut so that the rifle's head space (length from bolt face to shoulder) is within specification. But it must also be cut to the proper diameter, particularly in the throat or leade. If too wide, the bullet will yaw as it leaves the case mouth; if too narrow, the bullet will be squeezed; if off-center, the bullet will be shaved — any of these three will cause the bullet to diverge from a true flight path. How the chamber is cut is therefore a very critical consideration when choosing a barrel and gunsmith.

Note: Head space specifications are set by different institutions. In the United States they are most commonly established by the Small Arms and Ammunition Manufacturer's Institute (SAMMI) for civilian firearms. SAMMI specifications are derived with the idea that ammunition of a specific caliber from a wide number of manufacturers will be fired in a wide variety of firearms of that caliber. SAMMI specifications are somewhat of a compromise. You will notice that when comparing SAMMI head space specs with military head space specs that the former tend to be a bit looser than the latter.

Misunderstanding what is happening, many gunsmiths will increase the diameter of the gas port to compensate for the added depth, which may worsen the problem. In fact, the correct procedure with a heavy barrel is to slightly bell the mouth of the gas port. This allows the gas stream to expand slightly and thus flow faster.

When the front sight assembly base is fitted over the barrel, the vent in the rear leg (gas tube bracket) must fit so that the gas vent in the barrel is centered exactly, see Figure 5-16. The set screw on our custom rifle (arrow), makes certain that the front sight assembly stays centered and in place.

Barrels are sold as rifled blanks only or blanks with rough cut or short chambers. Many custom gunsmiths prefer to cut their chambers from scratch to their final shape and specification. The chamber is first roughed to shape. Then a finish reamer equipped with a long pilot is inserted into the chamber, see Figure 5-17. The pilot fits into the bore ahead of the chamber. As the reamer is advanced, the pilot guides it exactly in line with the bore. The fin-

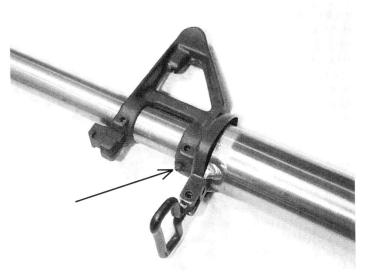

Chamber — Virtually every custom gunsmith building the M16/AR15 match rifle will have his own tried and true method for cutting chambers.

Fig. 5-16. Front sight and gas vent assembly on the Grüning Precision custom match AR15 rifle. Note that the set screw holds the front sight assembly tightly in proper alignment, and that the ferrule is welded to the hand guard tube and does not touch the barrel.

It can be as simple as matching the chamber length to bullet length so that the bullet has "x" distance to "jump" from the case mouth to the leade or it may be too complicated to be understood by the "layman" — meaning the gunsmith wishes to keep it a secret.

When ordering a custom M16/AR15 barrel, quiz your gunsmith about the method he uses to cut the chamber. If he refuses to discuss his methods, ask for the names and phone numbers of other customers for whom he has built rifles and check to see if they are happy. If he refuses to provide names

ish reamer also cuts the throat or leade, which is the taper at the front of the chamber leading to the lands. The leade positions the bullet when it is fired and guides it into the bore.

The depth of the chamber is governed by the head space specification which in the case of the M16/AR15 is the distance from the bolt face to the sloping wall of the chamber that cradles the shoulder of the cartridge case, see Figure 5-18. Head space specifications for both military and civilian M16s and AR15s are shown in Table 5-2. Head space gages for the M16/AR15 are shown in Figure 5-19 and Appendix E.

Fig. 5-17. M16/AR15 chambering reamers

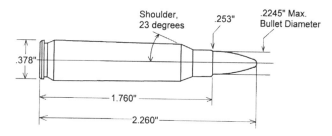

Fig. 5-18. The chamber must be cut to fit exactly the dimensions of the particular cartridge which will be used with the rifle. This drawing provides the dimensions for the .223 Remington (5.56 x 45 mm NATO) cartridge.

Table 5-2 M16/AR15 Head Space Gage Dimensions	
Go Gage	1.464
No Go Gage	1.470
Field Gage Military Civilian (SAMMI)	1.473 1.474

leaves the barrel. Secondly, if the crown is not cut absolutely perpendicular to the bore, as the bullet leaves the muzzle, gas will escape first from the low side and push the bullet in the opposite direction. Your gunsmith should be capable of cutting the crown to within 0.0003 inch true to the bore's axis. And the crown should be recessed at 11 degrees to provide additional protection to the muzzle, see Figure 5-20.

Fig. 5-19. Headspace gages for the M16/AR15 rifle: top to bottom: Go (1.464), No Go (1.470), military field (1.473) and SAMMI (1.474).

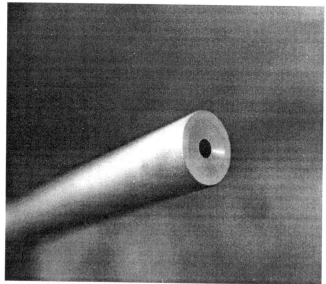

Fig. 5-20. The crown on this 1000 meter match AR15 rifle was cut to 0.0003 inch true to the bore by custom gunsmith Jim Gronning of Grüning Precision. He cuts all his barrel crowns with the same precision.

Selecting the Barrel — Once you have completed your analysis, hopefully based on the considerations discussed above, you are ready to select the barrel blank. There are numerous companies today making barrel blanks in a wide variety of shapes and materials. Selecting a material — 4140 steel or 416 stainless steel — requires that you consider the depth of your pockets as stainless steel barrels are more expensive, the

Crown — The barrel's crown is of equal importance to the chamber where accuracy is concerned, for two reasons. First, the crown helps to protect the delicate end of the lands and grooves. Any deformity in this area will divert the bullet as it

amount of shooting you will do and the loads you will shoot.

In addition, the companies that manufacture M16/AR15s often offer their barrels for sale. The standard barrel configurations are shown in Figure 5-21 and were developed by Colt, the upper two for the U.S. military and the lower as part of their sporting line of A2 rifles.

If you are an active match participant with an eye on Camp Perry in August, then you will shoot upwards of a 1,000 rounds per month in practice, not to mention matches. That rate of shooting definitely demands a stainless steel barrel.

If you just like shooting ultra-accurate match-quality rifles at your local range once or twice a month, then a 4140 steel barrel will serve you just as well.

If you intend to shoot very light bullets at speeds approaching 4,000 fps or very heavy bullets over 600 yards, then choose the stainless steel barrel because you will start to see throat erosion in carbon steel barrels at between 1,500 to 2,000 rounds. If you will be shooting standard commercial or military surplus ammunition at 100, 200 or 300 yard targets, you can get by with 4140 steel barrels for upwards of 10,000 rounds.

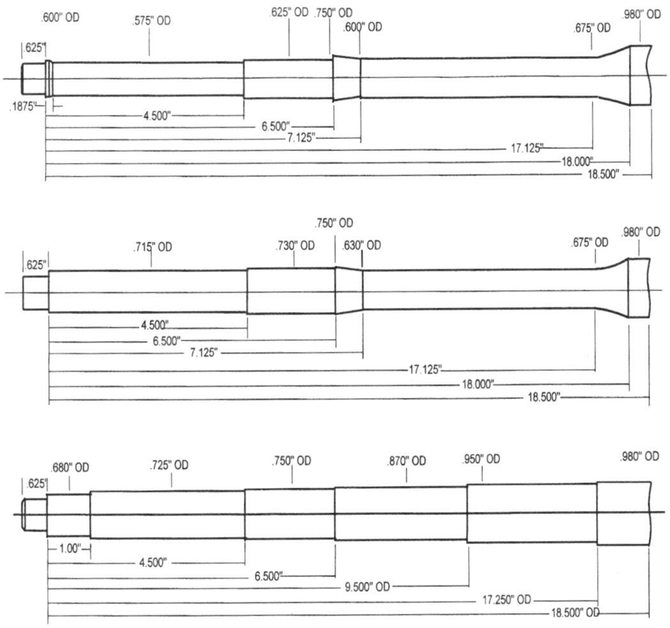

The author is very partial to K&P barrels but has also used Obermeyer, Hart, Douglas, Schneider, Krieger and Walther barrels in .223 and other calibers. It is the author's contention that any barrel from a major manufacturer with the rifling twist suited to the ammunition, properly chambered and throated and free-floated will provide less than minute-of-angle accuracy in the M16/AR15. How much less than minute-of-angle? Well, that's why you are paying your gunsmith the big bucks.

Chrome Plated Bores and Chambers — One final note: many military M16/AR15 barrel chambers and bores are chrome-plated to resist erosion and extend barrel life because soldiers in combat are not always in a position to clean their rifles. But chrome-plating a match barrel, or one from which you expect to wring the utmost accuracy is a no-no as it adds a layer of metal to the bore, thus reducing its diameter. Even if you could make the bore oversized to allow for the chrome layer, there is no way to assure that you can lay down the right

amount of plating to bring the bore to the correct specification, .219 — .224 inches in diameter. In addition, the chrome plating tends to accumulate at the bottom of the grooves, further aggravating the accuracy problem. A slight decrease in accuracy is not a military consideration as soldiers rarely fire rifles at targets more than 300 meters distant. But a match shooter does and that slight loss of accuracy could make the difference between being in the black at 600 meters or not.

Don't chrome-plate a match rifle barrel. See the sidebar overleaf for instructions on how to determine if an M16/AR15 bore and chamber are chrome-plated.

Bolt Carriers and Bolts

Opinions vary considerably among match shooters and custom rifle smiths about how a bolt carrier affects accuracy. So far as the author can tell there are a lot of opinions but few facts. The bolt carrier's job is to lock and unlock the bolt head. What we do know is that the bolt carrier affects reliability, which is just as important in match competition as accuracy. A bolt carrier that is too loose in the receiver track will bind and cause misfeeds. It also loses its lubrication at a faster rate adding to the misfeed problem.

A bolt carrier that is too tight will also tend to bind, particularly as it heats up. Again, lubrication becomes critical. As the too-tight bolt carrier heats up, the lubrication flashes off more quickly, increasing the friction during cycling.

The bolt carrier also cocks the hammer. Unless the ramp is machined at the proper angle, it will be chewed up by the hammer which is made of harder steel. Finally, it is critical that the bolt carrier rails fit those in the receiver properly and are square and straight.

The bolt itself holds the cartridge in alignment with the bore. The M16/AR15 bolt must be slightly smaller than the inside diameter of the bolt carrier. The bolt ring groove must be cut to an exact depth so that when the bolt rings are installed, a gas tight fit is achieved with the bolt carrier. You can test this easily by checking to see if the bolt will move side-to-side in the bolt carrier. If it does, the fit is very sloppy and combustion gases will leak back through the bolt.

Fig. 5-21. Top to bottom, barrel contours for M16A1/AR15A1, M16A2 and AR15 Sporter II

A more precise test is recommended. Remove the bolt from the carrier, then remove the firing pin, extractor and ejector parts. Make sure the bolt is lightly lubricated. Insert the bolt into the carrier, then slowly tip the bolt carrier down. If the bolt slides out, it's time to replace the rings.

If you are still having trouble after replacing the rings, the bolt ring groove in the bolt may not have been cut properly, or the bolt carrier bolt tunnel is oversized and one or both will have to be replaced.

Accuracy will be reduced if the bolt lugs do not mesh perfectly with the lugs in the barrel extension. The custom gunsmith achieves this by lapping the bolt lugs into the barrel extension lugs so that contact is as even as possible around the circumference and friction is reduced to the lowest level achievable.

The custom rifle smith has a plethora of bolt carriers to choose from. G.I. bolts include those manufactured by Colt and Fabrique Nationale, plus those manufactured by companies in other nations using the M16 and which have been imported into the United States. We would have included a photograph, but there are no significant outward differences in any of the bolts and carriers examined.

There are also a number of commercial manufacturers of AR15 components, including bolts (refer to Table 3-1) and numerous aftermarket suppliers, some of whom manufacture bolts and other parts. Then there are the suppliers who are simply resellers of used G.I. and new aftermarket parts. When purchasing parts, try and determine into which category the seller falls before paying good money.

National Match Bolts — You should know one thing about bolt carriers and bolts right from the start. There is no such thing as a "National Match" anything as far as the M16/AR15 is concerned, at least at the time this was being written. I am using "National Match" to mean blessed by U.S. Army, Marine Corps, Air Force and/or Navy regulations. No U.S. military service has yet published National Match standards for the M16/AR15. Each service works to their own set of rules and specifications, and to the author's knowledge, these have not been published in the same sense as those National Match standards have been for the M1903, M1 Garand and M14 Rifles.

A number of commercial concerns have used the phrase "National Match" for their bolt carriers and bolts to signify that theirs hold to tighter dimensions. But just stamping "Match" or "National Match" on a bolt carrier does not mean that it does. Dimensions must be checked carefully against manufacturer's claims and specifications for service rifles to make certain that what you receive for your money is not just a surplus bolt that has been so marked, then chrome-plated.

One bolt that we tested and found to meet and exceed military specifications for dimensions and hardness and finish was that from Young Manufacturing in Glendale, Arizona. Their bolt carrier is manufactured in their own production facilities, and two variations are offered: the first is called the "National Match Bolt Carrier" and it is 0.2 oz. heavier than the stock M16/AR15 bolt. The second variation is termed the "National Match Light" and weighs 0.6oz. less than the standard GI bolt carrier. It was designed for use in combat shooting where cycling and faster lock time is desired. We might mention that the Young's Manufacturing bolt carrier is the only one that is patented.

Owner Dan Young is a precision machinist trained in the aerospace industry — his company provides components to the aerospace industry on contract. He became interested in the mechanics and problems of the M16/AR15 bolt a few years ago while manufacturing parts for a well-known custom rifle maker. Applying his aerospace training, he developed what

---

Military M16 and some civilian AR15 chambers and bores are chrome-plated to resist erosion and wear. Those that are can easily be determined by examining the markings on barrels or by examining the bore and chamber.

To determine if the chamber and bore are chrome-plated, clean throughly and dry with clean patches. Use a strong white light (sunlight is best) and examine the bore and chamber. Bores will have a flat, pewter appearance if chrome-plated but will gleam if not.

If the barrel is made by Colt, you can also check the markings as follows: approximately 1 inch behind the compensator you will find a marking stamped in the barrel which will tell you the rifling twist rate, the caliber and a code indicating whether or not the chamber and/or bore is chrome-plated.

SAK MP C 5.56 NATO 1/12
C MP C 5.56 NATO 1/7

SAK or **C** indicates the manufacturer; **MP** indicates that the barrel was inspected for flaws by Magnetic Particle Inspection, the following **C** indicates a chrome-plated chamber; 5.56 NATO is the caliber and 1/7 indicates a rifling twist rate of 1 turn in 7 inches.

The letters **RUC** or **RNC** may also be stamped on the barrel to indicate a chromed chamber.

If you see this marking:

C MP B 5.56 NATO 1/7

the **C** and **B** indicates that both chamber and bore are chrome-plated. Or the marking **CB** alone, indicates a chrome-plated chamber and bore as do the words, **Chrome Bore**.

he and a great many match shooters feel is an improved bolt carrier.

Young Manufacturing National Match bolts are machined from 8620 steel and heat treated to GI mil spec standards. The bolt is fluted at the upper end, then ground and polished smooth and hard chromed, see Figure 5-22. This provides more con-

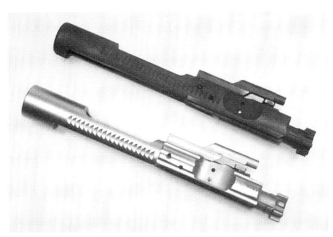

Fig. 5-22. Custom-made AR15 bolt (below) made by Young Manufacturing compared to standard AR15 (upper) manufactured by Colt.

tact in the upper receiver and holds the cartridge in better alignment with the bore than a standard GI bolt. The hard chrome plating promotes smoother functioning. Finally, a full hammer ramp is machined so that there is no chance of the firing pin hanging up on the hammer, see Figure 5-23. The ramp also assures that the new titanium firing pins can be used without being damaged.

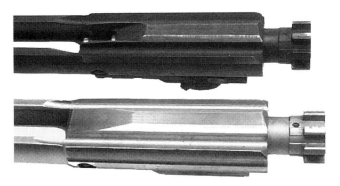

Fig. 5-23. The full hammer ramp machined on the underside of the Young Manufacturing bolt carrier (below) is compared to the hammer ramp on a standard AR15 bolt carrier (above).

Sights

Front Sights

The issue front sight for the M16A2/AR15A2 is a great improvement over that for the M16A1/AR15A1. The flat sur-

faces of the former's sight post provide a crisper sight picture than the round front sight post of the latter. The only drawback to the A2 configuration front sight is that fact that adjustments can only be made in 1/4 minute of angle increments — four flat surfaces — while the A1 front sight post can be adjusted for any degree of change.

Either sight when viewed through the overly large issue short range aperture on the rear sight is easy to "top," i.e., to look over the top of the sight rather than across it. This, of course, causes you to shoot low. The only cure for this is a smaller aperture as described below.

The service front sight is fine for casual target shooting or for combat, but competition work demands a narrow post. Competition front sights with precision ground sides are available from a number of suppliers. The most popular widths are 0.52, 0.62 and 0.72 inches. There is no hard and fast rule as to which size is best. It is a subjective determination that your eye and brain will make. Try all three sizes, starting with the widest to see which performs best for you. Fortunately, front sight posts are not expensive. Be sure to check the sight post with both apertures to make certain your eye/brain remains happy with its selection.

The ground sides of the A2 front sight post will show a steely white color which is sometimes a help against the black bull if you hold center but which may disappear into the white if you hold the bull atop the post. For that reason, or if sun glare is a problem, simply blacken the sight post. Cold bluing solution works well and is certainly less messy than carbide sight blackeners.

Grúning Precision will manufacture any width AR15 sight desired by its customers — a 0.52 inch front post was installed on our custom match service rifle. And Grúning Precision takes it a step further, if desired. A small hole is drilled beneath the front sight post and tapped, and a set screw is inserted and tightened down to prevent the front sight from being moved inadvertently once "zero" has been achieved. This is just another bit of "gremlin-proofing" that you should do if you intended to compete with your rifle.

Rear Sights

The new windage adjustable rear sight developed for the A2 proved a boon to match shooters. Windage adjustments can now be made in 1/2 minute of angle increments and elevation adjustments in 1 minute of angle increments. But when elevated to the maximum for ranges beyond 600 yards, the A2 rear sight proved to have as much as 2 minutes of angle in left-to-right play while the M14's combat sight had less than a tenth that. The reason lies in the fact that the sight itself is mounted on a single threaded pillar. The further it is extended, the more wobble develops.

Richard Smith of Smith Enterprises, Phoenix, Arizona has developed improved A2 rear sights with a more finely threaded pillar screw, see Figure 5-24. Jim Gronning of

Fig. 5-24. A standard Colt-manufactured rear sight pillar (L) for the AR15 compared to one manufactured by Smith Enterprises (R). Note the much finer thread on the Smith rear sight pillar.

Grúning Precision has added two precision ground guides to Smith's fine thread pillar which eliminates all side-to-side play and keeps the rear sight rock steady even at maximum elevation, see Figure 5-25.

Fig. 5-25. Grúning Precision has modified the Smith Enterprises rear sight with the addition of two precision ground steel pillars (arrows). Even at extreme elevations of 1,000 yards and more there is no left-right play.

Another problem with the rear sight has to do with the fact that the aperture is mounted on the windage screw. Every time you change apertures, you turn that screw 1/4 turn (or 1/4 minute of angle), and that causes a change in the point of impact. In theory, the long range (smaller) aperture is offset to compensate, but the author has discovered that the compensation is approximate at best and cannot be relied on. This may not be too important at short ranges (at 100 yards it is only about 1/4 inch) but at longer ranges it can spell disaster.

The one quarter turn of the windage screw caused by changing apertures will produce, at 800 yards, a change of about 2 inches in the point of impact— enough to take you right out of the black, especially if the wind is crosswise.

Why change apertures at all? The two different apertures on the A1 or A2 rear sight allow more or less light through the peep sight depending on which you select, see Figure 5-26. The large diameter hole works best at ranges up to 200-300 yards, the smaller aperture at ranges beyond. But it is really a matter of personal preference and a bit of experimentation will tell you which is the best aperture for you.

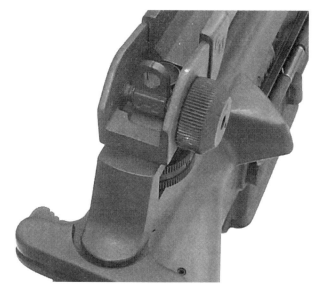

Fig. 5-26. Standard M6/AR15 rear sight aperture

Once you know, do not change apertures after the rifle is sighted in. If this is not practicable, i.e., you are using the small aperture on an heavily overcast day, remember to take into the account the 1/4 minute angle of change when you select the other aperture, i.e., if you are shooting at 400 yards and change apertures the sight will move one inch (two clicks) to the right on the target. Therefore, you would move the windage two clicks left to compensate.

Competition shooters usually prefer narrower diameter apertures than those installed on military or civilian M16/AR15s. There are three ways to achieve this. Substitute a "L" arm with apertures reduced to your liking. The problem with this methods is that you cannot always be sure that the smaller apertures will work well in reduced or variable light.

The second method is to have the existing aperture drilled out and tapped for an insert, or the easier way, to simply replace the "L" with one already drilled and tapped. Screw-in apertures in varying sizes ranging from 0.36 or smaller to 0.52 or larger are available from a number of sources such as Quality Parts/Bushmaster, Brownells or ArmaLite.

The third method, and one popular with those of us whose vision is no longer that of a teenager, is the sighting system developed by B. Jones of Phoenix, AZ. His system literally puts a corrective lens into the aperture. Using the existing "L," you drill out the largest aperture, thread it and screw in the lens holder, see Figure 5-27. Into the lens holder goes a corrective lens matched to your vision requirements. No more squinted, squinching and squeezing to position your glasses so that you can see through the proper aspect. Since the lens is in the sight, your head position remains consistent from shot to shot. A variety of ready-made lenses to correct most vision problems are always in stock, and in various colors to suit a variety of lighting. And if the ready-made ones do not work, Bob will grind one to your exact specifications.

Fig. 27. B. Jones rear sight system. A corrective lens is inserted into the holder which is threaded into the rear sight.

For those bolt-action rifle match shooters whose windage knobs turn the "right way," that is, left to right, and dislike the AR15 because its windage knob turns right to left, B. Jones is now supplying left-hand threaded windage knobs that function exactly the same as the windage knob on your favorite bolt-action rifle.

B. Jones also provides a variety of other "corrective rear sight" aids. For law enforcement tactical shooters, a similar rear sight system has a shorter hood and the lenses are held in with an "O" ring. The lens and hood are mounted on the short stroke of the "L" which permits the sight to be flipped so that the shooter can use the "base" aperture for close-in shots or other cases where there is no need for the "improved" image.

A wide variety of other types of sights are available for the AR15. For the combat shooter, "Trijicon® Rifle Sights" has tritium inserts to provide sight visibility in low light conditions. Match shooters (but not service rifle match) who want improved "iron sight" have their choice of wide range of receiver rear sights including the quick detachable base by J.P. Enterprises for the AR15 that holds the Lyman #90L receiver sight. This sight can be removed from base and reattached without loss of zero. J.P. Enterprises also provides a quick detachable front sight mount for the Lyman #93 Globe front

sight. They manufacture another that clamps securely on Weaver-style bases as well. These and other sights and accessories for the AR15 are available from Brownells, perhaps the largest gunsmithing accessory source in the world (see Appendix F).

Triggers

The only criticism ever levied against the M16/AR15 trigger of which the author is aware is that it is a single stage trigger while the M1 Garand and the M14 were equipped with two-stage triggers. The two-stage trigger is considered more conducive to aimed fire because it allows you to bring the trigger to the point of releasing the sear (first stage), hold it there while you steady your aim and control your breathing, and squeeze (second stage). The single stage trigger does not provide this "peaking" that tells you that the sear is about to release. Even so, it is possible to adjust the issue trigger on the M16/AR15 not only to the desired "pull weight," but an experienced custom rifle smiths can smooth it to the point where pull and sear release are accomplished in one smooth motion. Fortunately, you can have it either way. For those shooters who prefer the two-stage trigger (the author is not one) it can be easily installed.

Many out-of-the box AR15s (and M16s) arrive with less than adequate triggers no matter the manufacturer. Mating surfaces are frequently rough and produce a hard, creepy pull. Corporation for the Promotion of Rifle Practice and Firearms Safety (CPRPFS) rules require a minimum 4.5 lb trigger pull for National Match competition. So, the obvious solution is to stone a rough trigger smooth. But you have to be very careful. As with any trigger assembly, angles are carefully calculated and machined to provide a safe and consistent let off. Changing the angle of the trigger/sear interface is dangerous and can result in inadvertent firing, doubling or other malfunctions.

Trigger parts for the M16/AR15 are case-hardened for long wear. Stoning through the case into the softer metal may provide a "smooth" trigger initially, but it will soon turn hard and creepy again as the softer steel wears. And malfunctions will quickly follow. To avoid this situation, some custom gunsmiths add an insert of hardened alloy steel to the bearing surface of the trigger. The insert can then be stoned to a mirror polish without fear of cutting through the case hardening.

Since we opted for a single-stage trigger, we asked Jim Gronning of Grúning Precision to install his variation. He provides an excellent single stage trigger using the existing AR15 or M16 trigger assembly. He begins by lightening the hammer to provide faster lock time. He then checks — and regrinds the mating surfaces to specification if necessary — then stones the mating parts to a glass surface. If too much grinding is needed, he will substitute parts. He then installs a trigger over-travel screw on the selector switch axis. The result is smooth trigger with about 0.125 inch takeup and a crisp release at 4.75 lbs, see Figure 5-28.

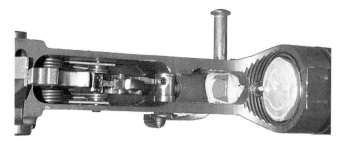

Fig. 5-28. Grúning Precision trigger work. Note the lightened hammer and the trigger stop on the selector lever axle. Note the glass bedding at the rear of the receiver to insure that the upper and lower receivers match perfectly.

William's Trigger Specialties of Atwood, IL provides both single and two-stage triggers of unmatched quality. For Mouse Gun advocates, bench rest shooters and varmiteers, they also offer one of the slickest set triggers for the AR15 that the author has ever encountered. The author's AR15A1 with a William's set trigger breaks like a glass rod at exactly 1.25 lbs every time. The best thing about the Williams set trigger is that it can only be set when the safety is in the "ON" position. You set the selector to SAFE, push the trigger forward, then flip the selector to FIRE, see Figure 5-29.

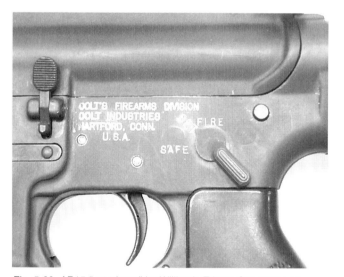

Fig. 5-29. AR15 "set trigger" by William's Trigger Specialties of Atwood, IL

For those who prefer the two-stage trigger, one of the most popular is the Compass Lake Engineering Competition Trigger. Formerly available through Quality Parts/Bushmaster, it is now available direct from Compass Lake — See Appendix F. Another two-stage design that is well liked by competitors, including the Army's Marksmanship Unit, is the Milazzo-Krieger two-stage design. Both the Compass Lake and Milazzo-Krieger designs include a lighter weight hammer for faster lock time.

The key to selecting any type of new trigger, or even a rework of the existing trigger, is sear engagement. Anything

that reduces sear engagement will cause the bearing surfaces of the parts affected to wear faster. To overcome this, the new parts must be made of hardened steel alloys or existing trigger parts should be professionally rehardened, if possible.

Magazines

The M16/AR15 rifle is naturally muzzle heavy with the magazine well slightly behind the point of balance, unlike the M14/M1A and the FAL which locate the magazine at midpoint. Because the magazine is behind the point of balance, the point of aim does not tend rise as severely as does M14 or FAL as the magazine empties during rapid fire. And, as the lower receiver serves only to hold the trigger assembly and the magazine is directly in line with the chamber, different magazines do not tend to cause a change in the point of impact to the extent that they do in rifles with a one-piece receiver. Therefore magazine selection is usually limited to making certain that the magazine is clean and properly lubricated, the follower moves up and down without binding and the feed lips are not deformed. Even so, the wise competitive shooter will test and select his or her magazines with care, label them with the rifle's serial number or other identifier and keep them segregated, see Figure 5-30.

Fig. 5-30. AR15 magazine identified to a specific rifle for match shooting. The author uses white typing correction fluid.

The twenty round magazine is used by most competitors although ten round magazines may become popular in states such as California that have outlawed the sale of new magazines with a capacity of 11 rounds or greater after January 1, 2000. Aluminum GI 20 round magazines appear to be the most popular on the range, but again, every competitor has his or her own preferences. Thirty round magazines are too long to be used in the prone position, and there are no stages in any NRA or Corporation for the Promotion of Rifle Practice and Firearms Safety (CPRPFS) sanctioned matches that require more than a twenty round magazine. Few of the several plastic magazines available are seen in competition, probably because most are of the thirty round variety.

The Final Results

After working through the analysis outlined above, we selected our custom gunsmith and developed a set of specifications for both rifles as follows.

Service Match AR15

Our service match rifle was built on a Colt Model MT6601 Target HBAR Rifle. It was unfired when we began the project. After breaking the stock AR15 in with 150 rounds of Lake City military ammunition, we fired a five shot group at 100 and 200 yards for record using Federal Gold Medal match ammunition from a rest. The 100 yard group measured 0.96 inches in diameter. The 200 yard group measured 2.10 inches in diameters, see Figure 5-30.

Fig. 5-31. The K&P stainless steel match barrel machined to final shape, just before installation.

Fig. 5-30. Craig Riesch fires the stock AR15 during its break-in period prior to being rebuilt by custom gunsmith Jim Gronning, owner of Gruning Precision, as a service match rifle.

After reviewing the winning rifles shot in several regional matches and Camp Perry in 1999, we selected our custom gunsmith, Jim Gronning of Grúning Precision, Riverside, California. We have to admit that we were influenced by the fact that he had already built three M1A match rifles and an outstanding Elk rifle for us.

For the barrel, we selected a K&P heavy stainless steel barrel with a unchromed bore. Jim turned it to the proper diameters, machined the chamber to exacting shape and specifications that he has developed and which contribute greatly to the accuracy of his rifles, see Figure 5-31. The barrel is 0.998 inches in diameter at the rear for 2.60 inches, stepping down to 0.980 for 8.775 inches and stepping down in three more steps to a final diameter of 0.720 inches with an overall length of 19.89 inches. The head space dimension — go gage to barrel shoulder is 0.752 inches. The was installed to the upper

receiver. An A.H. Merchant hand guard tube and barrel nut, as described above, was installed. The barrel nut was torqued to the proper specifications and the gas tube alignment checked, see Figure 5-32.

Fig. 5-32. Closeup showing the A.H. Merchant hand guard tube and barrel nut installed.

He machined the rear sight base at the back of the upper receiver perfectly flat in relation to the line of the bore, then installed his own modification of the Smith Enterprises rear sight with the twin, precision ground pillars as we anticipated a great deal of long range shooting, see Figure 5-33. A 0.52 inch wide front sight was chosen, which Jim ground himself and installed with a set screw below to prevent its inadvertently being turned.

A B. Jones sighting system was installed in the rear sight with a +1.75 correction lens that worked like a charm. For the first time in years, I was able to shoot without eyeglasses or a telescopic sight and actually see the target bull well enough at 600 yards to shoot "10"s and an occasional "X." Thank you Bob Jones!

The stock trigger was converted to a slick, single stage trigger that breaks crisply at 3.75 pounds. The set screw in

Fig. 5-33. Machining the rear sight base absolutely flat.

the selector switch axis limits overtravel to 2 mm. The hand guards were mounted on an extension tube threaded onto the receiver. A Young Manufacturing bolt assembly completed the project. Empty, the service match rifle weighed 9.86 pounds, see Figure 5-34.

We tested the rifle extensively on the 100 and 200 yards ranges at the Maywood Gun Club in Riverside, California and at the 300 and 600 yard ranges at the West End Gun Club at Upland, California. Testing was done from all positions as well as from a steady rest, see Figures 5-35 and 36. At all ranges, the rifle shot sub-minute of angle groups. The following figures are taken from testing performed while firing from a rest. At 100 yards, group sizes averaged 0.47 inches; at 200 yards, averages were 1.3 inches. At 300 yards, averages were 2.10 inches and at 600 yards, 4.9 inches. Black Hills 69 grain match was used for all testing which was conducted on slightly overcast spring days with little or no wind. We would emphasize this is the same rifle that in the hands of 18 year old Joe Bartoli won the Alice Bull Cup given for the highest aggregate score in the National Trophy Individual Rifle and President's Matches at Camp Perry in 1999.

1000 Yard Match Rifle

The 1000 yard match gun followed a similar building procedure. Again, a K&P barrel was selected as a rifled blank. It was set up between centers on the lathe and the exterior machined straight in line with the bore, then cut to shape. The 24 inch barrel was cut straighter than the service rifle barrel with only two steps leading to the gas port. The gas block (Figure 5-37) was heated with a propane torch to expand it slightly,

Fig. 5-34. Top, The finished product, the Grúning Precision Service Match Rifle, below, Fig. 5-35, the 1000 Yard Match Rifle.

Fig. 5-36. Doug Curry, retired Los Angeles County Sherrif's Deputy checks out our Grúning Precision Service Match AR15 at the West End Gun Club, Upland, California

then mounted and centered on the barrel for an exact shrink fit. As an added precaution, it is held securely in place with set screws. This set screws are probably superfluous but Jim Gronning prefers to take every precaution. Murphy rules in competition.

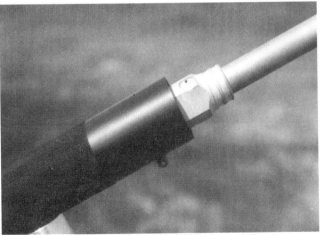

Fig. 5-37. The gas block installed by shrink fitting to an AR15 1000 yard space gun barrel.

The lower receiver selected was the DPMS AR15 410 stainless steel model in a black Teflon finish. The upper receiver was the ArmaLite AR15A4 in a matt black anodized finish. This model is a flat top receiver, so the DPMS flat top riser mount with Weaver rails was selected to raise the telescopic sight high enough for comfortable shooting. The DPMS mount slides right over the ArmaLite Weaver-style base and fastens down with fore and aft thumbscrews, see Figure 5-38. The trigger treatment was the same for the service match rifle except that the trigger was set to break at 1.75 pounds. A steel

free-floated hand guard was installed after Jim machined it to accept a hand stop of his own design. A Sierra Precision pistol grip was also installed. A Leupold Vari-X II 3 x 9 telescopic sight was mounted using Leopold rings.

Fig. 5-38. The DMPS Flat Top Riser mount raises the weaver-style rings high enough for comfortable shooting with a telescopic sight.

Fig. 5-39. Custom gunsmith, Jim Gronning (r) confers with two experts over a fine point in his design for an AR15 service match rifle: Col. Kenneth Erdman, USMC, Ret., Past President of the California Rifle and Pistol Association, National Champion, Camp Perry and Distinguished High Master (l) and Lt. Col. Robert Frushon (center), USMC, Ret., past Vice President of the California Rifle and Pistol Association and past Chairman of the High Power Rifle Association and a Distinguished Master high power shooter as well.

6. SHOOTING THE M16/AR15

The M16/AR15 Sight

The M16/AR15 rifle, no matter the manufacturer, is zeroed at the factory before shipping. Unless major repairs or custom work have been performed, only minor adjustments should be necessary to bring the point of aim to where you want it. If the barrel or front or rear sights have been replaced, or ammunition other than M193 Ball for M16/AR15 and M16A1/AR15A1 rifles with a 1:12 rifling twist or M855 for the M16A2/AR15A2 with a 1:17, 1:77 or 1:9 rifling twist is used, then reestablishment of the basic zero may be necessary.

Sight picture is a matter of personal preference. Some prefer a center hold on the target bull (USMC hold), others prefer to align the bull atop the front sight post (US Army hold), see Figure 6-1. Be consistent and sight all your rifles — and pistols— in the same manner. More about "Sight Picture" later.

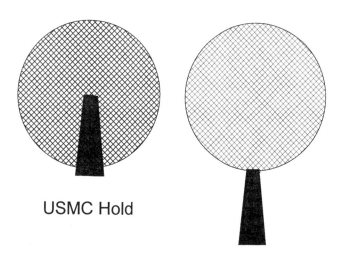

USMC Hold

U.S. Army Hold

Fig. 6-1. Front sight and target as seen through the rear sight aperture.

Note: Before starting, it is extremely wise to record all final sight settings in terms of X-number of clicks up from the bottom and X-number of clicks right or left of dead center. Write the numbers down in a notebook, in your range book if you keep one, and on a strip of masking tape attached to the butt stock of your rifle. Really savvy shooters also record the sight settings on a strip of plastic with indelible marking pen and keep it in the butt stock compartment. Don't depend on your memory.

Adjusting the Sights

The standard M16/AR15A1 front sight is a round, tapered post, and while it does not provide as sharp a sight picture as the later A2 sight, it can be adjusted up or down without worrying about the proper profile. The standard front A2 sight is a tapered square post, and it must be turned up or down in 1/4 increments. If you have installed an aftermarket front sight with front and rear sides narrower than the left or right sides, it must be turned in 1/2 minute increments to present the proper profile.

The front sight adjusts easily with the M16/AR15 front sight adjusting tool. If you do not have one, use a bullet tip or a small punch to depress the detent and a pair of masking tape-covered needle nose pliers to carefully turn the sight. Be careful not to scratch the finish. As a general rule of thumb, if the rifle is shooting high, the front sight post needs to be adjusted down; if shooting low, it needs to be adjusted up.

The A1 Sight System — The A1 rear sight is not adjustable for elevation but is adjustable for windage in 1 minute of angle increments. Use a bullet tip or other tool to depress the detent and turn the wheel on the right side of the receiver. The A1 rear sight was intended originally for combat shooting, and an elevation adjustment was not thought necessary due to flat-shooting characteristics of the .223 cartridge. Elevation adjustments when necessary were made by raising or lowering the front sight, and then only by a qualified armorer. If you need to adjust the elevation on your M16A1/AR15A1, skip the next section and go to "How to Solve Problems" below and use that information, ignoring references to adjusting the rear sight. The M16A2/AR15A2 rear sight is adjustable for both elevation and windage as it was intended to be used over longer ranges that the A1 rifle. However, the basic zero is still set by adjusting the front sight first, then the rear sight.

After adjusting the front sight for elevation and the rear for windage to achieve basic zero, you may find that the rear sight has moved too far to the left or right. If so, you will need to consult a competent gunsmith experienced with the M16/AR15, or return the rifle to the manufacturer for repair. You cannot compensate by adjusting the front sight for windage on the standard A1 or A2 rifle.

The A2 Sight System — The A2 sight can be adjusted for elevation in 1 minute of angle increments by turning the horizontal range dial under the rear sight. The range dial is marked "8/3." The 300 indicates 300 meters which is the battle sight setting; the 800 (when the elevation range dial is turned a full revolution) indicates 800 meters range. The range dial is also marked"4," "5," and "6" indicating hundreds of meters. These range settings will only be accurate when the rifle is properly zeroed as described in the following paragraphs.

Adjustments to the A2 rear sight for windage are made in 1/2 inch increments by turning the windage knob on the right side of the receiver right or left.

Some aftermarket range dials, such as those manufactured by Smith Enterprises, do not have range markings. As these rear sights are made primarily for target shooting, the assumption is that the shooter will prefer to turn the elevation and windage dials to zero and count click stops to desired elevation and windage settings.

Establishing the Basic Zero

"Sighting in" to achieve a basic zero can be an exercise in frustration unless done correctly. The following methods work very well. Shooting may be done from a rest or from a prone or sitting position. A rest works best and will require less expenditure of ammunition to achieve a centered group. Use sandbags or a commercial rifle rest to rest the handguard on, not the barrel. Try and pick a still day to eliminate the effects of wind on the bullet in flight.

Note: do not rest the rifle's hand guard on a hard surface. Use either a pad or your hand, between the hand guard and rest.

Set up a target at 25 yards. Twenty-five yards? Yes. The flight path of a bullet is an arc crossing any two points of equal altitude in space as it appears to rise and fall along your line of sight (actually, the flight of the bullet is a straight line but gravity pulls it into a curve). Since most bullets will cross the same altitude point at 25 and 100 yards, you can make use of this phenomenon to quickly sight in virtually any rifle at 25 yards where you can easily see the results. It is easy and quick to rezero for 200 or 300 yards.

This first system is the standard procedure developed by Colt to zero the M16/AR15 at the factory. It should always be followed after the installation of a new barrel or new sights. The second method works well when reestablishing the basic zero for nonstandard ammunition or when minor adjustments are needed.

Factory Method

Turn the elevation knob to the 8/3 (or 6/3 for carbines) mark, then up one click. The 3 indicates three hundred meters. Do not move the elevation knob for the rest of this procedure.

Turn the smaller, unmarked aperture on the sight leaf to the vertical position.

Turn the windage knob until the line on the sight leaf is in line with the index line on the rear sight base.

With the target at 25 yards and the rifle firm on its rest, center the sights on the target's X-ring. Fire ten rounds carefully to establish a group, readjusting the rifle to the same point of aim after every shot.

Compare the ten shot group with the center of the bull. If they are the same, further adjustment is not necessary. Otherwise, find the center of the group and draw a vertical and horizontal line. Measure vertical distance to the center of the X-ring, then horizontal distance, see Figure 6-2.

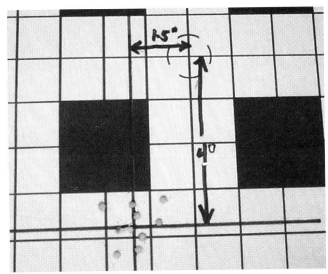

Fig. 6-2. Establishing Basic Zero. The center of this ten shot group fired at 25 yards was 4 inches low and 1.5 inches to the left. To bring the sights on target, use the Change in POI figures in Table 6-1 . . . 10.6 clicks up and 12 clicks right.

Calculate the number of clicks need to move the front sight up or down to set the elevation and left or right to set the windage using Table 6-1, overleaf [(can be used for either M195 Ball (55 grain bullet) or M855 Ball (62 grain bullet)].

For instance, if your group is centered 4 inches high and 1.5 inches to the right, divide 4 inches by 0.375 = 10.6. Turn the *front sight* using the front sight tool up (clockwise) 10 clicks. Turn the windage knob 12 clicks counterclockwise.

Fire another 10 shot group and repeat the above procedure until your group is centered on the target bull. Your rifle's basic zero is now set for 0 to 200 meters. Leave the windage knob set.

Write down both elevation and windage settings as the number of clicks above bottom and from right or left of the center line. Turn the elevation knob down one click to 8/3 (6/3 on the carbine) and flip the peep sight to bring up the large aperture. Your rifle or carbine is now zeroed for any distance from 100 to 300 yards and at 800 yards. Additional elevation and windage changes can be made by with the rear sight elevation and windage knobs.

Making Elevation and Sight Changes for Non-Standard Ammunition

If the basic zero has been established with military ball ammunition, you may wish to reestablish it for match ammuni-

Table 6-1
Establishing Basic Zero
Sight Adjustment Increments Target Distance
M195 Ball (55 grain) or M855 Ball (62 grain bullet)

Elevation Adjustments	
Target Distance	**Change in POI per Front Sight Click**
25 meters	9 mm (0.375 inches)
100 meters	1.8 cm (1.375 inches)
200 meters*	7 cm (2.75 inches)

Windage Adjustments	
Target Distance	**Change in POI per Windage Click**
25 meters	3 mm (0.125 inches)
100 meters	1.25 cm (0.5 inches)
200 meters**	2.50 cm (1 inch)

* Add one click to compensate for the difference between meters and yards
** Add two clicks to compensate for the difference between meters and yards
Data taken from M16A2 Rifles and Carbines, Operation and Unit Maintenance Instruction, 2nd Edition, 1988, Colt's Manufacturing Company.

tion or your own handloads. Set up a clean target at 25 yards. Turn the elevation adjusting screw down until the rear sight bottoms, then turn back up 2-3 clicks. Turn the windage knob until the center index mark on the sight leaf is directly in line with the center index line on the sight base. Fire a five shot group with the ammunition on which you wish to standardize.

Find the center of the five round group and measure the distance to the center of the target. Dial in the appropriate number of elevation and windage turns to bring the sights to point of aim using the above table. The click adjustments may not be exact but will be close enough.

Assume the same shooting position and fire another five shot group. This one should be centered in the bull. If not, make the necessary additional corrections.

Now shift the target to the 100 yard line. As before, assume the exact same shooting position and fire a five shot group. Because you have already brought the sights into near alignment, the five shot group should at least be on the paper. Measure the distance from the center of the five shot group to the bull and adjust the sights accordingly. Since you are firing at 100 yards, one click elevation will equal 1 inch and 1 click windage will equal 1/2 inch, or as close to that as necessary.

Fire another five shot group from the same position and make any final adjustments. You have now established your basic zero for this rifle with these sight settings and this am-

munition at 100 yards. To find the basic zero at for 200 or 300 yard center group, repeat the procedure you used for sighting the rifle at 100 yards at the desired distance. To find the basic zero with a different type of ammunition with a different bullet weight and/or powder charge, repeat the procedure for sighting the rifle at the desired distance.

Setting the Range Dial

Once you have established your basic zero for the ammunition type(s) you intend to shoot, you may notice that the elevation knob does not read 8/3 (6/3 for the carbine). It is helpful but not necessary to reset the M16/AR15A2 elevation or range dial — the circular, horizontal drum inset into the rear sight mount. Doing so will allow you to dial additional ranges quickly without counting clicks.

To do so, begin by recording your basic zero elevation setting as X clicks from the bottom. Do the same with the windage knob by counting the clicks back to the center index mark. Record the basic zero windage setting as X clicks right or left of center.

Turn down the rear sight elevation knob until the sight bottoms.

The elevation knob on the A2 is secured with a 1/16th inch allen screw which holds the two halves of the knob together (refer to Figure 4-5).

Flip the aperture leaf so that the smallest diameter aperture is vertical. Looking down on the rear sight from above, note the small hole just ahead of the aperture. When the elevation knob is turned with the 8/3 (6/3 for carbines) mark in line with the index mark on the left side beneath the rear sight housing, the allen screw will be directly beneath that hole. Insert the allen wrench and back off the screw 3-4 turns. Leave the allen wrench in the screw so that the upper portion (numbered) of the elevation knob will not turn. Turn the bottom of the elevation knob the number of clicks up or down to bring it to your new basic sight setting. Tighten the allen screw. The rear sight basic zero is now at the 8/3 mark (6/3 mark for carbines).

Note: A bit of white paint or typing correction fluid applied to the range and windage knobs markings makes them much more visible, especially on overcast days or in low light conditions. Clean the scribed lines first with alcohol, wipe dry and apply the paint. Rub excess off with your thumb, leaving the paint in the recesses. When the markings get dirty or the paint chips away, simply clean the old paint off and reapply. You can also apply a line of paint to designate the zero range setting for the windage knob if it is to the left or right of the center line.

Sight Picture

There are two sighting methods in common use: center hold and bottom hold. It is a good idea to experiment with both to see which works best for you, then standardize on it for both rifles and handguns.

The U.S. Marine Corps teaches the center hold. The front and rear sights are aligned so that they bisect the target bull. The U.S. Army teaches the bottom hold in which the target bull sits atop the front sight post. Either is just as effective when mastered, refer to Figure 6-1.

With the rifle against your shoulder look through the rear sight aperture. Line up the front sight with the black bull on the distant target. The object is to keep the top of the front post centered in the aperture with either the target bull bisected by the top of the sight post or sitting on it, whichever method you have chosen. Center the front post vertically. Your eye will take care of centering it horizontally by subconsciously measuring the amount of light on either side of the post and instructing your brain to make the adjustments.

Many new shooters complain that it is almost impossible to hold the rifle still enough to keep the sights on target. Improving upper body strength will minimize the amount of movement as will the proper use of a sling, proper breathing and proper stance. For instance, wearing a shooting coat and using a sling correctly will reduce muzzle waver by several orders of magnitude.

The muzzle of a rifle will describe a figure 8 when aimed at a target. How small that figure 8 is depends on you, your physical condition and the shooting aids you employ. Practice and more practice will teach you to hold the muzzle steady. Some shooters allow the front sights to pass across the target bull and squeeze the trigger just before it does so. This is not a good practice in target shooting and should be avoided. Instead, concentrate on holding the muzzle as steady as possible.

Breathing and heart rate also influence sight picture. You cannot aim correctly when your lungs are expanding and contracting, particularly at long ranges. Therefore, as you aim your rifle and release the safety, take a slightly deeper breath than normal. As the sights come onto the target, release one half the breath and hold the rest. Center your sights and fire.

When you are under pressure, adrenaline production increases and your heart rate speeds up. The average adult heart weighs about three-quarters of a pound and beats at an average rate of 72 times per minute — up to 120 to 130 times per minute under stress — and moves about 12 pounds of blood through the body. You can observe the effect of heart beat on sight picture best from the prone position. No matter how still you are, you will see the front sight post rise and fall against the target bull in time with your heart beat. If you observe long enough, you will see that the movement is not continuous. Your heart pumps and the sight moves up, then down. In that split second before the heart beats again, the rifle sight is still. That is the time to fire.

With practice, you will be able to control your breathing and to feel your heart beat so that you know when to fire.

Shooting Equipment

If you are serious about shooting well, you will need to add certain pieces of equipment. If you are a casual shooter, you will need only a few of the items mentioned below. But if you are a match shooter determined to win a High Master rating, then you will need all or more, see Figure 6-3.

Fig. 6-3. A well-equipped shooting kit is essential if you are a serious target shooter. Always check match rules to see what equipment you are allowed to take to the firing line.

Shooting Glasses and Ear Protection

No one should ever fire any gun without shooting glasses and ear protectors. Primers and cartridge cases can burst, no matter the amount of quality control employed by the manufacturers. In the M16/AR5 breech, you are dealing with white hot gases pressurized to 52,000 pounds per square inch every time you fire. Every modern rifle is designed to contain these gases and in the event a cartridge case ruptures, channel the escaping hot gases away from the shooter. But why takes chances? You only get one pair of eyes. Only a fool does not wear protective glasses when shooting.

Buy only shooting glasses with safety lenses. Your optometrist or ophthalmologist can supply safety glasses to your prescription and in a range of colors. If you live where bright sunny days are the norm, consider glasses with grey or green tint. Amber works best for foggy or overcast days.

Safety glasses should ride comfortably on the bridge of your nose in all shooting positions. If you wear prescription glasses, ask your doctor to move the optical center of vision in the lenses. You may have to demonstrate the positions so that he can determine the proper center. Inform the doctor before hand and take along an empty stock in a case, rather than a whole rifle. The doctor might not mind a target rifle in his examination rooms but other patients may object.

Hearing protection is just as important as eye protection. Although the author was convinced in his mid-twenties by an ex-Marine Corps gunnery sergeant who taught him to shoot to wear ear plugs at all times, it turned out not to be enough protection and he now suffers from tinnitus. Tinnitus is a disease on the inner ear in which you hear a constant buzzing, whistling or other sound, and it is common in most older shooters, rock and roll band members and fans of the Grateful Dead over 45. Wearing just ear plugs or head sets may not be enough. The author now routinely wears both and recommends the same procedure to all shooters. It doesn't take many high decibel blasts before your hearing is irrevocably damaged.

Spotting Scope

Almost any kind of shooting you do will require a good spotting telescope, or at least a good pair of binoculars. Even if you like exercise, you will not have time to walk 100 to 200 yards or more to the target between every shot or group of shots. And if you do not keep a constant check on how you are shooting, you will have no way to discover and correct mistakes.

Spotting scopes are expensive and can range from $125 to $500 and more. Your pocket book will guide you better than I can, but remember, you get what you pay for. The scope should be at least 20X to be useful — conversely, scopes beyond 60X are useless because of heat shimmer and mirage. Variable power scopes allow you to take advantage of cool, still days to magnify the image more than on hot, shimmering days. The scope should be mounted on sturdy rest. Most shooters who participate in matches prefer a stand with a vertical extension that allows the scope to be moved up for standing

Fig. 6-4. A shooting stool is almost a must at long matches. It can hold a water bottle, ammunition, tools, towel, safety glasses, etc., and provide a place to sit and relax.

and sitting, or down for prone positions. A "wind spike" can be screwed onto the bottom of the stand and pushed into the ground to keep the scope and stand from tipping over on windy days.

Shooting Gloves

A person new to the shooting sports chuckled at the author's shooting glove one day a few years ago, hinting that it was somehow not manly to wear one. By the end of his first hour practice session with the sling, the newby's hand was red and sore and he had changed his mind. You might push through the pain until your hand toughens up, but I've noticed that by the end of long matches, shooters without gloves usually are favoring their off hand. The pain surely must have some effect on their scores.

Shooting gloves are designed to protect the off hand when shoved against the forward sling swivel. It also provides a nonslip palm surface to cradle the hand guard or forend. Most shooting gloves leave the fingers exposed.

Shooting Mats

After you have stretched out once or twice on the cold, stony ground at most shooting ranges, or the concrete pads at the better equipped ones, you will understand the value of a shooting pad. High Power match rules do not allow you to use a pad that provides firm support but do allow you to protect your elbows and knees from abrasion and your body from cold and damp. Excellent shooting mats are available from many of the suppliers listed in Appendix F.

The shooting pad should be constructed of heavy material to resist the wear and tear of stones, roots, and your boots. It should conform to all High Power match rules, even if you do not intend to participate, and it should roll up into a small package for storage and transportation. If you do not want to pay for an expensive shooting mat, consider the closed-cell foam pads made for use under sleeping bags. Check your nearest sporting goods or Army surplus store.

Shooting Stool

The ultimate in convenience and comfort at the range, the shooting stool not only provides a place to sit but serves as storage container for everything from ammunition to tools to shooting glasses, bottles of water and insulated containers of coffee or tea . . . not an required item, but certainly a very handy one, especially at day-long matches, see Figure 6-4.

Note: A word here about stimulants containing coffee at matches. Unless the coffee or tea is decaffeinated, don't drink it. Caffeine stimulates the production of adrenalin which will increase muscle tension and give you the shakes. No matter how inured you think you are to caffeine, it is best avoided. The same goes for soft drinks. Most contain caffeine unless they specifically state they do not. The best liquid to drink is water, and plenty of it. For the same reason, do not smoke while shooting. Nicotine dulls the senses and slows your reactions. And of course, never mix alcohol and firearms.

Shooting Box

A wide variety of shooting boxes are available, ranging from the high-end Pachmyer box to the inexpensive plastic boxes offered by MTM. All work admirably and choice is a matter of personal taste and the number of tools you wish to carry. The author prefers to use a top opening metal tool box with three drawers, see Figure 6-5.

Fig. 6-5. Murphy rules at matches and tactical shoots. Be prepared. The author's shooting box contains a variety of hand tools and parts to make repairs on the spot.

At a minimum the shooting box should contain safety glasses, ear protection, cleaning rods, tips and cleaning solutions and patches, also a small hammer, screw driver(s), pliers, heavy duty stapler for tacking up targets, black marking pen, steel ruler in decimal inches for scoring targets, notepad, scorebook and targets. Other tools can be added as need and experience dictates. The author always includes a damp towel in a plastic bag, bar of soap and a bottle of water or Gatorade.

Always check match rules regarding the type and size of box you are allowed to carry onto the firing range.

Shooting the M16/AR15

The M16/AR15 is an easy rifle to shoot. Civilian versions are invariably semiautomatic which means that the rifle will fire once for each pull of the trigger as long as cartridges remain in the magazine. Recoil is light, the sights are excellent and functioning is smooth. For this reason, the rifle can become so familiar that you might forget you are handling a deadly weapon.

These **basic rules** apply to all firearms.

1.   Always assume that all firearms are loaded until you have personally checked and double checked to make certain they are not. If you do not know how to open the breech, do not touch the gun.

2.   The safety should be in the "ON" position at all times until the moment before you fire. Only combat soldiers expecting a fire fight carry a loaded weapon with the safety off. Anyone else who does so is a fool, and a dangerous one.

3.   Do not load a magazine until you are at your shooting position, and do not insert a loaded magazine into the rifle until you are ready to shoot. Turn the selector switch to the SAFE position (toward the muzzle) before inserting the magazine or loading a round.

4.   Always make certain the muzzle is pointing in a safe direction, even when the rifle is unloaded.

5.   Never aim a firearm at anything you do not intend to shoot, whether the firearm is loaded or not, and especially not in fun. Doing so is the mark of a fool.

6.   Never aim a firearm at anything you cannot clearly see and identify. Firing "sound shots" is the mark of a dangerous fool.

7.   Always make sure that you have a safe backstop. Keep in mind that a bullet fired from an M16/AR15 at a 30 degree up angle will carry as far as three miles with sufficient force to wound or kill. A bullet fired from an M16/AR15 can penetrate up to two inches of mild steel or up to one inch of armor steel at ranges up to 300 yards.

8.   Always remove magazines when you are finished shooting. Always inspect magazines to make certain they are empty. The .223 (5.56 mm) cartridge is small and easy to overlook.

Before you shoot, wipe the rifle's bore with a clean patch on the end of a cleaning rod to remove excess oil. This is good practice to standardize on as it assures that bore is free of all obstructions.

To load the magazine, lay cartridges one at time on the magazine floor plate and press down so that they pass below the feed lips, see Figure 6-6, overleaf. Take care not to snag the cartridge rim on the rear of the magazine. It is good practice to load one less cartridge than the magazine's capacity to prevent any possibility of malfunction.

If you have cartridges in the military-style clip, fit the bottom, expanded end of the clip over the top of the magazine. Hold the magazine in one hand on a solid surface and place the thumb of the other on the top cartridge, just ahead of the rim and push down smoothly until the last cartridge is below the feed lips, see Figure 6-7, overleaf.

Note: You can load one cartridge at a time in the M16/AR15 using the "Naval Academy" method. With the bolt locked open and the magazine in place, tilt the rifle to the left and drop one cartridge into the open ejection port on top of the magazine follower. Release the bolt which will then chamber the round. This method is useful during matches when with practice, it is quicker to load in this manner than to insert a new magazine with only two rounds.

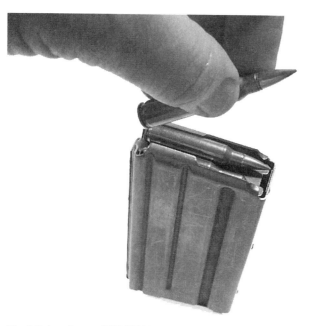

Fig. 6-6. Loading an M16/AR15 magazine

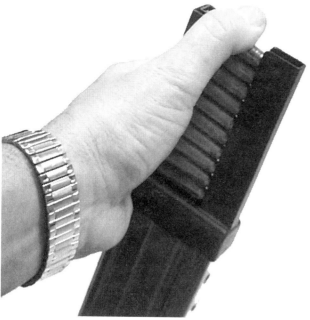

Fig. 6-7. Loading a magazine with cartridge clip.

Turn the selector lever to SAFE (toward the muzzle). Cock the rifle by drawing back on the cocking handle until the bolt locks open. Push on the bottom of the bolt release switch (left side of the receiver) to hold the bolt back.

Insert the loaded magazine into the magazine well and push upward until it snaps home. It is good practice to slap the bottom of the magazine to make certain it is engaged. Few things are more embarrassing than to have an improperly seated magazine fall out as you start a course of fire, or worse, cause a cartridge to misfeed and jam.

To load the first round, push the top of the bolt release switch and let the bolt fly forward. Do not hold onto the cocking handle as this may cause a misfeed.

Whether you shoot the rifle in a standing, sitting, kneeling or prone position, the basics are the same. If using a sling, it should have been adjusted before loading the rifle. Raise the rifle to your shoulder and fit it against the inside curve of the sheath of muscle covering the shoulder joint. Your off hand should cradle the hand guard and your shooting hand should comfortably encircle the pistol grip, as high up as possible so that the trigger finger extends as straight as possible.

The rifle should be in a vertical plane. Canting it to one side or the other will cause it to shoot in that direction. Lay your cheek on the stock so that your eye is level with the rear sight. You should be able to see the front sight post without having to stretch or strain.

Take up your sight picture. With the thumb of your shooting hand, turn the selector to FIRE (straight up). Lay the ball tip of your trigger finger lightly on the trigger as you take a slightly deeper breath than normal. Exhale one half as you center the front sight post on the target and let your eye adjust the amount of light on either side as seen through the rear sight aperture.

Squeeze your trigger finger slightly to take up any slack, then continue the motion, applying as much force as necessary to cause the trigger to break. Do this in a slow, sustained manner so that you do not jerk the trigger. When the rifle fires, hold your position for the count of two and continue to watch the target through the sights.

If you are not going to fire again immediately, turn the selector lever to SAFE.

If you legally own a select fire M16 rifle, follow the same procedure as above to fire in the semiautomatic mode.

After the last round in the magazine is fired, the follower will rise to prevent the bolt from returning to battery as a signal that the magazine is empty. Eject the empty magazine by depressing the magazine release on the right side of the receiver. If you intend to continue firing, load a new magazine and depress the bolt release to allow the bolt to go forward and load a new round. It is good practice not to let the empty magazine fall to the ground.

To fire in the full automatic mode, turn the selector lever to AUTO (toward the butt stock) on those rifles so equipped. Keep in mind that even though the recoil is mild, the rifle will climb up and right about thirty degrees unless you control it carefully. At that elevation, bullets can fly down range for up to three miles or more.

There is rarely a need, short of actual military combat, to fire more than three or four rounds in the full automatic mode. Unless the rifle is mounted on a bipod, the majority of shooters will not be able to fire accurately on full auto without proper training.

As soon as you finish firing, immediately turn the selector lever to SAFE.

Breaking in A New Rifle

When you buy a new car, you drive it at reasonable speeds and avoid sudden acceleration for the first several hundred miles to allow the engine and other parts to "wear in." You should do the same with any rifle. Trigger parts have to wear against each other to smooth out minute burrs and jags. The barrel's bore will be slightly rough from machining and rifling operations, unless it has been honed. This roughness will cause minute quantities of bullet material to adhere to the rifling — leading and copper fouling — which affect accuracy and raise chamber pressures by increasing the friction with the bullets passing through the bore.

So, if you want the smoothest, most accurate barrel possible, follow these rules with all high power rifles.

For the first ten rounds, clean the bore after every shot. Use a bore guide, a coated cleaning rod fitted with a Parker-Hale-type jag (round, not slotted) and a tight fitting patch. Do not spare the patches. Use a cleaner like J-B Bore Cleaner that has a soft abrasive added to it. Clean until the patches show no discoloration. For the next ten rounds, clean after every two rounds; the next fifty rounds, clean after every five rounds. Finally, clean after every ten rounds until you have accumulated 200 shots (130 additional rounds). It sounds like a lot of work, and it is, but your reward will be a very accurate rifle barrel with a very low rate of copper fouling.

If you use molybdenum disulfide (moly) coated bullets, don't fire them through a new rifle bore until you have completed the breaking-in procedure described above. If you decide to use moly-coated bullets, it is best to stick with them to the exclusion of non-moly-coated bullets in that particular firearm. It takes a lot of shooting and cleaning to rid your barrel of residual moly.

We have had great luck with Black Hills ammunition, both moly-coated and non-coated in .308 and .223 calibers. In our experience, rifles fired with moly-coated bullets retain their accuracy for longer between cleanings.

Position Shooting

Most casual shooters fire either from a standing position or from a rest, such as a shooting bench. Target shooters who are serious about their marksmanship will learn all four service match shooting positions — standing, sitting, kneeling, and prone. If you are a hunter, standing and kneeling are the two most used positions, but kneeling is rarely used in match shooting. When assuming a shooting position, bone should contact bone to make the steadiest platform. In other words, elbow should press against kneecap, forearm against thigh bone or rib cage and so on. Study the following photographs to see how Bruce Bigelow, First Sergeant, USMC (Ret) and a member of the US Marine Corps Reserve Shooting Team from 1982 to 1998, works each position to create as much bone-to-bone contact as possible.

Standing

Shooting accurately from the standing position is very difficult. Your body is a column balanced on two legs while holding a heavy object at a right angle to a supporting post — your spine. Its no wonder the muzzle wavers. So add a cantilever.

To shoot well from a standing position, stand facing 90 degrees away from the target with your feet spread a shoulder's width apart, see Figure 6-8. Distribute your weight evenly on both legs. Relax your knees rather than bend them. Your hips must be kept level and in line with your shoulders — as your shoulders turn, so must your hips.

Fig. 6-8. Standing position: notice how the off-hand elbow presses against the rib cage for additional support. This is the cantilever that helps carry the weight of the rifle.

Turn slightly from the hips to the left so that your offhand shoulder turns toward the target. Raise the rifle to eye level. Snug the rifle butt into your shoulder and grasp the pistol grip with your shooting hand (finger off the trigger). Your off arm will carry the rifle's weight. Your hand should cradle the forearm with your wrist straight. Do not squeeze the hand guard. The elbow of that arm should rest against your rib cage so that the contact is bone-to-bone, forming the cantilever. A sling adjusted properly enhances this position — use of the sling is discussed below — but remember, it is not legal in service rifle matches.

Your head should be erect so that you are looking straight ahead through the sights. Adjust the placement of your feet until the rifle points naturally at the target. Test your position by aiming the rifle at the bull, then close your eyes for a moment. When you open them, the rifle should still be pointing at the bull. If not, adjust your stance and repeat the test.

To fire, pull the rifle tight against your shoulder, release the safety, take a deep breath, let half out and squeeze the trigger when the sights are in alignment. Do not jerk the trigger, squeeze it.

Kneeling

When in the kneeling position, your center of gravity is much lower than in the standing position, which lends added stability, see Figure 6-9. There are three variations of the kneeling position, high, low and forward. The high position is popular among hunters for quick shots and among older veterans of the service rifle match circuit as it is not as wearing. The low and forward positions are only seen in matches where you need more stability and have the time to assume the position.

Fig. 6-9. In the kneeling position, your center of gravity is lower, so your stability is enhanced. Notice how the elbow is anchored to the bone just behind the knee cap.

In the **high** position, turn 45 degrees from the target and sink down so that your knee touches the ground at a 60 degree angle from the target. Your heel should contact the base of your spine. The off leg should be nearly in line with the target, lower leg up and thigh forming a platform.

Raise the rifle to the shoulder. The off hand cradles the rifle while its elbow is just behind the knee, on the bone. The shooting arm should be held so that the elbow presses against

the rib cage while pulling the butt solidly against the shoulder. The spine should be bent just enough to bring the head into alignment with the rifle's sights. Test your position by aiming, closing your eyes for a moment and checking to make certain that the rifle is still in alignment with the point of aim.

Notice that Sergeant Bigelow has his right knee planted firmly while he sits back on his left ankle. His back is straight and his head erect, tipped only slightly to see the sights. The hard bone-to-bone contact of offhand elbow and knee —cantilever — and the right side knee opened to a 45 degree angle provide a great deal of steady support.

The **low** position starts with you facing slightly to the side of the target with the leg on the shooting side bent so that you are sitting squarely on the foot which will carry your body's weight. Bend forward with the off leg pointed almost directly at the target and the foot angled forward. This will allow you to move your off hand further forward on the handgrips for added stability.

The **forward** position is very stable but requires a few moments and a degree of suppleness to get into, and therefore is usually used only in service rifle matches. Face the target and angle the leg on your shooting side about 15 degrees away from the target. Sink down so that the buttock on the shooting side rests squarely on the shooting side's foot. The off leg should be pointed almost directly at the target. Depending on the degree of your physical conditioning, bend forward as far as you can reach comfortably. The shooting elbow should rest against the ribs when the rifle is against the shoulder, and the off elbow should rest solidly behind the knee. This is a very stable position and after the prone position, probably the steadiest from which to shoot.

Sitting

Sitting is the easiest position to master. Some shooters consider it steadier than the kneeling position although it does not provide the same tripod-like support.

To assume the sitting position, stand with hips and shoulders at right angles to the target with the rifle sling in place over the outside of the left wrist and high on the left upper arm. Cross your left leg over your right at the ankles and assume a sitting position. Rest your left elbow on your right knee and the right elbow on the right knee (elbow behind the knee cap), see Figure 6-10. The sling should pull tight enough to draw the left arm in slightly. Rest the butt securely against the right shoulder. Now lean forward as you look through the rear sight. Sling tension should be sufficient to hold you at this position. The further forward you can lean, the steadier the position becomes, see Figure 6-11.

Examine the two photographs. Notice that Sergeant Bigelow has his ankles crossed, shooting side ankle over offhand ankle to act as an anchor. Figure 6-11 illustrates the degree to which he has leaned forward and shows his elbow and knee in good solid alignment.

Fig. 6-10. To assume the sitting position, cross your ankles and sink down; the off-elbow should plant against the off knee . . .

Fig. 6-11. . . . and the shooting elbow against the same side shin bone. The further forward you lean, the steadier the position.

Prone

Your center of gravity is as low as you can get it when lying flat, so you can't ask your body to provide a steadier shooting platform. Your arms and shoulders will form two sides of a triangle and your extended body the other, see Figure 6-12.

Face the target, place the butt of the rifle on the ground where your shooting elbow will go, kneel and fold forward. Push your off elbow slightly ahead and snug the rifle into your shoulder. The shooting elbow will fall into its proper place.

Your head and neck muscles should be relaxed. Angle around until the base of your spine is 10 degrees off a line from the target to your head. Bend your shooting side leg to relieve the strain from the shooting side elbow. The offhand should cradle the forend. In International Match Shooting, the off hand must be at least 6 inches above the ground.

Fig. 6-12. The prone position is the most stable you can take up. Shoulders, arms and back forms the sides of a triangle with a center of gravity at ground level.

To test the position, aim, close your eyes for a moment and open them. The rifle should still be pointed at the target. If not, adjust your position by moving the entire body, not just your shoulders.

You can do everything from this position — change magazines, check the target through the scope, record your shots — without having to move your body or the position is incorrect.

Check Figure 6-12 once again. Sergeant Bigelow is in a comfortable position and his rifle is rock steady. His shooting side leg is bent at the knee and drawn up to relieve the strain on his shooting arm. When ready to shoot, he will draw his knee up to his elbow to achieve bone-to-bone contact that will provide an increased measure of steadiness.

Slings

The use of a sling with the M16/AR15 is a bit different than with other military style rifles. In the standard M16/AR15, the forward sling swivel is attached to the front sight assembly on the barrel. When the sling is drawn tight, it can cause the barrel on a standard M16/AR15 rifle to bend and even to shift slightly in the upper receiver. For these reasons, the M16/AR15 is never shot with a sling drawn up as tightly as you would for an M1 Garand or an M14/M1A. The exception is, of course, a rifle barrel that has been free-floated and fitted with a hand guard tube — with sling swivel — attached to the upper receiver.

The standard nylon sling issued for the M16/AR15 is usually avoided by match shooters because it stretches. For hunters who use the sling to carry the rifle rather than to steady aim, the standard nylon sling is ideal as it is very light and strong. Match shooters should use either the cotton canvas M1 sling designed for the M1 Garand or the M14 rifle, or a variation on the Model 1907 sling, see Figure 6-13. Original M1907 slings, besides being more than fifty years old now, are becoming expensive collector's items. Several companies — Boyt, Brownells, Uncle Mike — manufacture the M1907

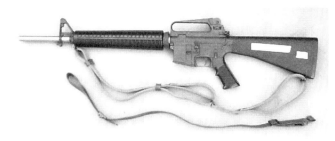

Fig. 6-13. The M1907 leather sling is shown rigged on the rifle with the M1 cotton canvas sling below. Either sling is preferable in competition to the nylon sling developed for the M16.

sling for competition work. Those for the M16/AR15 are slightly longer. I am six foot tall with an average reach for my height, and I find the M1907 sling made originally for the M1903 right at its useful limit. If you are taller or bulkier, use a M1907 sling made for the M16/AR15.

The M1 Sling made of cotton canvas is an ideal sling for match shooting with the M16/AR15. It is light, does not stretch and can be adjusted instantly. The M1 sling has a metal quick release clip on the bottom end. Slip this over the rear sling swivel, thread the upper end through the upper sling swivel and back down and through the metal keeper. The keeper should open toward the rifle, not away. This prevents the keeper from accidentally being snagged and pulled open.

While you can't form a closed loop for your upper arm with the M1 sling, you don't really need it. Loosen the sling and insert your off arm beneath the magazine well. Slide your hand back through so that the sling crosses your wrist and grasp the hand guard. Adjust the metal keeper to the desired tension. You can adjust the overall length of the M1 sling using the buckle on the lower end. A bit of experimentation will find you the right combination. If you prefer, let the bottom end of the sling hang free by unsnapping the metal clip.

If you purchase a new leather sling, work it well to remove the stiffness and make it supple. Clean it with saddle soap and preserve it with a very light application of mink oil, rubbed in thoroughly. The cotton canvas M1 sling can be washed in a mild detergent or cleaned with any of the commercial home dry cleaning products.

When using a sling to steady your aim, envision it as the base of an inverted triangle with the other two sides your upper arm and forearm. Rig the sling on the rifle and leave it loose. The upper end of the sling should pass through the sling swivel from the front and back through the fastener. The bottom should pass through the lower sling swivel in the same manner. The upper end should have a large loop. The idea is for the sling to take up some of the rifle's weight and carry it back to the upper arm so that the rifle is supported by the stronger shoulder and back muscles.

The sling should pass above the offhand elbow as high as possible then forward and over the back of the offhand wrist. The sling should be tight enough to draw the shooting arm inward against the rib cage to provide bone-to-bone contact.

If you are using a M1907 sling, the loop should not be so tight that it interferes with circulation in the upper arm.

Before assuming a shooting position, remove rings, watches and bracelets that might catch in the sling, and wear a shooting glove.

Before assuming the prone position, don the sling and grasp the rifle. Kneel and place the rifle butt on the ground or shooting mat. Your offhand should be in position hard against the forward sling swivel. Lean forward using the rifle butt to steady yourself. Use the offhand elbow and shooting hand to lower yourself prone.

When you assume a shooting position using the sling, it should draw up to the right tension without further adjustment. Each position will require that the fastener be moved to a different place on the sling. You should determine the holes for the fastener and mark them on the sling with indelible marking pen, or, in the case of the fabric slings, with white paint or a sewn thread or tag. You will then be able to quickly adjust the sling to the proper tension for sitting or kneeling or the prone position.

Tactical Slings

In Chapter 4 we discussed the GI tactical sling; a definite improvement is the "Snap Sling" designed by Ed Verdugo of GRSC in Yucaipa, California (see Appendix F). Ed's sling design allows the M16/AR15 (or any other tactical rifle) to be carried in the cross-chest position with the weight of the rifle taken up by back and shoulder muscles. The Snap Sling also overcomes the greatest limitation of the GI tactical sling — difficulty in deploying the rifle or carbine in an emergency — by the use of a cleverly designed quick release system based on a single spring clip. From the cross-chest carry position, you simply push the rifle forward sharply and up into position. The snap sling releases and readjusts instantly for the shooting position.

The sling requires two sling adapters, which are furnished, to rig it on the off-side of the weapon. The butt stock is removed and the adaptor slipped over the extension tube. The front sling swivel is removed and another adaptor inserted between the bayonet mount and the sling swivel lugs. The adaptor is then secured with a screw and nut. A set screw bottoms against the barrel to stabilize the assembly. The sling is then clipped onto both sling adaptors.

To use, you slip the two outside straps over your head and left shoulder and adjust the slide until the buttstock rides comfortably under the armpit on the shooting side, the muzzle points safely downward and the rifle or carbine rides flat against the chest, see Figure 6-14. The sling can also be adjusted to carry the rifle backpack style — flat against the back, muzzle down.

Another design, the V-Tac sling, attaches to the front of a load-bearing vest when wearing a fully loaded back pack. It works in the same manner as the Snap Sling.

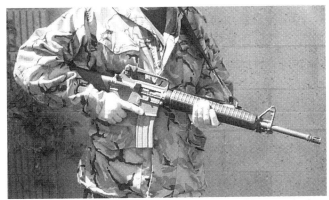

Fig. 6-14. The Ed Verdugo-designed tactical Snap Sling permits the rifle to be carried comfortably in the cross-chest fashion with the weight being carried by back and shoulder muscles.

To deploy the rifle, you simply push it sharply forward and bring the butt up against your shoulder. The quick release clip allows the sling to lengthen instantly, see Figure 6-15. To return it to the carry position, you grasp the quick release and snap the slide back into place.

Fig. 6-15. To deploy the rifle, simply push forward sharply as you lift the rifle to the shoulder. The quick release snaps loose instantly.

The front adaptor has a modified weaver mount for attaching flashlights like the Sure Fire or MagLite, see Figure 6-15.

Fig. 6-16. Flash lights or other sighting aids attach to the Weaver mount.

All in all, the GRSC Snap Sling is a great tactical sling that can be adjusted for any number of different carry positions. Its best feature is fact that it allows the rifle to be deployed instantly in an emergency.

Physical Conditioning

To shoot well, you must be in good physical condition. Rifles are heavy, particularly match rifles, so upper body strength is very important. A protruding stomach in the prone or sitting position will not provide a stable platform and will squeeze your lungs, making breathing difficult. You should be able to hold your breath for 60 seconds minimum without gasping for air at the end. If you can't, get out and start running or walking.

You must be able to isolate the muscles of your trigger finger and command them to deliberately squeeze the trigger to the point of sear release, hold at that point, and then apply the final amount of pressure as the sights align. You must practice until you can call the trigger break every time.

You cannot improve your shooting ability without improving your physical condition. You will be calling on leg, arm, shoulder, neck and back muscles to serve in unaccustomed positions for long periods of time. Not only must you be limber enough to gain these positions, but your muscles must be strong and resilient enough so that you do not stagger into the next position as if you were afflicted with arthritis.

Work on upper body strength, with special attention to your neck muscles. Make stretching and calisthenics a regular part of your daily routine. Since breath control and pulse rate affect your shooting, you should run or walk at least five to ten miles per week and include at least three sets of 50 yard wind sprints during each outing to build lung capacity.

Your heart beat can and will disturb your point of aim, particularly if your pulse rate is elevated. The better physical condition you are in, the slower your heart will beat and the more time you will have to release the trigger between beats. Yes, between beats. Practice while lying on your living room rug. Set up a paper target a few feet distant and with an UNLOADED rifle and without a magazine, practice aiming at the target while feeling and listening for your heart beat. Apply the final amount of "break" pressure to the trigger between beats. It will take several practice sessions before you become adept.

One final benefit to be derived from getting into shape: your significant other will stop complaining about the time and money you spend shooting as your health and appearance improves. Trust me. By the way, check with your doctor before beginning any exercise program

Storing Your Rifle

All firearms must be kept under lock and key when not in use. Even if you do not have children in the house, they may visit. And if they do not, there will be occasions when sales people, repair people and visitors, invited or uninvited, will be in your home. Even if they do nothing more than mention to another that you have a "gun," that person may pass the information on to another and so on until it comes to the ears of the wrong type.

Also, be aware, if a government official, police or fireman comes to your house for any reason and observes a firearm that is not securely stored, he or she is bound by law in most jurisdictions to report it. That puts you into the law enforcement computers with all that it means today. If the police are called to your home at a later date by a neighbor — friendly or unfriendly — they may arrive with a SWAT team in the middle of the night.

Play it safe; keep all firearms locked away and out of sight.

If you are going to store your rifle for a lengthy period, check to make certain that it is unloaded. Then turn the selector switch to the "semiautomatic" position. Point the rifle in a safe direction and squeeze the trigger so that the hammer goes forward. This will relieve all tension on the mainspring.

Clean the rifle thoroughly and coat the bore with a gun oil. Leave a thin coat of oil on the bolt, bolt carrier and the trigger mechanism. Remove magazines. If magazines are to be stored for long periods of time, remove the floor plates and allow the springs to extend. Coat the magazine parts inside and out with a thin coat of oil and store in airtight plastic bags or other containers.

For long term storage of firearms, they can be placed in silicone-treated bags such as "Bore-Stores." Silicone prevents rusting.

Never store a firearm in a plastic or leather carrying case as moisture will condense inside and cause rust and corrosion. Canvas or other "breathable" storage cases may be used, but spray the interior thoroughly with silicone oil. Never use WD-40 or other light lubricants. Not only do they evaporate quickly, but many contain kerosene which will thin or even remove bluing and paint.

Do not place the muzzle cap on the rifle when in storage. It will cause moisture from the air to condense inside the barrel and drip down into the action. Use the muzzle cap only in the field to protect the bore from dust and grit. If you are concerned about dust in the bore while in storage, cover the muzzle with a single layer of cheese cloth or other wide weave material. Cover it, do not plug it.

For safety's sake, do not store the rifle and ammunition in the same container. Ammunition should be stored in separate locked containers and never in the same area as the firearm. If a burglar does break into your home or business and finds the firearms, at least he or she will not be able to load them.

Training and Competition

If you are serious about match or tactical shooting or are a law enforcement officer, at some point you may want to attend a course of instruction in how to use the AR15 properly. The better courses will teach you, at a minimum, about proper use of the sling, zeroing techniques, telescopic sights, ammunition, ballistics, safe gun handling, basic maintenance and repair, the legal and ethical use of deadly force and liability.

Practical instruction will include proper carrying techniques, shooting stance and other positions, breath control, sight alignment and trigger control, target engagement to various ranges and rapid reloading techniques. More advanced courses will offer low-light and night firing techniques and long range shooting.

The Front Sight Training Institute offers the widest assortment of training courses throughout the year. Organized and directed by Dr. Ignatius Piazza (Four Weapons Combat Master), FSTI has extensive ranges at Bakersfield, California and Las Vegas, Nevada and offers two and four day courses in practical rifle. 800 987-7719.

Other firearms training groups reviewed by the author are listed below.

The Blackwater Training Center, 850 Puddin Ridge Road, Moyock, NC, 27958, also offers a complete range of courses in practical and tactical rifle. Phone 252 435-2488.

Gunsite, 2900 West Gunsite Rd., Paulden AZ 86334 (520 636- 4565) has for a number of years offered one of the best known programs in tactical and precision rifle training.

Firearms Academy of Seattle, PO Box 400, Onalaska, WA 98570 offers a wide range of firearms courses taught by outstanding instructors in the field (360 978-6100).

Competition is also great way to build skills, meet new friends and have a lot of fun. The National Rifle Association's main function is to organize firearms competitions at all levels. Various types and levels of competition are offered from .22 rimfire, 50 yard matches to 1,000 yard medium and heavy caliber competitions. Contact the NRA at 800 672-3888 for information.

The Civilian Marksmanship Program (CMP) has been in existence since the start of the last century and has an enviable history in firearms competition. The National Service Matches, the Palma competition and numerous groups and organizations are gathered under the aegis of the CMP. Contact them at 419 635-2141. Both organizations can provide local information geared to your area.

A few minutes spent with a good search engine like htpp://www.yahoo.com will provide a large number of leads to firearms training groups around the country. Type in "firearms+training." Also, check local resources. Many police departments offer training through their police associations. Gun stores and ranges are also source of information for training.

Don't overlook your local shooting ranges and clubs. Many have well-organized competition schedules on a year-round basis. Check your local yellow pages for "Ranges–Shooting."

7. TELESCOPIC SIGHTS FOR THE M16/AR15

Just about any telescopic sight can be used on the M16/AR15. A host of different accessories for mounting the scope fill the catalogs.

Perhaps the most familiar scope for the M16/AR15 is the Colt 1304 telescopic sight which perches atop the carry handle and needs no other mount, see Figure 7-1. This telescopic sight was designed and developed by the Realist corporation and was manufactured in 3X and 4X variations for more than two decades. It saw service during the Vietnam War and tops the rifles of many a police department sniper team, see Figure 7-2. Relatively inexpensive until recently, it has been challenged by a near copy manufactured in China. Our testing showed that the Chinese copy, while not as ruggedly built and with inferior optics, would certainly serve nicely for causal plinking and target shooting out to 300 yards.

Fig. 7-1. The Colt Realist telescopic sight. North Cape Publications Collection.

Fig. 7-2. The Colt Realist scope is ideal for short-range tactical work in good light. Its low magnification brightens and sharpens the target's image.

Over the years, Colt and the U.S. Military have experimented with a number of optical sighting aids for the M16 rifle. In 1967, 384 conventional telescopic sights, also made by Realist, were sent to Vietnam to be tested in-country with 125 accurized M14 rifles equipped with the M84 scope developed for the M1D Garand, see Figure 7-3.

At least three mounts were designed for use on the M16 rifle that should be mentioned, all by Leatherwood. The first mount slotted into the carry handle and was secured by a knurled knob and flat spring. The second was a modified Weaver system that mounted on a handleless upper receiver and the third also slotted into the carry handle and was secured by the knob and flat spring. But this mount also had a front projection that extended down to rest against the front of the upper receiver for added stability, see Figure 7-4. Although the testing showed the desirability of a telescope-equipped M16, the nod went to the accurized M14s which were later developed into the standard sniping weapon of the Vietnam War and is still in use as an secondary sniper weapon in U.S. Military service today, the M21.

Through the 1980s, more than eighty sighting systems were tested with the M16 rifle, including the British Trilux and SUSAT sights, the Canadian ELCAN and No. 78 and wide range of night vision and heat-sensing devices, see Figures 7-4, 7-5, 7-6, 7-7 and 7-8.

In the 1980s, Colt developed and issued the "Delta" HBAR for police tactical use which was introduced as a "countersniper rifle." It was equipped with the same 20 inch heavy barrel as the Target Match HBAR and a 3-9X rubber-coated Tasco telescopic sight. It had a duplex crosshair reticle and new base designed by Richard Swan that attached to the carry handle. It also had an ambidextrous plastic cheek piece which

Fig. 7-3. The M1D, developed to late for service in the Korean War, was tested in Vietnam.

Fig. 7-4. Leatherwood scope mount with a No. 78 Mk 1 Telescopic Sight mounted for test purposes. Courtesy Canadian Ministry of Defense.

Fig. 7-5. An M16E1with Swarovski 6 x 42 mm scope on an A.R.M.S. mount for testing by the U.S. Army. Photo courtesy U.S. Army.

Fig. 7-6. An M16A1 with an AN/PVS-4 passive night vision sight mounted. Photo courtesy U.S. Army.

Fig. 7-7. Experimental M16 being tested with a prototype Thermal Weapon Sight (TWS). Photo courtesy, U.S. Army.

Fig. 7-8. Various sighting aids being tested on the M16 Commando and the M16A1. Photo courtesy, U.S. Army.

was undercut at the top for the charging handle. The cheek piece was designed and manufactured by Cherokee Accessories and is described below.

Choosing a Telescopic Sight

There are two reasons for using a telescopic sight: 1) to brighten the sight picture — especially necessary for aging eyes and 2) to magnify a distant target to increase accuracy, especially at long ranges.

Before purchasing a telescopic sight, you should determine which of the two above reasons applies most in your case. If you do a lot of long distance shooting, a powerful telescopic sight is called for — keep in mind that you are not allowed to use a telescopic sight in service rifle matches.

If you are past the forty year mark, your eyes probably are not quite as good as they used to be at resolving distant images. If you shoot mostly at distances under 300 yards, then a low to medium power scope will probably serve you well. If you also occasionally shoot at longer distances, consider a scope that allows you to increase the magnification as needed (variable power). If you are hunter who likes to make long shots or a law enforcement rifleman, you will want to use a range-finding, adjustable power telescopic sight with as much light gathering power as possible.

Light Gathering Power

Light gathering power is probably the most important factor in choosing a telescopic sight. The more light that enters the objective lens (the one at the front) the brighter will be the image you see. Many of today's scopes have large objective lenses ranging up to 60 mm in diameter, and more. They are especially effective at dawn or dusk and on heavily overcast days, see Figure 7-9.

Fig/ 7-9. This Leupold Vari-X III with a 40 mm objective lens was developed for the FBI Hostage Response Teams (HRT). North Cape Publications Collection.

Magnification

Magnification is probably the second most important factor in choosing a telescopic sight. Two types are manufactured: fixed power and variable power. An example of the fixed power scope is the Colt "Realist"-type scope with its 20 mm objective and 3 or 4 power magnification. An example of the variable power scope is the Leupold Vari-X III with magnifications varying between 3 and 10 power (3-10X) or 4.5 to 14

power (4.5-14X). These Leupold scopes are equipped with either a 40 mm or 50 mm objective lens depending on the model.

The first inclination is to select the scope with the greatest magnification. But that is not always the correct answer. Few scopes can be used satisfactorily at much beyond 4 power unless the rifle is placed on a solid rest because the increased magnification causes an apparent increase in oscillation. Remember our description of the rifleman as a column (the spine) supported on a bipod (the legs) holding a 7 to 12 pound weight at a right angle without benefit of a cantilever support? Now add another pound or so of weight for the scope and mount and watch the magnified sight picture dance around. That's oscillation.

Unless you are shooting at ranges beyond 300 yards or your eye sight is dimming substantially, your best bet is either a 3 or 4X scope or a variable that starts at 3X. In either case, the sight picture will improve dramatically without excessive oscillation.

Long range shots made from a rest (bipod or other steady surface) can benefit from much higher magnifications. In fact, if you are having trouble learning to detect and feel your heartbeat as discussed in the chapter on shooting, a high power scope will show it too you instantly.

For years, the experts would advise you to purchase fixed power scopes as they provided brighter, sharper images, were hardier and would seal in the inert nitrogen gases used to keep out moisture far better than variable power scopes. That is no longer true, nor has it been for the last 15-20 years. Variable power scopes today rank with the best of the fixed power scopes in every instance.

Controls

The sight should have sufficient adjustment range to reach 1,000 yards — yes, 1,000. Sooner or later you are going to want to try it, even if you are not a match shooter. Several mounts for the M16/AR15 now allow you to adjust the scope's tilt before you touch the elevation knob and put the 600 yard range right in the center, or lower, of your scope's range. If you are using the M16/AR15's carry handle as the mount for your scope, it is an easy matter to slide a shim under the rear of most scope bases to achieve the same effect. As a rule of thumb, a 0.001 inch shim under the base will equal one minute of angle on the target. Its not a very exact rule in the case of the M16/AR15 but close enough to help you dial in.

Another factor to consider is the amount of elevation adjustment you are able to make decreases as windage is dialed in. When large windage corrections are needed — a problem far more acute in the M16/AR15 than in the M14 as the 5.56 mm NATO bullet is far more prone to deflection by the wind — you may find yourself unable to make sufficient elevation correction to reach beyond 300 yards.

For example, if at zero windage you are able to make a

full elevation adjustment between 12 and 6 o'clock, at extreme windage adjustments you may only be able to make adjustments between 8 and 10 o'clock. The solution is an adjustable windage base — or shims. The only windage-adjustable AR15 mount of which the author is aware as this was written is scope rail by High Performance International which has a 12 MOA slant which allows you to zero at 600 yards.

Mounts

The flat top A4 upper receiver is ideal for the kind of elevation adjustment mount described immediately above, see Figure 7-10. The Picatinny Arsenal mount accepts a wide variety of bases and even other Picatinny Arsenal-style mounts like the DPMS Flat Top Riser which increases scope height to compensate for the low stock-receiver-barrel line. The DPMS rig slides over the flat top rail. Two thumbscrews, one each fore and aft not only provide a secure attachment but make it easy to add shims under the rear, if necessary.

Simple, effective and inexpensive mounts for the M16/AR15, both carry handle and A-4 flat top versions, are manufactured by the B-Square company. The carry handle mount provides a tunnel for iron sight use and accepts Weaver rings. Two variations are made for the flat top upper, one with integral rings and the other which accepts weaver rings. Both types clamp onto the Picatinny Arsenal mount and are located with large diameter, vertical split pin. If you need to shim either of these, you must insert the shim in the rear ring under the scope body in the conventional way.

Reticle

Finally, decide on what type of reticle you want in the telescopic sight. Figure 7-11 shows the five types commonly used today. The standard cross hair or duplex cross hair are perhaps the best for long-range target work with the duplex having the slight edge. Under poor light conditions, the heavy segments of each cross hair are easier to see and lead the eye naturally to the center.

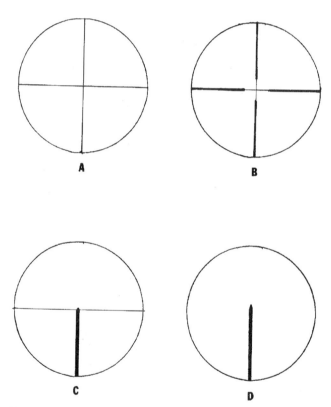

Fig. 7-11. Reticle types: A) Standard crosshair, B) Duplex target, C) Crosshair and post, and D) Post.

A new entry in the cross hair debate is the mil-dot reticle, see Figure 7-12. It is similar to the duplex reticle except that a specific number of beads (usually eight or ten) are strung on the cross hairs 0.25 mils apart. Each bead is also exactly 0.25 mils long. A mil (or milliradian) covers exactly 3.6 inches at

Fig. 7-10. The M16/AR15A4 flat top upper receiver has a Picatinny Arsenal mount (above) which accepts a variety of Weaver-style bases. Shown here is the B-Square mount (below).

100 yards, 7.2 inches at 200 yards, 10.8 inches at 300 yards, 14.4 inches at 400 yards and so on to 36 inches at 1,000 yards. This allows you to judge the distance to the target. Say the target's height is 12 inches and one-mil dot covers it exactly; this indicates an estimated the range of about 350 yards. You can also adjust for windage in the same way. A 10 mph cross wind will deflect a 55 grain bullet 21.1 inches. Divide 21.1 by 3.6 = 5.86/2 = 2.93 mils. Your windage correction then is the right edge of the second mil-dot.

Fig. 7-13. As your eye moves in relation to a line drawn between the target and the reticule, your line of sight will also move, causing the apparent displacement of the target.

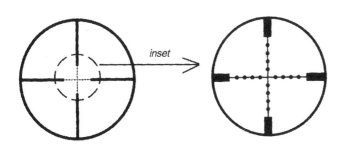

Fig. 7-12. The Mil-dot reticle allows the shooter to measure the height of the target and quickly calculate the range.

With a little practice, estimating the distance and doing the math becomes easy and quick. Because the author is terrible at math, he prefers to think in metric terms in which 1 mil equals 9.14 cm, close enough to 10 to make the arithmetic easier. Thus our 12 inch high target becomes 30.5 cm high divided by 10 equals 3.05 mils or 300 meters (or 328 yards). Close enough.

As in choosing a rifle or a custom gunsmith, do your homework before laying out cash. Talk to others who use telescopic sights the way you intend to, read what you can and even ask for advice from the gunsmith you choose to build your rifle.

Cheek Pieces

When using a telescopic sight, parallax is probably the long-range shooter's greatest problem and is also most likely the least understood. *Parallax is the apparent displacement of an object as seen from two points of view.* When applied to a telescopic sight, if for one shot, your eye is directly in line with the crosshair and the target's center, then all else being equal, the bullet will strike the center of the target. If for the second shot, the eye is displaced one degree above a direct line from the target center to the crosshairs, then the shot will strike low, see Figure 7-13. And the amount of displacement increases as the distance lengthens.

Why should the eye be in a different place for the second shot? Unless you place your cheek in exactly the same spot against the stock every time, your eye will be in a different place for every shot. The Monte Carlo stock with its protruding comb was developed to enable the shooter to hold his head

in the same relation to the crosshair for every shot. Likewise, the cheekpad on the M1 Garand and the M14 rifle was developed for the same reason. Tactical shooters speak of "cheek weld" when referring to shot placement. They simply mean placing your cheek against the stock in the same place every time if you wish to achieve consistent results.

The problem of parallax is exaggerated with the M16/AR15 as its straight line stock is so low in relation to the sight line through a telescopic sight that it is impossible to achieve a "cheek weld." Most shooters are surprised to discover when they mount a telescopic sight to the AR15s that their group sizes are often no smaller than if they were using iron sights, and the reason is, parallax.

To solve the problem of parallax-induced changes, before Colt introduced the Delta HBAR Tactical Rifle in the 1980s, they approached a small company named Cherokee Accessories to acquire the cheek piece the company had just developed.

Called the "Delta Cheekpiece," this trademarked design has been widely imitated, see Figure 7-14. But the original with its forward-swept cheek rest is still the best. Made of a strong, lightweight plastic, It fits easily onto all M16/AR15 stocks that hold to the original Colt specifications. It weighs less than 8 ounces and can be installed or removed in about one minute. To do so, you remove the lower butt plate screw and slide the rear sling swivel out. Slip the Delta Cheekpiece onto the stock and secure it with the two screws provided. Reinstall the rear sling swivel and lower butt plate screw.

Fig. 7-14. The Delta Cheekpiece is manufactured by Cherokee Accessories. Its distinctive forward sweep is tradmarked and cannot be copied. The raised comb provides a solid rest for your cheek, thus helping to eliminate errors due to parallax.

Attach your telescopic sight and lay your cheek against the stock. The raised cheek piece helps to assure that you will lay your cheekbone on it in the same place every time, centering your eye from shot to shot. You will see that your group sizes will close up immediately.

Cherokee also produces a cheek piece for the collapsible M16/AR15 stock called the "CAR-15" that simply snaps on. Try using a telescopic sight on a collapsible stock without a cheek piece and you will find it is nearly impossible to hold better than a two minute group. Clip on the cheek piece and those wild shots you were blaming on the shorter barrel will disappear.

Two other products are offered for use with telescopic sights on the AR15, see Figure 7-15. The first is the "Hawk Delta Pro Cheekpiece" which can be snapped on an off the stock without tools. The original sling swivel is replaced with a locking tab which is held in place with the lower butt pad screw. The Delta Pro Cheekpiece is then snapped over the stock. The locking tab holds it securely in place. The cheek piece has its own rear sling swivel plus a tubular compartment at the top for storage.

Fig. 7-15. Top to bottom: Cherokee "Tacstock" with an adjustable cheekpiece; "Delta Pro" Cheekpiece, "Hawk Delta Pro" Snap-on Cheekpiece and "CAR-15" Cheekpiece for collapsible stocks.

The second product is a buttstock with a fully adjustable cheek piece, the "Tacstock." This unit replaces the original buttstock, a simple operation that can be performed quickly by removing the butt pad and sliding the original stock off the receiver extension, taking care not to lose the rear takedown pin spring. The Tacstock slides onto the receiver extension and is held by the buttpad screws, just like the original stock.

The Tacstock has a fully adjustable comb that can be raised or lowered depending on the type of scope or the optical sight used. For instance, the Colt Realist scope when mounted requires the comb be raised to an intermediate height. But if a starlight scope is mounted in its place, the comb can be raised to accommodate its higher sight line.

To adjust the stock, the locking knob on the right side is loosened and the adjusting knob on the bottom is turned right or left to raise or lower the comb. When the proper height is found, the locking knob is tightened to hold it securely in place. The adjusting knob on the bottom of the stock is large enough to serve comfortably as a grip for the off-hand when in the prone position or shooting from a bipod or rest. If something happens to the scope and the shooter must switch to the iron sights, simply loosen the locking knob, unscrew the adjusting knob completely and lift the cheek piece off.

If you want to shoot the M16/AR15 accurately with a telescopic sight, you need to use a cheek piece.

Bipods

For serious long range field work with a scope, a bipod is essential. The standard military issue M16 bipod described in Chapter 4 should only be used in an emergency.

The Harris Bipod is considered an old standby simply because it is effective, relatively inexpensive and quite versatile. It is adjustable for height, allows the muzzle to be swung through a wide enough arc to be useful and is sturdy. Each leg can be adjusted individually on uneven terrain. The Harris bipod is widely used by federal, state and local law enforcement agencies.

The Parker-Hale bipod is even sturdier and far more expensive. It is preferred by many European police, counterterrorist and military tactical shooters. It is also heavier and bulkier and for that reason, is most often found on larger caliber tactical rifles than the M16/AR15.

A new bipod entry for the M16/AR15 tactical rifle is the Cherokee Accessories Tactical Bipod which mounts to either the original hand guard or a replacement hand guard for the M16/AR15A2, Figure 7-16. The replacement hand guard is molded from a sturdy, high temperature-resistant plastic and is grooved to allow the bipod to fold up and tuck away (or nest) so that it does not snag on brush, etc. A special mounting system allows the bipod to swivel so that the shooter can track with the muzzle, and it can be mounted at either the front or rear of the hand guard. While the legs are not individually adjustable for height, the convenience of being able to fold the bipod legs up into the hand guard goes a long way to offset that factor. The bipod is molded in a process called Metal Injection Molding (MIM) which consistently produces strong, void-free castings.

Fig. 7-16. Cherokee Accessories folding bipod.

8. .22 CALIBER AR15 RIFLES

As suburbanization creeps ever outward, we are losing more and more shooting ranges. Twenty years ago, there were four large ranges within a thirty minute drive of the author's home. Today there are none. The range he belongs to now is a hour's drive away. Five years ago, there were a dozen shooting areas on federal property within an hour or so drive of his home; today, in spite of Federal laws to the contrary, there are none. The Forestry Service and Bureau of Land Management have closed them all (curious how this happened during the intensely antigun Clinton administration). Ten years ago, most of the desert lands in Southern California were open to public shooting. Today, more than 90% of the desert is closed to all recreational uses.

As outdoor ranges disappear or move away, indoor ranges are springing up to at least provide a place for hand gun practice. But few indoor ranges are equipped to handle a rifle as powerful as the M16/AR15. So when you get tired of snapping in your match or service rifle on your living room floor, where do you go to practice? How about your local indoor range?

Almost every indoor range will allow .22 rifles. So why not add a .22 rimfire conversion kit or upper receiver to your AR15?

Conversion Kits

M261 — The U.S. military uses a drop-in conversion kit designated the "Conversion Kit (Caliber .22 Rimfire Adapter) M261, see Figure 8-1. The unit was designed by John Foote of the U.S. Armament Corporation. In testing, it edged out a similar design by Max Atchisson of the Military Armament Corporation.

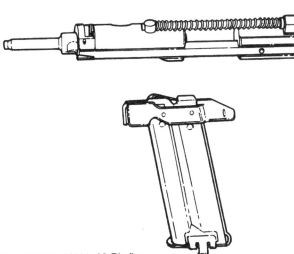

Fig. 8-1. The M261 .22 Rimfire Conversion Unit.

The M216 is a drop-in unit which replaces the 5.56 mm NATO bolt assembly with a blow back bolt unit. A special ten round magazine is used which fits into a 30 round M16/AR15 magazine without tools. When used in the M16A1 which does not have the spent case deflector, a special rimfire spent case deflector is clipped onto the upper receiver and a boxlike funnel directs the spent .22 cases down and away from the shooter's face.

A civilian version of the M261 was sold by Colt in previous years.

Atchisson .22 Caliber Conversion Unit — The Atchisson .22 Caliber conversion kit for the M16/AR15, see Figure 8-2, may have lost out in the Army trials to the M261, but it has been a commercial success.

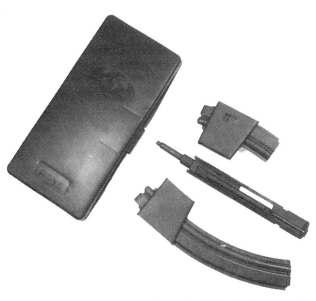

Fig. 8-2. Atchisson .22 Caliber Conversion Unit with storage case and 10 and 30 round magazines.

This relatively inexpensive unit, like the M261, consists of a blow back bolt unit that replaces the bolt carrier in your standard M16/AR15. A ten or thirty round magazine slides into the magazine well rather than the magazine. The .22 rimfire cartridge feeds from the magazine into a chamber that, externally, duplicates the shape of the .223 cartridge. When the hammer strikes the firing pin in the blowback bolt unit, the cartridge ignites and propels the bullet down the bore. As the external diameter of the .22 rimfire bullet is .221 inches, accuracy beyond twenty-five to fifty feet is problematical. But for indoor practice, it is more than sufficient.

You install the unit by first opening the receiver and removing the .223 bolt. Leave the bolt handle in place but draw it about two-thirds of the way back. Insert the Atchisson unit so that the chamber slides into the barrel's chamber and push the bolt handle home, see Figure 8-3. Pull the handle back and observe the friction points where the Atchisson unit rides in the receiver. Remove the unit and coat these sparingly with gun oil or a light grease. Reinsert the .22 conversion unit and close the receiver. Cycle the bolt several times to distribute the lubricant.

Fig. 8-3. The Atchisson .22 conversion blow back bolt installed.

Conversion Kit Problems

You may encounter any or all of five problems with either the M261 or the Atchisson .22 conversion unit, but the problems are easy to solve.

Problem 1: your rifle's upper and lower receivers close so tightly that the blowback bolt cannot cycle. If this happens, obtain a spare rear receiver pin and turn its diameter down until the bolt cycles when the receiver halves are pinned together. You can reduce the diameter by chucking the pin in a lathe, or if you do not have one, in an electric drill. Hold a file against the spinning pin at a 40 degree angle and move from one end to the other as the pin is spun. Or, take it to a gunsmith or machinist and ask him or her to do it for you.

Problem 2: there is gas blockage. The .22 rimfire round is quite dirty. After several hundred rounds, functioning may become sluggish or stop altogether. If you are an out door range, replace the .22 caliber unit with the 5.56 mm unit and fire several rounds of full-power ammunition to clean the unit. You may have to cycle the bolt manually for the first or second shot. Always clean the blow back unit after every shooting session.

Problem 3: you develop leading in the bore. Use cartridges

with copper-jacketed .22 rimfire bullets whenever possible. Check the bore often and clean whenever leading is apparent. I have one rifle that never shows any leading but does develop copper fouling and another that leads up after ten shots.

Problem 4). there are misfeeds. This is usually due to two problems. The first is a tight fit between the upper and lower halves of the receiver that squeezes the bolt unit against the rails enough to slow it down during its cycle. The other cause is the presentation of the .22 rimfire round at an "up" angle to the line of the bore. As the bolt snaps forward, it pushes the round from the magazine up the ramp to the chamber. If the bullet tip strikes the ramp at the wrong angle because the ramp is too steep, too rough or because the bolt is moving too slowly, the bullet tip will strike the top edge of the chamber entrance and either be deflected, bent or crushed.

If the bolt moves too slowly, lubricate it. If this does not solve the problem, the receiver halves may be just tight enough to slow the bolt down as it cycles. The solution is discussed in Problem 1. If the ramp is causing the problem, try polishing it with wet 600 grit emery paper to make it as smooth as possible. If this fails, take it to a gunsmith as the angle of the ramp may have to be modified for your rifle. Don't try it yourself or you will make the problem worse.

Problem 5:. accuracy will be problematical with either of the drop-in units because of four factors. First, the .22 rimfire round is much shorter than the .223 cartridge, see Figure 8-4. To solve that problem, the chamber of the drop-in unit is shaped like a .223 cartridge. But this chamber is not rifled which means that when the cartridge is fired, the .22 bullet has to jump 1.2 inches (arrow) before it encounters the barrel's rifling, See Figure 8-4. This jump is known as "free bore."

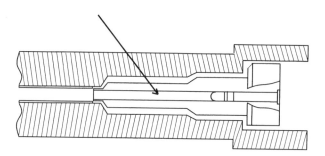

Fig. 8-4. Cross-section view (not to scale) of the .22 rimfire blowback chamber. Note the long jump (1.2) inches the bullet must make (arrow) before encountering the rifling.

The second factor has to do with bullet size. The .223 bullet is 0.224 inches in diameter while the .22 rimfire is only 0.221 inches in diameter. The 0.003 inch difference almost guarantees that the .22 rimfire bullet will not be gripping the lands to any appreciable extent.

The third factor affecting accuracy has to do with the rifle's twist. The 40 grain .22 caliber bullet works best at a slow 1:16 twist. If the drop-in unit is placed in an M16/AR15A2, the bullet will be spun at a rate of one turn in seven inches (1:7). If used in the M16/AR15A1, it will be spun at a rate of 1:12. Either rate will have a substantial effect on accuracy, especially when coupled with the excessive amount of free bore.

The fourth factor is fouling. Powder fouling develops very fast in rimfire rifles. It will develop even faster in the M16/AR15A2, and only a little more slowly in the M16/AR15A1 with its slower 1:12 twist. The solution is to use copper-jacketed bullets and clean the rifle's bore often. Watch for copper fouling with jacketed .22 rounds. A better solution is to use the M16A1/AR15A1 for .22 caliber practice.

Cleaning the .22 Rimfire Conversion Unit

As everyone knows, the .22 rimfire is a dirty round. The M16/AR15 vents gases into the receiver through the gas tube which is not blocked by the conversion unit. When the outside lubricated .22 rimfire cartridge is fired, a certain amount of the waxy lubricant is vaporized and sucked back into the action where it is deposited as a sticky layer of wax. So, pay careful attention to maintenance.

Fig. 8-5. AR15 with a .22 caliber rimfire magazine, and an upper receiver built by Derrick Martin at Accuracy Speaks. At fifty yards, one hole groups are standard.

Clean the .22 conversion unit thoroughly, then scrub the barrel. Finally, using a toothbrush or the nylon cleaning brush made for the M16/AR15, clean the powder and debris from the receiver. If the fouling is heavy, spray one of the new aerosol powder solvents inside the receiver and let it stand for a few minutes, then clean.

The right to manufacture the Atchisson unit is owned by Jonathan Arthur Ciener, Inc. They also manufacture .22 conversion units for the Ruger Mini-14, Government Model 1911, Beretta M92/96 and Taurus PT92/99 and the Glock series of pistols.

Production .22 Caliber M16/AR15s

Two companies, to the author's knowledge, manufacture .22 caliber versions of the M16/AR15: Parker-Hale, Ltd. in England and Leightner-Wise Rifle Company in the United States. Both are described in Chapter 3.

Custom-Built .22 Caliber AR15s

A few custom gunsmiths in the United States and Canada build .22 caliber versions of the M16/AR15. The author is most

familiar with those built by Jim Gronning of Grúning Precision and Derrick Martin at Accuracy Speaks. Both companies provide complete new upper receivers with barrels bored exactly for the .22 rimfire round and rifled to the proper 1:16 twist. The barrels used are made especially for the .22 caliber rimfire cartridge and do not have gas vents which reduces the fouling in the lower receiver.

Both companies install a .22 rimfire conversion unit, but with the lengthy chamber extension removed. A proper chamber is then cut in the .22 rimfire barrel which avoids the excessive free-bore problem of the drop-in conversion units. The magazine built for the conversion unit used is retained.

We tested the Accuracy Speaks and Grúning Precision rifles, both of which were set up as competition service rifles, see Figures 8-5 and Figure 8-6. The Accuracy Speaks .22 was identical to the owner's Service Match Rifle down to the weights in the butt stock. Because he used it for match practice between trips to a more distant and longer shooting range, he wanted it be as close to the .223 service match rifle as possible. At 50 yards, using PMC standard velocity .22 rimfire ammunition, we came close to shooting one hole groups in windless conditions and at 100 yards, near minute of angle shots were common. The rounds fed from the magazine without a bobble.

The Accuracy Speaks .22 AR15.

Accuracy Speaks had done an excellent job of balancing the Colt conversion blow back unit to the puny .22 rimfire. The

Fig. 8-6. Colt .22 rimfire conversion installed by Accuracy Speaks.

Colt conversion unit, which is no longer manufactured, was the civilian version of the M261 military unit.

The owner tried a wide variety of .22 rimfire brands before settling on the PMC standard velocity. His comment was "the more expensive the ammunition, the worse it shot from this rifle."

The Grúning Precision .22 Rimfire Rifle

After the passage of the 1999 California Assault Rifle legislation (see the following side bar) we decided to build a .22 caliber AR15 rifle that could be legally used on any rifle range in the state. While it is possible register an AR15 (provided it was not made by Colt) before the end of 2000, and the shoot it legally in California, the law is so vague and poorly written concerning the definition of an "assault rifle" that a person legally owning a registered rifle could have it confiscated by a law enforcement officer unsure of its status. Not even taking into account such factors as poor record keeping, worse inventory control and crowded court schedules, it would cost a great deal of money to have a court order the return of the rifle. Many law-abiding gun owners would have to abandon their legal property to the police. One chief of police in a large California city was overheard remarking that he "looked forward to adding a great many rifles to his department's inventory at no cost" in this way.

So, after a discussion with Jim, we decided to duplicate our .223 match service competition rifle (see Chapter 5) in .22 rimfire as that caliber rifle is not subject to the 1999 California law. We selected a DPMS cast upper receiver and a 20 inch Douglas Supreme airgauged, stainless steel barrel with a 1:16 inch twist installed ahead of the Atchisson .22 conversion unit but with the chamber extension removed. The front sight post was ground to 0.52 inches and installed with a set screw below to hold it in place, just as on our .223 service match rifle.

Fig. 8-7. The Douglas Supreme match grade .22 rimfire barrel being rough cut to shape in a lathe.

Jim cut the Douglas blank to the same diameters as our .223 service match rifle, see Figure 8-7. The difference in the two barrels lay in the fact that the .22 rimfire lacked a barrel extension. The ramp was milled into breech end and the chamber was bored, see Figures 8-8 and 8-9. The breech was then reduced to the same diameter as the barrel opening in the upper receiver. The barrel was drilled and the indexing pin fitted. The A.H. Merchant hand guard tube and barrel nut was installed, a standard A2 barrel nut assembly followed and the hand guards were fitted.

Fig. 8-8. Above, the feed ramp being cut . . .

Fig. 8-9. . . . below, the .22 rimfire chamber being reamed.

A B. Jones sight system was installed in the rear aperture to match that on the .223 competition service rifle. The upper receiver unit was matched to our .223 competition service rifle lower receiver and stock. The addition of a few ounces of lead weights in the buttstock provided the .22 rimfire upper/lower combination with the exact feel of the rifle with the .223 upper receiver mounted. In use, the .22 rimfire upper receiver felt almost identical to its larger .223 cousin in everything but recoil.

Shooting tests at Evan's Gunsmithing/Shooter's World, an indoor range in Orange, California established two things.

Fig. 8-10. The upper receiver, barrel and bolt ready for final fitting. The extension on the bolt will be removed.

indoor 25 yard line, one ragged hole groups were the norm from a prone position. On the Tucson Rifle Club rifle range on a hot but calm, spring day, at 50 yards, the average group size from three five shot strings was 0.47 inches using the Ely Tenex cartride and 0.55 using the Remington Yellow Jacket. At 100 yards, three five shot strings averaged 0.90 inches with the Ely Tenex and 1.05 inches with the Yellow Jacket cartridges.

There you have it. A properly-constructed .22 rimfire upper should provide you with trigger/hold/breathing and, at ranges up to 50 yards and 100 yards on windless days, with live fire accuracy practice as well.

First, like the Accuracy Speaks rifle, our .22 upper receiver functioned without a hitch with every brand of .22 ammunition tested. We then tested a range of ammunition from ultra-precision match to standard velocity lead bullets for accuracy and found that the best results came from Ely Tenex and Remington High velocity .22 rimfire ammunition.

When using what we thought was copper-jacketed .22 bullets, we saw evidence of copper fouling. But after discussing the problem with a member of Remington's technical staff we discovered that .22 rimfire rounds are not jacketed. Rather the copper "jacket" is really powdered copper or brass which binds mechanically to the lead. The fouling was easy to clean with standard cleaning methods.

At Remington's suggestion, we tried their "High Velocity Golden" .22 rimfire cartridges which are coated with brass powder, and had no further problems.

The Grúning Precision .22 rimfire upper matched the Accuracy Speaks rifle in the "accuracy" department. On the

Fig. 8-11. The author testing the new Grúning Precision .22 rimfire AR15 at the Tucson Rifle Club range in Tucson, AZ. Photo by Roy Marcot.

The .22 Rimfire and California's Assault Rifle Legislation

In 1999, the California legislature passed an all encompassing bill outlawing the sale or possession of "assault rifles." Exceptions were those semiautomatic, high capacity magazine rifles not previously banned by the 1989 law and which had been duly registered, and those semiautomatic, high capacity magazine rifles not on the 1989 list and which were in the owner's legal possession before January 1, 2000, and registered before January 1, 2001.

In effect, the law banned all further acquisition of military style, semiautomatic, high capacity magazine rifles. It also made it illegal for anyone under 21 to possess or register such rifles — which shut down all junior service rifle teams in the state on the first day of the new century and severely limited participation in service rifle and other match competition by law-abiding citizens.

The law did, however, exempt semiautomatic .22 rimfire rifles, no matter their configuration. In a conversation with the California Department of Justice, Firearms Branch, the author was told that a .22 caliber rimfire AR15-type rifle would continue to be legal in California as the law specifically exempted .22 caliber rimfire rifles and pistols. Also, that a .22 caliber rimfire upper receiver placed on a standard AR15 lower receiver would remain legal as the rifle was no longer in the banned category by virtue of the fact that it now fired a .22 caliber rimfire cartridge — providing the lower receiver was not banned by the 1989 law or had been legally registered at that time. And finally, that the .223 upper receiver would not have to be registered as it was not a "firearm" as defined by the law.

So there you have it, Californians. Keep your AR15 rifle registration-free by substituting a .22 rimfire upper barreled receiver for the .223 barreled upper receiver. Shoot the .22 within California's borders, and the .223 without.

9. PROTECTING YOUR RIGHT TO OWN AN AR15 RIFLE

The Bill of Rights, which comprises the first ten amendments to the Constitution of the United States, guarantees you certain rights. Certainly the right to assemble peacefully and speak your mind is known and accepted by all American citizens without question, as is the right to be safe and secure from arbitrary government actions that interfere with your safety and well being. No one suggests that "government" should be able to enter your home without a warrant signed by a magistrate upon proof of good cause, or that you be arrested without just cause, forbid you to practice your own brand of religion or meet and associate with those you choose in a law-abiding manner.

But over the past thirty-five years, government at all levels has come to believe that it can deprive you of your right to own a firearm, a right guaranteed by the 2nd Amendment. A growing number legislators and bureaucrats are convinced that the 2nd Amendment does not apply to individuals but to the states. They are wrong, and unless *we all* fight to stop them, within another decade or so, they will have legislated your right away.

Everyone who believes that the Constitution of the United States must not be tampered with in the name of expediency must become involved in the fight to protect the 2nd Amendment whether they own firearms or not. Tamper with one right, and they are all in danger.

Those who own and enjoy the legal use of firearms bear an even heavier burden whether they be collectors, target shooters, hunters, trap, skeet and clay shooters, cowboy action participants or those who own firearms only for self defense. No matter your reason for firearms ownership, you must take part in the battle or lose that right. For those who hunt with bolt action rifles, shoot wild fowl with shotguns or collect antique weapons and do not believe their firearms rights will be affected by current and future laws, may we respectfully suggest you check what happened in England and Australia recently, and is happening now in Canada.

First Step

To protect your right to own firearms, if you are not registered to vote, do so now. Voting is one of the most important things you can do to help win the fight. Want an example? John F. Kennedy won the 1960 Presidential election by 50,000 votes. That amounts to one vote in each voting precinct in the United States. Your vote counts, so use it.

Second Step

Join a gun rights organization. The National Rifle Association is the strongest and the most effective. You may not like everything they do and say, but then you probably do not like everything your political party or candidate does and says either. The point is the NRA fights to preserve the 2nd Amendment, and you owe them your support. Membership is only $35.00 a year — the cost of two or three boxes of ammunition. If you cannot afford that, then you cannot afford to shoot. If they ask for contributions to support the fight, give as much as you can. If every gun owner gave just the cost of one box of commercial .223 caliber ammunition every year, the antigunners would not stand a ghost of chance. Call 1 800 672-3888 to join or renew your membership.

If you do not want to join the NRA, then join the Second Amendment Foundation (1-800-426-4302) or Gun Owners of America (703-321-8585). But join some pro-firearms group and lend your support.

Third Step

Every gun owner is well aware that media is not on our side. Every time they present a biased report, or show a handgun in the background when talking about crime, they persuade more and more people that firearms are evil and must be done away with. Most of us fuss and fume but do nothing about it.

Don't make that mistake. Radio and television make use of the public airwaves. They are required by federal law to present material which conforms to community standards. As more than fifty percent of the population owns a firearm, biased, antigun positions are not in conformance with community standards.

What can you do about it? A great deal. Every time you see or hear a biased, antigun news report or watch an antigun dramatic radio or television program, phone the station and complain. There are two reasons why your phone call is effective. First, the station must compile all comments received from the public about the programing and present it to the Federal Communications Commission at the time it renews its broadcasting license. If the list indicates that the station is not meeting "community standards," the broadcast license may not be renewed. Millions of dollars are at stake.

Secondly, radio and television producers live and die by their "ratings." Virtually all news staff members, including on-air personnel, work on one or two year contracts. If your complaint suggests that you will stop watching that station, or at least that news program, it impacts their ratings. On a normal night, a big city television station will receive from 25 to 100 comments regarding a news segment (more if it is controversial). If fifteen or more calls are received protesting a biased news account — well you do the math. If this happens every time an antigun segment is aired, how long do you think it will take the producer to change his or her approach, before the station owner's do it for him or her.

Is your phone call really effective? In the metropolitan area where the author lives, a large, independent station ran a news segment researched and written by a staff reporter. The antigun bias was very obvious. The author was contacted by the reporter for information, which the reporter promptly disregarded. The author persuaded a dozen people to watch the news segment and then phone the station over the following several days to protest the inaccuracies and bias in the story. A second weekend presentation was canceled.

Making an impact on your local radio or TV station is very easy to do. In your yellow pages, look up "television stations and broadcasting," then make a list of the phone numbers for the local radio and television stations you watch most. Do the same for "radio stations and broadcasting." Keep both lists by your favorite chair. When you see or hear a news program with an antigun bias, call the station and register your complaint.

Be polite and to the point. Don't launch into a lecture; the person taking the call is simply there to record your comments. He or she usually has no say in how the news is written or presented.

Now, persuade your friends to do the same thing. Then as the complaints mount, watch the way the station's point of view changes.

The national radio and TV networks are susceptible to the same pressures, but the numbers of complaints have to be greater. If CNN, NBC, ABC or CBS airs an antigun news segment, make it known you disapprove.

Making the same impression on your local newspaper is more difficult because they do not use the public air waves and most large newspapers today pretty well control their market. Newspaper editorial boards are notoriously immune to local opinion as expressed in letters to the editor and comments in other forms of the media.

Small, local news weeklies often carry antigun stories and messages simply because they pull them off the wire services or the Internet and lack the staff to check facts. If you find a wrong or misleading article, let them know by phone or mail. You will probably be thanked if you are polite and can back your criticism with facts from sources that can be checked quickly.

Note: If your telephone yellow pages does not list all of your local TV and radio stations, you can call information for their phone numbers and addresses. Most local newspapers also carry a list of radio and TV stations in the area, complete with phones numbers and addresses. These are usually printed in entertainment sections on Saturday or Sunday.

You can also check the Internet. While not all TV and radio stations maintain Internet web sites, they will be listed somewhere. The author prefers the Altavista search engine (http://www.altavista.com) because it is easy to use and thorough, but any web search engine will do. First try to locate the station through the "Internet Yellow Pages." Most will be listed there. Supply the station call letters and the city and state. If this does not work, try a general search using the call letters and the state, only. A search for KNBC, California provided the following: KNBC Channel 4 News, Los Angeles, 818 840-3425.

Once you have compiled your list, why not make copies and drop them off at your favorite gun shop and range? Copy or summarize these two pages with the list so that others will be encouraged to make calls as well.

Follow these three steps and you will have done your part to protect the 2nd Amendment and your right to own and enjoy your firearms.

10. THE .308 AR15

When Eugene Stoner developed the AR10, he proved that a semiautomatic rifle was capable of providing accuracy nearly equal to the best U.S. sniper rifle then available, in each and every military rifle issued to a GI. But military planners in the mid-1960s were torn between the desire for accuracy and the need to provide a heavy volume of full automatic fire. When they managed to achieved both objectives, they were so wrapped up in internecine squabbling,

Fig. 10-1. Eugene Stoner's first successful military rifle was the AR-10 in 7.62 mm NATO.

further obscured by a raging war, that no one understood what had been achieved. The AR10 was adopted only by a handful of small nations and passed into obscurity. Nearly thirty years would pass before Eugene Stoner's original .30 caliber design would achieve the respect that it deserved.

The Stoner-25 .308 Precision Rifle

The work performed in the 1970s on the development of a new sniper rifle for the US Army at the Government-owned Rock Island Arsenal, as so often in the past, provided the catalyst for private industry. Working with the engineers and production people at Knight's Manufacturing Company of Vero Beach, Florida, Eugene Stoner modified the AR10 system in its original .308 caliber for production as the SR-25 (Stoner Rifle, AR10 plus AR15 equals 25). By doing so, he achieved outstanding accuracy and consistency and the rifle has been adopted by match shooters and by numerous police special weapons squads around the country

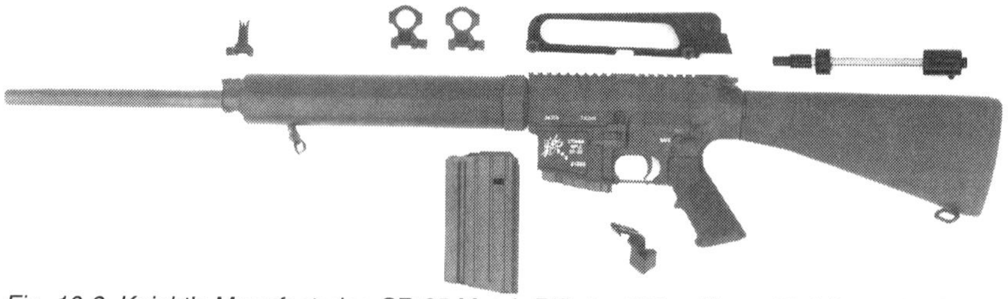

Fig. 10-2. Knight's Manufacturing SR-25 Match Rifle in .308 caliber with (above, L-R) detachable front sight, KMC 30 mm scope rings, detachable carry handle, precision bore rod guide and (below) 20 rd magazine and shell deflector.

for the purpose originally foreseen at Rock Island — as a sniper rifle.

Components

The heart of any rifle is the receiver. The SR-25 lower receiver is manufactured in one piece from high-tensile strength 7075 T6 aluminum alloy. It is identical to that of the AR15/M16 receiver except for the larger magazine well. The upper receiver's manufacture starts with an extruded bar of 7075 T6 aluminum alloy 8.375 inches long. The bar is machined in a computerized numerically controlled (CNC) machine which produces a finished upper receiver cut to precise standards. The only difference between the SR-25 upper and the M16/AR15 upper is the missing carry handle tunnel and lack of forward assist plunger housing. The top of the upper receiver is machined for a full length scope rail based on the Picatinny-Weaver rail system.

Almost sixty percent of the SR-25 components — everything but the two receiver halves, hammer, the barrel assembly and the bolt carrier/bolt — are interchangeable with the standard AR15/M16 rifle. The SR-25's hammer is thinner, and according to Knight's, more efficient than the hammer used in the AR15. The bolt carrier/bolt assembly of AISI 8620 carbon steel with a Rockwell C-scale hardness of 60-62, is nearly identical to the AR15 bolt except that it is sized for the larger .308 cartridge. The bolt is driven into the barrel extension by the recoil spring. The action of the cam lug causes the bolt to turn in the carrier, locking its seven lugs into the seven slots in the barrel extension.

Remington 5R Rifling

Rifled barrel blanks are manufactured for Knight's by Remington and are identical to those used in the Army's M24 Sniper Rifle. The blanks are turned at Knight's to final shape. The result is a 24-inch heavy barrel made of 4140 high carbon steel with the famous Remington "5R" rifling which has five grooves with radial, or rounded, rifling — a rifling system adopted from the Russian AK74 rifle. The twist is to the right and it makes one turn in 11.25 inches

(1:11.25) which both Knight and Remington consider ideal for the .308 bullet weighing between 150 and 173 grains.

The barrel is screwed into a barrel extension which in turn is indexed into the upper receiver for proper alignment, as with the M16/AR15. A barrel nut then locks the barrel to the receiver. The free-floated hand guard is attached to a shroud fitted between the barrel nut and the receiver. The hand guard includes an attaching point for a Harris bipod and sling swivel.

The gas block sleeves onto the barrel and is indexed into position against a pedestal that flares from the barrel's surface. An interesting feature of the gas block assembly is that its upper surface is milled into a Picatinny-Weaver-style rail to allow a quick-detachable front sight to be mounted.

The magazine that Knight's selected for the SR-25 is the original AR10 magazine. Pre-ban 20 round magazines (new steel type) were originally issued until they ran out and were replaced by ten round magazines in mid-1996 to comply with the provisions of the Violent Crime Control Act of 1994. Original AR10, twenty round capacity magazines can still be found on surplus market and are legal under federal law as their manufacture ended well before 1994. But check your own state's laws.

The firing controls of the SR-25 are very similar to the AR15/M16 rifle. When we tested the SR-25, we found that the only real differences between it and the AR15 had to do with weight and balance. All the firing controls were right where our fingers searched for them.

Fig. 10-3. The ArmaLite, Inc., AR-10(T) Match Rifle in .308 with the ST95 telescopic sight and mount. Photo courtesy of Armalite, Inc.

The SR-25 field-strips and cleans the same way as the AR15/M16: 1) remove the magazine. 2) Check inside the receiver to see that it is unloaded. 3) Push the rear receiver pin out to the right. 4) Push the forward receiver pin out to the right. Separate the upper and lower halves of the receiver. 5) Remove the bolt. Reassemble in reverse order.

The SR-25 is a match-quality rifle that can break one minute of angle with 168 grain match ammunition right off the shelf. Shoot several hundred rounds through the SR-25 and watch the group sizes close up as the rifle wears in. And the rifle was designed to hold this degree of accuracy for 10,000 or more rounds if properly cleaned on a regular basis. If accuracy begins to suffer at that point, a new barrel can be installed and head spaced easily.

The SR-25 uses a single-stage trigger set to 3.6 pounds. On our SR-25, there was no creep, and let-off when it came, was crisp. Because of the rifle's weight and straight-line stock

the recoil was less than from an M14/M1A.

In addition to the Match Rifle, Knight's also offers a Lightweight Match Rifle with a 20 inch barrel which weighs 1.25 pounds less than the Match rifle; the Stoner Carbine which began life as a semiautomatic hunting rifle and proved so popular it has been adopted also as a compact lightweight (7.75 pounds) tactical rifle and the Sporter Rifle (the barrel is not free-floated) which retains the traditional AR15/M16 look, but without a flash hider and bayonet mount to comply with the 1994 Violent Crime Act.

ArmaLite AR10 Series

The ArmaLite company of Geneseo, IL also manufactures a very fine .308 M16/AR15 type rifle. All parts are built to Mil-Spec standards or better. The uppers are forged and machined to shape and both upper and lower are hard coat anodized.

At the time this book went to press, eight models were offered and are described in Table 3-1. The include three rifles (one match) and three carbines. All models are furnished with chromemoly barrel in varying lengths from 16 to 24 inches. Two models with carry handles are offered, and the remainder are flat top upper receivers with Picatinny Arsenal Weaver style mounts (also on the front sight base). ArmaLite's two-stage match trigger is available as well. All barrels are rifled either with a 1:11.25 or 1:12 twist. And all are built with the same attention to detail found in the company's .223 series of rifles and carbines as well.

Testing the .308 Stoner Design

Our test rifle was a Stoner-24 Match rifle from Knights (new in the box). An ArmaLite rifle was not available to us before deadline time. The Stoner-24 mounted a Redfield 4 x 12 Variable Scope in KMC Scope rings locked to the upper rail. These rings provided a perfect line-of-sight/cheekweld position. During our test, we shot five successive groups of three shots each using Federal Match 168 Grain .308 at both 100 and 200 yards. At 100 yards, the smallest group was 0.95 inches in diameter, the largest 1.35 inches. At 200 yards, the smallest group was 1.75 inches in diameter, the largest was 2.1 inches.

There was no doubt in our minds that a custom gunsmith specializing in theM16/AR15 rifle might, with a little tweaking, here and there, improve on these results.

11. WHERE DO WE GO FROM HERE?

The M16 will probably be the last U.S. military rifle available to civilians shooters. The next U.S. military service rifle will be a select fire weapon combined with a 20 mm grenade launcher in one package.

Since the establishment of the Springfield Armory in 1798, developing an improved battle rifle has been a never-ending project. And in accordance with that tradition, even before the M16 rifle was standardized, development of an improved battle rifle has been a Defense Department goal.

By all reports, Eugene Stoner was never completely satisfied with the M16/AR15 design. He wanted to make a number of improvements and design changes but the military, fighting a war in Southeast Asia, needed the new rifle as soon as possible and were willing to make only those changes needed to get the rifle out to the troops.

Apparently ordnance officials also felt that there was great deal of room for improvement in the ArmaLite design because over the years since its introduction, a wide variety of programs have developed an amazing number of concepts, ranging from the multi-projectile SPIW to the M231 Firing Port Weapon to open bolt HBAR M16 Light Machine Gun to the successful M203 single shot, 40 mm grenade launcher. The rifle has been shortened, lengthened, lightened and skeletonized. More accessories have been mounted on and hung from it than virtually any other military rifle in history.

The first "improved M16" design was the AR18, see Figure 11-1. Almost as soon as the M16 was standardized, Eugene Stoner, still at ArmaLite, wanted to eliminate the raw gas flow impacting against the bolt face that carried carbon and unburned powder particles into the join between bolt and bolt carrier. His first step was to eliminate the direct gas takeoff which had been borrowed from the Swedish Model AG42B Ljungman rifle. He settled on a gas piston concept similar to that used by the American designer, John C. Garand (M1), the Belgian, Dieudonné J. Saive (SAFN and FAL) and the great Soviet designers, Sergei Gavrilovich Simonov (SKS) and Fedor Vasilevich Tokarev (SVT1938/40). In all four systems, a gas piston was interposed between the expanding bleed gas and the bolt face. The gas moved the piston which moved the bolt and vented to the atmosphere, eliminat-

ing any possibility of gas blowing blow back into the breech.

To deal with bent or dirty cartridges that could prevent the bolt from closing, a "forward assist" device had been incorporated into the M16 design. In the AR18, Stoner combined the forward assist device and cocking handle into one crank-like bolt handle which provided a positive purchase on the cartridge case and increased the rifle's reliability in the field. The AR18 rifle was designed to fire the M193 55 grain cartridge and so was rifled with a 1:12 twist, like the M16A1. Its magazines (20 and 30 round, plus a 40 round magazine) were identical to and interchangeable with those for the M16.

Special forces troops, hostage-rescue and SWAT teams often expressed concern that the M16 rifle's stock could not be folded for close quarter work. Colt had developed a telescoping stock for the M16, but even so, the stock still protruded from the rear of the receiver.

The AR-18's stock folded to the left side on

Fig. 11-1. Eugene Stoner considered the AR18 to be an improvement over the M16. North Cape Publications Collection.

a sturdy hinge at the back of the receiver, see Figure 10-2. The safety and fire selector switch were made ambidextrous so that the folded stock would not interfere with their functioning. This folding stock is probably the second best feature of the weapon and is comparable in quality to that used on the Fabrique Nationale FNC rifle.

A 2.75 X 20 mm scope was developed for the AR18 by Realist. A spring and rod attaching system allowed the scope to be mounted and dismounted quickly without loss of zero.

Fig. 11-2. The AR18 with the stock folded.

The AR18 rifle was made to be produced cheaply and quickly from sheet metal stampings that required little finish machining. But unfortunately, the AR18 did not offer enough significant improvements over the M16 design and so did not prove a successful military rifle. A few thousand were manufactured by ArmaLite, and by Howa in Japan and Sterling in Great Britain, under license, for civilian and police sales as the AR180.

Stoner left ArmaLite shortly after the AR18 design was completed and started a new company, ARES, Inc. in Port Clinton, Ohio. One of his first projects was the development of an advanced assault rifle for the U.S. government. The new design was designated the Future Assault Rifle Concept and it laid the foundation from which planning for all future M16 replacements would start. The new rifle had an integral muzzle brake and compensator, a folding bipod which nested in the hand guard, a spring-loaded dust cover that automatically closed over the ejector port between shots and an built-in reflex collimator sight. Two prototypes were built for testing before the program was discontinued during the defense department funding cuts in the mid-to late 1970s.

In the early 1980s, development work began on an Advanced Combat Rifle (ACR). Exploratory contracts were awarded to Heckler and Koch and to AAI Corporation. The ACR rifle had a gas operated firing pin that could be set to fire a three round burst, to fire full auto from an open bolt at 600 rpm or in the semiautomatic mode from a closed bolt. The rifle (and carbine) used a caseless 5.56 mm cartridge developed by Hercules Powder Company. The cartridges (70 grain 5.56 mm bullet or 28 grain, 4.32 mm sabot) were prepackaged in discardable magazines.

From this early beginning, The Objective Individual Combat Weapon (OICW) program developed. Today, the program's goal is to enhance the capability of the 21st century infantryman by replacing the M16 rifle, M203 grenade launcher, and M4 carbine with a new weapon combining the features of all three, see Figures 11-4 and 5. The new rifle system will provide a 500 percent increase in the probability that an enemy solider will be killed or wounded when fired upon at up too 1,000 meters. The new rifle system, which will combine a 5.56 mm rifle and a 20 mm grenade launcher in one package, will be substantially lighter than the M16/M203 combination. It will have day/night fire control (thermal and night vision capability) and an onboard computer for target acquisition and firing.

The soldier uses the built-in laser range finder to find the exact distance to the target, then determine whether to use the rifle or grenade launcher. If the later, the computer sets the grenade's fuse and tells the soldier when to fire.

The 5.56 mm rifle which forms the center of the kinetic energy half (read rifle) of the OICW is based on H&Ks G36 design which in turn is based on ArmaLite's long-underrated AR18. The rifle employs the same piston-driven Stoner rotating bolt as the AR18 although refined by a great deal of development work, and fires the same range of cartridges as the M16 rifle and M4 carbines.

The prime contractor was Alliant Techsystems Inc. who is responsible for developing the 20 mm grenade and its warhead and fusing system, as well as overall systems integration. Heckler and Koch (HK) GmbH and HK Inc. of Sterling VA are responsible for the 5.56 mm rifle. The Fire Control System is being developed by Contraves Brashear Systems Inc., of Pittsburgh, PA and Dynamit Nobel AG is developing the grenade ammunition. The program was in Phase 4/5 in June 2000 with the first complete rifles expected to be fielded in 2005.

Fig. 11-3. The Objective Individual Combat Weapon combines a 5.56 mm rifle with a 20 mm grenade launcher, laser range finder, thermal sight and fire control computer. Photo courtesy of Alliant Technosystems.

Fig. 11-4. An American soldier armed with the OICW will command as much firepower as a WWII platoon. Photo courtesy of Alliant Techsystems, Inc.

APPENDIX A
ASSEMBLY/DISASSEMBLY

The M16/AR15 rifle was designed to be easily disassembled for cleaning or repair. The U.S. military has established three levels of disassembly. Level 1 is used by the individual soldier; Level 2 is termed "intermediate maintenance" and is performed at the divisional. Level 3 is performed by specialized units trained and equipped to solve all problems with the M16/AR15, or at the factory level.

Level 1

1. Turn the selector switch to "SAFE," Figure A-1.

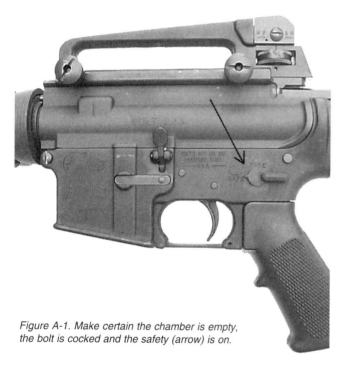

Figure A-1. Make certain the chamber is empty, the bolt is cocked and the safety (arrow) is on.

2. Remove the magazine. Check to make certain it is empty.
3. Draw back the cocking handle to retract the bolt. Look inside the chamber to make certain it is empty.
4. Press the bolt release on the left side of the receiver to allow the bolt to go forward.
5. Turn the selector switch to fire.
6. Press the rear takedown pin out of the receiver from the left and swivel the upper receiver forward, Figure A-2.
7. Pull back on the cocking handle and draw the bolt carrier out of the upper receiver.
8. Remove the cocking handle.

Fig. A-2. Push the rear take down pin out to the right.

9. Remove the front two-piece take down screw and separate the top and bottom of the receiver, Figure A-3.

Fig. A-3. Remove the front take down pin and separate the receiver halves.

Note: Some M16/AR15 rifles use a pivot pin rather than a two-piece screw. It can be disengaged by using the firing pin or a punch of the proper diameter to depress the detent holding it in place. Removal of the pivot pin is covered in Level 2, No.18.

10. To dismount the bolt assembly, turn the bolt head counter-clockwise as far as it will go. Remove the firing pin retainer pin (cotter pin) and draw out the firing pin. Remove the bolt cam pin and draw the bolt forward and out of the carrier, Figure A-4.

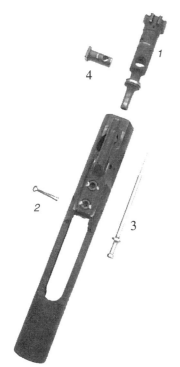

Fig. A-4. 1) Bolt head. 2) Firing pin retainer pin. 3) Firing Pin. 4) Bolt cam pin.

11. To remove the hand guards, have a helper hold the rifle in the vertical position. Pull down on the hand guard slip ring until the receiver end of one of the hand guards can be pulled loose. Repeat for the other hand guard, Figure A-5.

This completes the Level 1 disassembly. Reassembly in is reverse order.

Level 2

As many of the parts you will remove are quite small, use a magnetic tray or strips of adhesive tape to lay them on to prevent loss. All pins, with one exception, are removed by pushing out from the left and installed by pushing in from the right. The one exception is the receiver extension pin in the lower receiver of older M16 and XM16 models. It is driven out from right to left.

Note how the hammer spring tails fit into the grooves in the trigger pin.

12. Complete Level 1 disassembly after removing the magazine and checking that it and the chamber are empty.

Fig. A-5. Pull down the slip ring to remove handguards.

13. To remove the bolt extractor, disassemble the bolt as in Level 1, No. 10. Place your thumb on top of the extractor. Use the firing pin or a punch to remove the extractor by pushing out the extractor retainer pin, Figure A-6. Control the removal of the extractor so that the extractor spring is not lost. Remove the extractor spring from the extractor. Note that extractor spring contains either a separate rubber plug or a second spring. Don't lose either. Also note that the wide end of the spring must fit into the blind hole of the extractor.

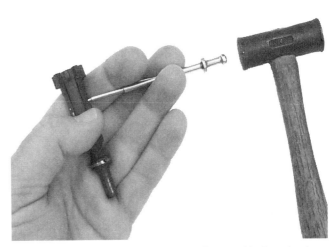

Fig. A-6. Use the firing pin or a punch to disassemble the extractor.

14. To completely disassemble the bolt, remove the ejector from the bolt, using a punch of the proper size to drive out the ejector pin. Place your thumb over the bolt face while withdrawing the punch as the ejector is under spring pressure. Ease the ejector and spring out.

The gas seal rings can be removed with a small screwdriver, Figure A-7. To replace a ring, hold it between thumb and forefinger with the split end up. Slide it over the firing pin tunnel and insert one end into the groove. Use the index finger of the other hand to gently push the ring into place until the other end snaps into the groove. Be gentle and do

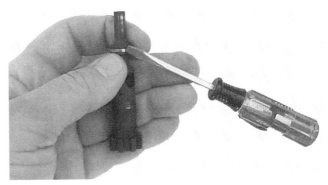

Fig. A-7. Use a small screwdriver to pry off the gas seal rings.

not hurry. Turn the rings so that the gaps are staggered. This will prevent loss of gas pressure. Fire several rounds to create an effective gas seal and to make certain the key is seated securely. You may have to operate the rifle manually until the seal is becomes effective.

Remove the carrier key by filing away the staked metal holding the bolts in place with a pointed Swiss file. Hold the bolt securely in a padded vise and make certain it is supported from below. Turn the socket bolts holding it in place out. Do not reuse the carrier key, but replace it with a new one. Tighten the socket head screws with a torque wrench to between 35 and 40 inch pounds. Restake the screws at the 2, 7 and 11 o'clock positions with a center punch.

Note: Do not remove the gas seal rings from the bolt or the carrier key from the bolt carrier unless they must be replaced. Replace only with new parts. Check to make certain that the staked screws securing the carrier key are tight and the carrier key has no play.

15.   To remove the action spring guide (buffer) assembly, push the buffer back and depress the buffer retainer, Figure A-8. Draw the recoil spring guide out, keeping in mind that it is under spring pressure. Separate the recoil spring from the buffer.

Fig. A-8. Depress the retaining plunger with a small screwdriver to release the recoil spring guide.

16.   To remove the butt stock, unscrew the top butt plate screw. Carefully pull the butt stock back and off the action spring guide tube so that the rear take down pin spring and detent, which are held in the lower receiver by the butt stock, are not lost, Figure A-9.

17.   To remove the pistol grip, invert the rifle and insert a screw driver with a wide blade into the bottom of the pistol grip and turn out the pistol grip screw and its lock washer. Pull up on the pistol grip slowly to remove it as the selector

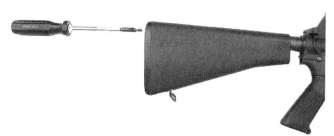

Fig. A-9. When removing the buttstock, do not lose the rear take down detent spring.

switch spring and its detent are held in the bottom of the lower receiver by the pistol grip, Figure A-10.

Fig. A-10. Remove the screw holding the pistol grip to the lower receiver.

18.   To remove a front pivot pin rather than the pivot screw, used a small punch to depress the detent holding the pin in place, and remove the pin. Control the removal of the detent and its spring.

19.   To remove the hammer, move the selector lever to the semiautomatic position and release the hammer. Use the firing pin nose or a proper size punch to push the hammer pin out from the left. Remove the hammer spring, paying particular attention to how it is installed on the hammer and how its tails lie in the trigger pin grooves. Draw a sketch if necessary, Figure A-11.

20.   To remove the automatic sear, turn the selector lever to the automatic position and push out with the firing pin or a proper size punch.

21.   To remove the selector lever, turn it to the rear as far as it will go. Use the firing pin or a proper size punch to push it out. If you did not remove the pistol grip and the selector lever spring and detent, you will have to do so now.

Fig. A-11. Use a small punch to press the hammer pin out from left to right.

22. To remove the trigger, trigger spring, disconnector and disconnector spring, use the firing pin or a proper size punch to push the pin out. Separate the components, paying attention to their relationship to one another.

23. Remove the bolt catch. Push the bolt catch pin out with a proper size punch. Push the pin forward toward the muzzle. Remove the components, noting their relationship to one another.

24. Remove the magazine catch by using a punch to push the magazine release button into the receiver from the right far enough that the catch can be rotated and unscrewed from the catch button and pulled out from the left.

25. Remove the trigger guard by pushing out the rear trigger guard pin with a proper size punch, Figure A-12.

Fig. A-12. Remove the trigger guard by depressing the detent at the magazine end and driving out the roll pin with a punch at the pistol grip end.

26. Rifle: Remove the extension spring tube (buffer tube) by driving out the roll pin from right to left (only on older M16 models; newer models do not have the roll pin). Use the M16/AR15 combination wrench with an extension handle or a socket wrench to grasp the square nut milled into the end of the extension tube and loosen it by turning counter clockwise. If you have not removed the buffer retainer detent and spring, hold it down while you unscrew the extension tube, then remove. Remember, it is under spring tension. When reinstalling the extension tube, hand tighten, then tighten again using a torque wrench to 35-39 ft/lbs.

Carbine: Remove the telescoping butt stock first by driving out the pin holding the release lever to the lock pin. Note that the carbine extension tube does not have the square nut at the end but is smooth. To remove it without damage, you need the carbine spanner wrench (Colt Part No. 62420) or a similar aftermarket tool (See Appendix F). The receiver extension tube is secured by a lock nut at the rear of the receiver which, if properly installed, has been staked. Remove the staking with a file and slide the lock nut back, being careful not to lose the selector lever spring and detent. Note the number of partial threads exposed before removing the extension tube and unscrew. When reinstalling, screw it in to that point so that the buffer detent moves up and down freely. Turn the lock nut back on and tighten with a torque wrench to 34-42 ft/lbs, then restake so that metal is upset into the slots provided at the front of the lock nut.

27. Remove the forward assist plunger from the upper receiver by driving out the roll pin from above with a proper size punch. As you withdraw the punch, control the plunger and its spring. The knob and pawl assembly are joined by a pin which can be removed if necessary. It should only be done to replace one part or the other.

28. Remove the butt plate and sling swivel from the butt stock by unscrewing the screw holding the butt plate to the stock. The XM16 and some very early M16s have solid butt plates and the sling swivel is held in place with a roll pin which can be removed with a punch. The sling is held to the base with a second roll pin. Figure A-13.

29. The forward sling swivel is

Fig. A-13. Remove the lower butt plate screw to free the rear sling swivel.

held to the front sight assembly with roll pin and can be removed with a punch.

30. The compensator on pre-1994 AR15s intended for non-military sales is screwed onto the barrel with a lock washer to hold it in place. Post-1994 AR15s may have the compensator pinned in place and it cannot be removed. Pre-1994 compensators can be turned off with a proper size box wrench or a crescent wrench using the flats milled on the compensator for that purpose, or with the M16/AR15 Combination Wrench. The middle slot in the compensator must be at top dead center (TDC). When reinstalling, use the combination wrench attached to a torque wrench and tighten to 15-20 ft/lbs minimum. The early XM16 and M16 three-prong flash hiders require the use of the Colt wrench, part no. 11010033.

31. To remove the front sight assembly, drive out the front and rear pins and slide the front sight assembly forward and off the barrel, Figure A-14. Remove the gas tube by driving out its retaining roll pin and pulling it back out of the front sight assembly and off.

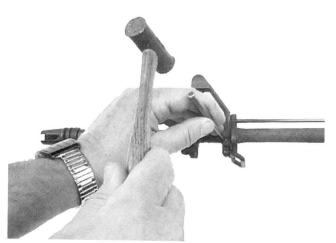

Fig. A-14. Drive out the two pins holding the front sight assembly and slide it forward and off the barrel after removing the flash hider.

32. To remove the front sight post, depress the detent in front of the sight post and unscrew. Be careful not to lose the front sight detent and its spring.

33. To remove the rear sight assembly, follow the procedures listed below:
A. A1 rear sight is not adjustable for elevation. Drive out the windage drum spring pin on the right side of the upper receiver. Remove the windage drum, detent and spring. Use a wide-bladed screw driver to remove the rear sight screw from the left. Press down on the top of the sight as you remove the screw as the sight is under pressure from a flat spring below.

B. To remove the A2 rear sight, turn the elevation knob to the 8/3 setting or to the point where the index screw hole in the elevation knob is visible through the front sight base when looking down at it from the top with the small aperture in the upright position. Drive out the pin holding the windage knob in place. Hold the knob as you do so and remove carefully so that the spring and detent are not lost. Remove the rear sight screw from the left being careful to control the rear sight with your thumb. Remove the rear sight and the flat spring beneath.

Remove the index screw with the proper size Allen wrench.

Drive out the elevation knob spring pin immediately below the elevation knob with a punch. Leave the punch in the pin hole, Figure A-15. Place your thumb over the top of the rear sight and slowly withdraw the punch, easing up the rear sight assembly at the same time until the spring is extended. Remove the sight base by turning the elevation knob up, then ease it off, being careful to capture the spring and detent at the front of the sight base. Remove the elevation knob to the left, watching for its detent and spring which will come up through the elevation index screw hole.

Fig. A-15. When installing the A2 elevation drum, place a punch in the pin hole to hold both parts of the drum in alignment.

Remove the index screw from the elevation knob and separate into two parts. Reassemble in exactly the opposite order, turning the upper receiver upside down to insert the elevation spring and then the elevation spring pin.

Level 3

This level of assembly and disassembly is best left to a trained gunsmith. The procedures will be described briefly.

34. Barrel removal and installation requires a set of vise jaws, combination wrench, breaker bar extension and torque wrench The Colt part numbers are 62695 for the vise jaws and 62965 for the combination wrench. The combination wrench has studs on its face. These must be fitted to the slots in the face of the barrel nut. A breaker bar should be attached to the combination wrench and turned counterclockwise to remove the barrel nut. The barrel and its extension can then be pulled forward out of the upper receiver.

To reassemble, reinsert the barrel into the upper receiver, so that the stud on the extension slides into the slot in the top of the upper receiver. Assemble the barrel nut assembly — barrel nut, slip ring, slip ring springs (3) and retaining ring. Use split ring pliers on this last to insert it into the slip ring. Slide the assembled barrel nut unit over the muzzle and along the barrel to the receiver face. Clamp the barrel in a vise using the barrel vise jaws.

Insert the bolt carrier in the upper receiver so that it locks into the lugs in the barrel extension. Insert a 0.177 in diameter by 2 3/4 inch long metal rod through the gas port opening in the barrel nut assembly, turning it until it enters the gas port hole in the face of the upper receiver and bottoms in the key on the bolt carrier.

Attach a 1/2 inch drive fitting to a torque wrench and attach the fitting to the lug on the combination wrench. Press the combination wrench against the barrel nut unit until all three lugs on the wrench engage the lugs on the barrel nut. You will have to press the wrench against the tension of the slip ring springs.

Make certain the lugs are engaged and turn the torque wrench clockwise, tightening the barrel nut, until a reading of 50 foot lbs is obtained for an M16/AR15A1 or 31-35 ft/lbs for the M16/AR15A2. Remove the rod from the gas port.

Note: No matter which model barrel you are installing, or reinstalling, after tightening the barrel to the recommended foot pounds, remove the torque wrench and replace it with a 1/2 inch drive wrench handle. Loosen the barrel until you can turn the combination wrench by hand.

Reinstall the torque wrench and retighten the barrel to the specified torque using the rod through the gas port into the carrier key to index properly. Repeat this procedure one more time — three times in all. This retightening procedure was developed by Colt to insure a better thread fit and prevent the barrel nut from working loose.

M16/AR15 Function Check

Your should perform a function check on the action of your M16/AR15 at regular intervals to assure safe performance. The test is simple and takes only a few second.

Remove the magazine. Pull the charging handle to the rear to cock the rifle. Check the breech to make sure it is unloaded. Turn the safety lever to the SAFE position. Squeeze the trigger. The hammer should not fall and you should hear nothing.

Place the safety in the SEMIAUTOMATIC position. Squeeze the trigger. You should hear a click as the hammer falls. With the safety still in the SEMIAUTOMATIC position, pull the charging handle to the rear and release. The hammer should not fall but be held by the disconnector. Release the trigger. You should hear light click as the hammer releases from the disconnector and drops to engage the trigger. Pull the trigger. You should hear a loud click as the hammer falls.

Repeat this test five times. The rifle should not malfunction. If the weapon *does malfunction* at any time during this test, consult a gunsmith.

If you have a full automatic M16 rifle, continue the function test. Set the selector Lever to AUTO. Cock the rifle by pulling and releasing the charging handle. Make certain the rifle is empty. Pull the trigger. You should hear a loud click as the hammer falls. Continue to hold the trigger back. Pull the charging handle all the way back then ease it slowly forward. You should hear a loud click as it reaches its rearmost position. Now release the trigger. You should not hear a click. Pull the trigger and again you should not hear a click.

APPENDIX B
CLEANING AND MAINTENANCE

Your M16/AR15 barrel will last as long as 15,000 - 20,000 or as few as 1,500 rounds depending on how you clean it and the equipment you use to do so. Whether your rifle is used for plinking or target shooting, take care of it.

Some basics you should understand. The M16/AR15 develops 52,000 pounds of pressure per square inch in the chamber when fired, and the gases produced by the burning propellant reach temperatures well over 2,000 degrees Fahrenheit. The combination of pressure and heat will eventually affect the best steels.

Proper barrel break-in is essential to barrel life. If you have a new rifle, please review the break in techniques described in Chapter 6, Breaking in a New Rifle.

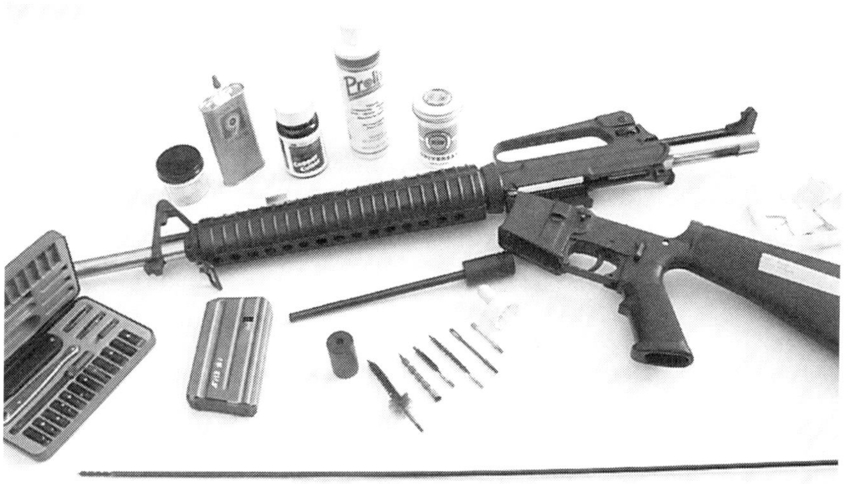

Once past the break-in stage, you will find that jacketed ammunition deposits a very thin layer of gilding metal on the lands and grooves in the bore. Gilding metal is a copper alloy. As each round is fired, more gilding metal is deposited, and as the layers build up, it requires more and more energy to force the bullet through the bore which in turn raises pressures and temperatures. A certain amount of copper fouling in many rifles will increase accuracy, but beyond a certain point accuracy suffers, and pressure increases cause excessive wear and can be dangerous.

Cleaning a high power rifle involves two tasks — cleaning the powder fouling from the bore and action and cleaning the copper deposits from the bore. Both are relatively easy to do but require time, patience, and the right equipment, Figure B-1.

Cleaning Equipment

A rifle should always be cleaned from the breech whenever possible to prevent damage to the delicate lands and grooves

Fig. B-1. Tools essential for keeping a match or tactical rifle clean are clockwise from top left: paste bore cleaning compound, lubricating oil, decoppering solution, bore cleaner and lubricant, light grease, cleaning patches, chamber bore guide, eye dropper, assorted cleaning jags and brushes, muzzle bore guide, screwdrivers and bottom, nylon-coated, one-piece cleaning rod.

at the muzzle. The M16/AR15 was designed to break open like a shotgun to allow a cleaning rod to be inserted from the breech.

The **cleaning rod** should always be softer than the barrel steel. Aluminum and copper rods work well, but the best are rubber- or nylon-coated rods. Aluminum and copper rods can leave scrapes of metal behind if they contact the lands, and which if not removed may bond to the steel when succeeding rounds are fired. Rubber- or nylon-clad rods may leave scrapes behind, but the hot propellant gases will vaporize them.

One-piece cleaning rods are far superior to jointed rods. Jointed rods bend easily and expose sharp edges at the joint which will wear the walls of the bore.

Cleaning rods should only be used in conjunction with **rod guides** which are available for the M16/AR15 from Brownells, Champions Choice, Creedmore and others, see Appendix F. Two types are made — chamber and muzzle — and they should be used to keep the cleaning rod centered in the bore. If you value accuracy, no rifle should ever be cleaned without cleaning rod guides installed.

Bore brushes are an often overlooked but very necessary accessory. The author prefers plastic bore brushes for the same reason he prefers plastic jags — they do not leave pieces of metal in the bore. The bore brush should be sized for the caliber of the bore to be cleaned and should have stiff, upright brushes and be very clean. I toss my bore brushes in the dishwasher silverware container and let them run through a cycle. Bore brushes are cheap but barrels are expensive, so I buy them by the handful.

Jags are those screw-on tips made with either a slot or corrugated surface to hold a cleaning patch. Again, they should be made of plastic. While they won't last as long as the steel or aluminum jags, they are so cheap that cost is not a consideration. Jags with corrugated surfaces will expose more patch cleaning surface than those with slots.

Cleaning patches should be made of soft cotton flannel or wool. For the M16/AR15, patches cut to 1.25 x 1.25 inches are best. Many jags are made oversize for the bore they are designed to clean, causing you to have to push hard to force the patch through. But this can cause the rod to flex and wear against the bore walls, even when using rod guides. Try several sizes of jags until you find one that, in combination with the clean patch, will slide through with only a medium amount of pressure. Then buy several.

There are many, many **bore cleaning solutions** available, ranging from good old Hoppes No. 9 to the latest whizbang, high-tech polymerized, starship drive cleaner and lubricant. All will do the job, as will soap and hot water and in a pinch, hand lotion. The author has actually used his wife's hand lotion at times. "Skin So Soft" works very well — and also makes an extremely good insect repellant. Try it; you'll be surprised.

Pick the cleaning solution you like and use it religiously. The same applies to **copper defouling agents**. Again, there are many to pick from. Read the labels carefully for ingredients and cautions. Some cleaning solutions and copper defoulers will remove everything from paint to plastic. Use with caution and dab a bit on the inside of the stock to make certain it won't damage the plastic.

Note: the best time to clean the bore is right after shooting, while it is still warm.

Cleaning Technique — Powder Fouling

Clear your M16/AR15 and remove the magazine. Check the chamber to make certain it is empty. Release the bolt and open the action. Brace the rifle so that the stock has dropped down out of the way. Remove the bolt carrier assembly.

Insert the chamber cleaning rod guide, Figure B-2. Some have a rubber O-ring at the breech end to seal the barrel so that gunk can't flow back into the chamber. Make sure it is well seated.

Attach a jag to your cleaning rod and wrap the patch around it, Figure B-3. Soak the patch with cleaning solution using an eye dropper. Never dip the patch or brush into a container of cleaning solution or you will contaminate it with fouling and assorted other crud that will probably wind up embedded in bore.

Push the patch through the cleaning rod guide and bore with one slow, steady and continuous motion. Let the patch drop away as it clears the muzzle, Figure B-4. Never reuse a patch or draw it back through the bore. Run at least three more soaked patches through the same way and let the bore soak in the cleaning solution for several minutes.

Attach a bore brush to the cleaning rod, soak it in cleaning solution using the eye dropper and push through the bore. I use the old Marine Corps rule of thumb – one pass for every round fired. Rewet the brush as needed.

Follow with four more patches well soaked in cleaning solution. Then let the bore soak until it has cooled completely. Dry the bore with at least three clean patches. If powder residue still appears on the patches, repeat the brushing and drying process until they are clean.

Once the bore is clean, use a chamber brush to clean the chamber. Remove the cleaning rod guide. Soak the brush in cleaning solution, insert it into the chamber and rotate 8 to 10 times or more. Never push back and forth or you will force crud into the bore. Dry the chamber using a clean swab or oversize patches wrapped around the chamber brush. If you use a swab, toss it in the dishwasher with your brushes. Run one more clean patch through the barrel to remove any crud that may have been pushed into the bore. Finally, with the rod guide back in place, run at least one clean patch soaked in gun oil through the bore to protect against rust and corrosion.

Note: If you are one of those people who must clean from the muzzle or whose rifle does not allow cleaning from the breech, always use a muzzle cleaning rod guide and make certain it is seated firmly. Use even more care when pushing the rod through the bore. Always remove the patch before pulling the rod back. Clean the chamber before cleaning the bore, then wipe chamber once more afterward.

Cleaning Technique – Copper Fouling

Copper fouling should also be removed depending on the how quickly copper residue builds up in your barrel. I have one rifle that only needs to be decoppered every 200 rounds. Another rifle needs it after every session. When groups begin to open up, check for copper fouling.

The technique is the same but the soaking periods are longer. Using the copper cleaner you have selected, install the rod guides in muzzle and breech, soak the patch with the solution and run it through the bore, letting it drop free. Repeat three more times. Be generous with the solution. The patches will show heavy blue discoloration which is the copper deposition.

After fifteen or twenty minutes, run three or four clean, dry patches through. If copper fouling remains, you will see traces of blue on the patches. If so, repeat the process with at least four clean patches soaked in copper defouling solution, waiting at least fifteen or twenty minutes before running clean patches through again. Repeat as necessary until the dry patches come out clean.

Cleaning the Bolt Assembly

Disassemble the bolt by removing the firing pin retaining pin (cotter pin on the right side) holding the firing pin. Remove the firing pin. Turn the bolt head counter clockwise and remove the bolt cam pin. Pull the bolt head from the bolt body.

Wipe all surfaces with cleaning solution including the firing pin and the firing pin retaining pin. Use a toothbrush to clean the bolt head, Figure B-5.

The hollow carrier key should be cleaned at least every other time you clean the bolt. Use the eye dropper to drip solution into the bolt carrier key tube. Cover the end with your thumb and shake it well. Clean the tube with a pipe cleaner and make certain that it is dry inside when you finish. Do not disassemble the bolt carrier key.

Lightly lubricate all bolt components and add one drop of oil to the bolt split rings. Use a pointed tool to turn the openings in the split rings so that they are offset from one another. Do not put any oil in the carrier key tube. Reassemble the bolt.

Cleaning the Gas Tube

Do not neglect the gas tube. It does not need as frequent cleaning as the bore, but does need cleaning. Remove the gas tube as described in Appendix A, Assembly/Disassembly. The front end will usually show the most fouling and can be cleaned with a pipe cleaner. Hold your thumb over the front end of the tube and use the eye dropper to fill the tube half full of cleaning solution. Cover the other end and shake vigorously and let it soak for a few minutes. Drain the solution away and clean both ends with a pipe cleaner. If the tube is clean, you are finished. If not, cut a 1.25 by 1.25 patch into narrow strips and tie in the middle with a strong nylon string. Work the string through the tube, soak the patch with an eye dropper and pull it through. Trim the patch if it is still too wide. You don't want to force the patch through the tube. It should slide through with a minimum amount of friction. Repeat as necessary and let the tube dry before reassembling.

Cleaning the Trigger Assembly

The trigger group can be cleaned easily with a tooth brush. In fact, the U.S. military issues a nylon bristle toothbrush with a back that is a bit narrower than the one with which you brush your teeth. These can be found in most gun stores and on tables at virtually every gun show. Failing that, an old tooth brush will do, Figure B-6.

Check the lower receiver carefully when you are cleaning. Nothing is more frustrating than to have the action jam solid during a shooting session because of a blown primer or other debris. Blow out the action with compressed air. If you are leery of driving to a service station with your rifle to use their air pump, take only the lower receiver or buy canned compressed air at a photo shop.

Use cleaning solution on a dry cloth to wipe the rifle's surface, paying particular attention to the sights, the compensator and the area around the cleaning kit door in the butt where dirt likes to accumulate.

Reassemble the rifle, point the muzzle in safe position and pull the trigger to release the bolt. Close the ejection port cover and the rifle is ready to store.

Cleaning the Magazine

Disassemble the magazine and wipe down all parts, inside and out, with cleaning solution on a clean cloth. Check the edges of the follower for burrs or nicks. If you find any, file them down and smooth with emery paper or a fine stone. Wipe the spring with the oily cloth and reassemble. Check to make certain that the follower moves smoothly up and down.

Cleaning the Sights

The rear and front sights should be wiped clean of dust whenever you clean the rifle. Use gun oil or, better yet, a dry lubricant powder to lubricate the rear sight as the cleaning solution may remove any paint or other markings you may have applied. If you have installed a B. Jones corrective lens or other optical sighting aid, remove the lens and rubber O-ring before cleaning this area.

A Final Caution

Do not store the rifle in a closed container if the barrel is still warm. Moisture will condense inside the case as the barrel cools. It will run down into the action and cause rust. Wait until the rifle has cooled before casing. Also, for long term storage, do not place the rifle in a closed case as moisture will condense inside due to temperature variations. If you must use a soft vinyl or hard metal or plastic case, leave it open so that the temperature will equalize.

Do not place the muzzle cap on the barrel when storing the rifle as this will also cause moisture to condense in the bore. Use the muzzle cap only to keep out rain and debris when in the field. If you mount a telescopic sight on the rifle, make sure the scope caps are the breathable type, otherwise moisture will condense and pool on the lenses and eventually will penetrate their seals.

Figure B-2. Bore guide inserted in chamber end.

Figure B-3. The patch should wrap completely around the jag.

Figure B-4. Let the patch fall as it emerges from the muzzle.

Figure B-5. Disassemble the bolt for cleaning.

Figure B-6. Use a toothbrush to clean the trigger assembly in the lower receiver. Blow out dust and debris with compressed air.

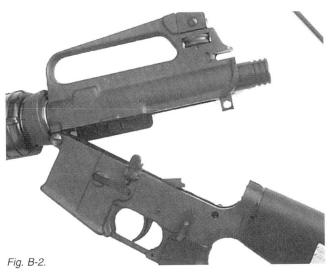

Fig. B-2.

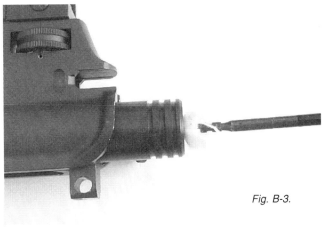

Fig. B-3.

Fig. B-4.

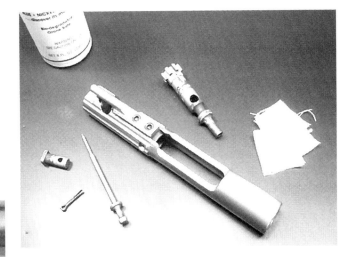

Fig. B-5.

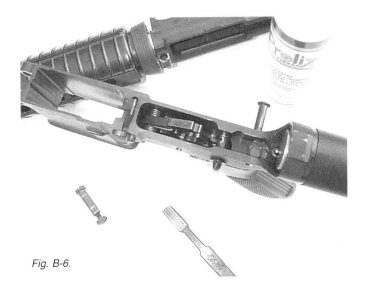

Fig. B-6.

APPENDIX C
TROUBLESHOOTING THE M16/AR15

Problem	Cause	Corrective Action
Failure to Fire	Selector Lever on SAFE	Move to firing position
	Damaged firing pin	Replace
	Firing pin not assembled properly, collar probably behind firing pin retaining pin	Reassemble properly
	Too much oil in the bolt firing pin recess	Disassemble bolt and clean out excess oil
	Fire control mechanism improperly assembled or parts broken	Remove and inspect the selector lever; inspect the trigger assembly for broken parts. Replace parts as necessary
	Trigger pin not installed properly	Inspect to make certain that the hammer spring tails rest in the grooves of the trigger pin to hold it in proper alignment in the receiver
Bolt will not unlock from barrel extension	Excess carbon from burned powder is fouling the barrel extension, bolt head or firing pin	Remove the magazine. Hold the rifle pointing up with the muzzle clear of all objects. Strike the butt squarely on the ground while pulling back on the charging handle. Clean the rifle thoroughly. (Make certain that everyone is clear of the muzzle at all times. Strike the butt squarely on the ground to prevent damage to the butt stock)
Failure to extract	Dirty or corroded ammunition	Remove offending ammunition, clean or replace. Also clean the magazine
	Carbon and dirt build-up in chamber	Clean chamber with cleaning brush
	Carbon and dirt build-up in the extractor recess or under the extractor lip	Inspect and clean
	Rubber insert or double spring not assembled in extractor spring	Reinstall with rubber insert at top of spring or thinner spring inside thicker
	Defective extractor spring or pin	Inspect and replace
	Cartridge rim sheared off	Inspect chamber. If pitted or corroded, consult a gunsmith
	Cartridge case separated leaving portion of case in chamber	May be due to excessive headspace or corroded or pitted receiver. Attach a cleaning brush to a cleaning rod and insert from the muzzle. If case is removed, inspect the chamber and if corroded or pitted, consult a gunsmith. If not removed, consult a gunsmith

Failure to eject	Broken ejector	Inspect and replace
	Jammed ejector	Inspect and clean
	Worn or broken ejector spring	Inspect and replace
	Short recoil	See "Short Recoil" in "Problem" column below
Failure to remain cocked	Worn, broken or missing parts in fire control mechanism	Inspect and replace parts or consult a gunsmith
	Hammer pin incorrectly installed	Inspect to make certain that the hammer is centered on the pin so that its blind spring enters the groove in the hammer pin
Failure to feed	Magazine not seated properly	Push in on bottom of magazine to seat it firmly. If the magazine still does not seat properly, push in on the magazine button, and rotate the catch on the left side clockwise to tighten
	Dirty of corroded ammunition	Remove ammunition and clean or replace. Clean magazine
	Dirty magazine	Disassemble and clean
	Defective magazine	If feed lips are bent out of shape or the magazine body is dented, replace
	Too many rounds in magazine	Use only 20 rounds in 20 round magazines, 30 in 30 round magazines
	Restricted buffer assembly	Remove, clean and lubricate buffer and action spring
	Short recoil	See "Short Recoil" in "Problem" column below
Double Feed	Defective magazine	Replace magazine
Failure to chamber a round	Defective magazine feed lips	Replace magazine
	Dirty, corroded or damaged ammunition	Remove ammunition and inspect. Clean or replace. Clean magazine
	Carbon build up in chamber	Clean chamber
	Bolt cam pin missing	Replace

	Restricted bolt carrier movement	Disassemble, clean and lubricate rifle. Remove charging handle, point receiver upward and install bolt carrier. Slowly slide the bolt carrier in the receiver to check alignment and movement for carrier key and gas tube. If binding is seen, consult a gunsmith
	Loose or damaged bolt carrier key	Consult a gunsmith
	Improperly assembled extractor spring	Disassemble, inspect and reassemble correctly. Make sure the rubber insert is installed correctly at the top (narrow) end of spring or the thinner spring is inside the thicker spring
	Bent gas tube	Consult a gunsmith
	Misaligned carrier and gas tube	Consult a gunsmith
Failure to lock the bolt closed	Dirt, carbon fouling or corrosion on barrel extension and/or bolt locking lugs	Inspect and clean
	Jammed extractor	Clean and lubricate
	Dirt on bolt face	Inspect and clean
	Jammed ejector	Disassemble and clean
	Restricted buffer assembly movement	Remove buffer and action spring, clean and lubricate. Also clean inside receiver extension
	Damaged ammunition	Inspect and replace
	Weak or broken action spring	Inspect and replace
Short recoil	Gaps in bolt rings not staggered	Inspect and stagger bolt ring gaps
	Carbon build-up or dirt in carrier key and on outside of gas tube	Inspect, clean and lubricate
	Restricted movement of bolt carrier group or buffer assembly	See "Failure to Lock the Bolt Closed" in "Problems" column
	Missing or broken bolt rings	Consult a gunsmith
	Loose carrier key	Consult a gunsmith
	Gas leakage due to broken or loose gas tube	Consult a gunsmith

	Restricted gas flow through gas tube due to propellant deposits	Consult a gunsmith
Bolt fails to lock after last shot is fired	Dirty or corroded bolt latch	Inspect and clean. Replace parts if necessary
	Faulty magazine	Replace magazine
	Broken bolt catch or spring	Inspect and replace
Fires when selector switch is set to SAFE	Worn or broken parts in trigger assembly	DANGEROUS. Unload rifle and consult a gunsmith immediately
With selector set to SEMI (M16) or FIRE (AR15), fires when trigger is released	Worn or broken parts in trigger assembly	DANGEROUS. Unload rifle and consult a gunsmith immediately
Selector lever binds	Dirt, corrosion or lack of lubrication	Inspect, clean and lubricate
Carbine sliding butt stock sticks	Sand, dirt or foreign matter	Clean and wipe dry
Carbine sliding butt stock release lever sticks	Sand, dirt of foreign matter in release lever detent well	Clean and lubricate

APPENDIX D
SOME M16/AR15 AMMUNITION
CONSIDERATIONS

Ammunition for the M16/AR15 is not as diverse as for other military rifles. The U.S. military has standardized on twelve types of service cartridges — there were ten 7.62 mm NATO cartridges and nineteen .30-06 cartridges for the M1 Garand. See Table D-1, overleaf, for a summary of current issue U.S. military issue ammunition

As we have seen, the lack of suitable ammunition delayed the widespread use of the M16/AR15 in match shooting for nearly two decades. Other than surplus military 55 grain ball ammunition, only a few other bullet weights were available until the mid- to late 1980s.

Today, ammunition is available in wide variety of bullet weights: 40, 52, 55, 64, 68, 69, 75 and 80 grains. The latter two bullet weights compare favorably in performance with 7.62 mm 174 grain match ammunition at ranges beyond 600 yards.

Beginning shooters, or those with limited time will be more interested in using commercial ammunition in spite of its cost. But eventually either your wallet or your increasing interest in improving your scores will demand better cost or performance than commercial ammunition can provide.

A Survey of Commercial Offerings

The author confesses to being one of those who lacks the time to hand load as he once did and so has had to rely on commercial ammunition of late. After trying a wide range, he has standardized on four varieties of .223 ammunition: Black Hills Ammunition, Inc., Federal Match, HSM and Canadian SS109.

Black Hills builds a 68 grain molybdenum disulfide coated (moly-coated) bullet that provided a 0.4 minute of angle (3 five-shot group aggregate) from his Grüning Precision-built AR15A2 service match rifle. Federal Gold Medal from Federal Cartridge Company (non-moly coated) loaded with a 69 grain Sierra Match King boat-tail hollow point bullet is also used extensively and gives almost as good results in a second service match rifle built by a now-retired custom rifle maker.

Another excellent 69 grain match cartridge is produced by a company called HSM of Missoula, MT. The HSM .223 match round also uses the Sierra 69 grain boat tail bullet loaded into new Winchester cases. We had just started serious evaluation of this round as this book went to press but the results look very promising. One HSM 69 aggregate group fired with the Grüning service match rifle averaged 0.45 inches.

The fourth type is Canadian-manufactured SS109, equivalent to the U.S. M855 62 grain cartridge. Available now and again on the surplus market, the author buys as much as he can afford whenever it appears and uses it for practice ammunition. The consistency is the best that he has found in testing various types of surplus ammunition and produces sub-minute of angle groups from his Grüning Precision-built AR15A2 and slightly over minute of angle groups from his standard Colt AR15A2 Match HBAR.

The Canadian SS109 is used in standard practice to 400 yards. The Black Hills, Federal Gold Medal and HMS is used at ranges beyond. Because the different weight bullets strike higher or lower on the bull at ranges to 400 yards (one click up or down at 100 yards plus one additional click for each additional one hundred yards), five to ten rounds of at least one of the heavier weight bullets are fired at the end of each practice session to check match sight settings.

The author's experience with the AR15 beyond 600 yards has been limited by the lack of 1000 yard shooting ranges in the area, but some trial and error has shown that in moderate winds, the 75 and 80 grain bullets follow the same ballistic tables as the 174 grain match bullet from the M14/M1A plus one to two clicks additional windage depending on whether the wind is weak (5-15 mph) or moderate (15-25 mph) gusts.

Reloading for the M16/AR15 Rifle

To wring the best accuracy out of your M16/AR15, you will probably hand load your own ammunition. When building commercial ammunition the designers have to take into account the varied chamber dimensions in which it will be fired. They must also deal with the fact that their ammunition, to be commercially viable, must be manufactured on high speed machinery which further loosens tolerances. The result is usually an excellent cartridge that will fit all rifles chambered for it but which does not deal with the differences in chamber diameters, diameter and length of throats and several other factors that make the difference between acceptable and excellent ammunition.

When you hand load, you can take all of these factors into account. You can chose bullet sizes, seat them higher or lower in the case, turn case mouths and vary case length and powder load and experiment with different primers in a quest to find the smallest group size.

Designation	Type	Bullet Weight (grains)	Cartridge Weight (grains)	Overall Length (inches)	Propellant (weight in grains)	Velocity (fps)	Indentifier
M193	Ball	56	182	2.26	WC 844 (28.5) CMR-170 (26.5)	3,250	Plain Tip
M195	Grenade	N/A	126	1.90	IMR 4475 (25)	140-165	Rose Petal Crimp
M196	Tracer	54	177	2.26	WC 884 (28.5) IMR 820M (25.3) CMR-170 (26.5)	3,200	Red
M197	High Pressure Test	174	174	2.26	SR7641 (16.7)	N/A	Plain Tip, Silvered Case
M232	Dummy	N/A	161	2.26	N/A	N/A	Overall Black Finish, No Primer
M755	Blank for M742 Riot Control Projector	N/A	112	1.90	Hi Skor 700X (12)	172-198	Rose Petal Crimp, Yellow Lacquer
M855	Ball	62	190	2.26	WC 844 (26.1)	3,025	Green Tip
M856	Tracer	63.7	191	2.26	WC 844 (24.7)	2,870	Orange Tip
M199	Dummy	N/A	150	2.26	N/A	N/A	6 Flutes in Case, No Primer
M200	Blank	N/A	107	1.90	HPC 13	N/A	Rose Petal Crimp
M862	Plastic	3.6	108	2.03	WPR 260 (8.7)	4,525	Blue Plastic Bullet
M995	Armor Piercing	52	180	2.25	WER 845 (27.5)	3,324	Black Tip

Table D-1
M16 U.S. Military Ammunition*

* Source: TM 43-0001-27, Headquarters, Department of the Army, Washington DC

To do so, you must know about hand loading and its vagaries and that is beyond the scope of this work. The author suggests you begin with one of the excellent reloading manuals published by Lyman, Speer or Hogdon. All are available at better gun stores or by mail from the Dillon Precision Products, Inc. (see Appendix F) who also manufacture and sell some of the finest reloading equipment and components available.

When reloading, you must consider the following:

Cases

Will you use new commercial or once-fired military brass? While military brass is cheaper by far, wall thickness, neck size and weight will not be the same as commercial brass. Only by sampling lots and measuring these points carefully, then loading and firing sample batches will you be able to make the proper selection.

Once fired military brass also have their primers crimped in place. The primers must be removed and the primer pockets swaged to an uniform size.

Primer

Believe it or not, primers have a great deal to do with ammunition accuracy. The flame they produce must ignite the powder charge instantly and evenly. They must fit the primer pocket well enough to sit slightly below the primer pocket rim. Again, experimentation is the only way to tell which primer will work best with which load in which rifle.

Powder Selection

Ball, flake, granular? Pressure, fouling and speed of burning plus many other factors come into play when selecting a powder. How much powder? How does powder type and weight affect accuracy? At what point does the search for more speed cause decreased accuracy? The reloading manuals will provide basic data and such useful texts as "Black Magic" by John Feamster and "The Competitive AR-15" by Glen D. Zediker will provide guidance and food for thought. (See Appendix G)

Bullet Selection

As we have seen in previous chapters, bullet selection is critical to accuracy and must be matched to the twist rate of your barrel's rifling. Weight, shape and seating depth are all critical. Speer for instance, offers 5.56 mm (.224 caliber) bullets in weights from 46 to 62 grains while Sierra's offerings range from 52 to 80 grains.

To Moly-coat or Not?

While the jury has not yet been presented with irrefutable evidence that coating bullets with molybdenum disulfide provides all the benefits so many of its adherents claim, there are reasons to consider their use, or at least test them on your own.

Two of the claims for moly-bullets are that they leave the bore cleaner and they wear the lands and grooves less because of lessened friction. The claim is also made that moly-coated bullets will achieve higher velocity because of reduced friction and even increased accuracy.

The author conducted a 500 round test with two AR15 Match HBAR rifles. In one, moly-coated bullets only were fired and the other, non-moly-coated bullets. Both types of ammunition used Sierra 69 grain boat tail hollow point bullets in commercially manufactured ammunition fired through 1:9 twist Colt HBAR barrels. Both barrels were cleaned thoroughly and decoppered before testing began. The rifles were then cleaned after every fifty rounds and decoppered after every 100 rounds.

Moly-coated bullets did appear to foul barrels far less than the uncoated bullets. As one means of determination, cleaning patches were counted after each cleaning. Only half the average number of cleaning patches were used with the moly-coated bullets and copper deposits were greatly reduced. There was no evidence of increased accuracy and the chronograph showed only a slight variance 30-40 fps in favor of the moly bullets, hardly enough to be considered significant. But it should be noted that the rifle reserved for the moly-coated barrel has seen an additional 214 rounds fired through it to date without cleaning and without an increase in group sizes. The rifle used to test the non-moly-coated barrels has racked up 225 rounds and the group sizes have opened about 20 percent.

The decreased fouling attributed to Moly-coated bullets may well be of interest if you are a match or varmint shooter. But the only way to be certain is to test them in your own rifle. You might find that it is possible to shoot an entire match without having to clean the bore.

If you decide to try Moly-coated bullets, clean your rifle barrel thoroughly and decopper it. Then fire at least 20 rounds of moly-coated bullets through the bore to coat it evenly, before beginning your testing. Keep in mind that once a barrel is coated with molybdenum disulfide, it will require a lot of cleaning solvent and a great deal of elbow grease to remove it all.

Moly-coated bullets are available as assembled ammunition from several manufacturers including Black Hills Ammunition. Moly-coated bullets as components are available from Sierra, Barnes and Hornady, among others. And molybdenum disulfide kits are also available for the real do-it-yourselfer.

HSM is now marketing a new bullet line with a proprietary "T-Coat." Bill Campbell, the company president, feels that it will provide all the advantages of a moly-coat without its disadvantages. For instamce, there is no break-in period with "T-Coat" bullets. See Appendix F.

Reloading Equipment

As important as quality components is quality reloading equipment. Don't stint here or in purchasing reloading dies as they will probably last for the rest of your life. Reloading equipment is very, very sturdy.

There are two types of reloading equipment for semiautomatic rifle shooters to consider, single-stage and progressive. Single stage reloaders have only one station in which you install each of three dies in turn in one holder for each operation — resizing, decapping/capping, powder loading, bullet seating and crimping.

A progressive reloader allows you to install all three dies plus the powder measure, and perform each operation in turn for a completed cartridge.

In past years, serious reloaders scorned progressive reloaders for their lack of precision. No longer, the new generation of progressive reloaders allow complete control over every aspect of the reloading process, and in fact, may turn out far more carefully crafted cartridges as each step is performed in precisely the same manner.

A key component of the reloading process is the reloading die set. For precision rifle cartridges, never use less than a three die set. Secondly, they must be precision manufactured and the author highly recommends the use of carbide dies only. They are a bit more expensive but will last a lifetime and the chances of having to pry out a stuck case are almost nonexistent. Third, fired cases must be cleaned thoroughly before reloading and then lubricated to pass through the reloading dies without sticking — yes, lubricate lightly even if using carbide resizing dies.

There are four critical stages to the reloading process: resizing the fired cases, trimming cases to the proper length, dropping an exact powder charge and seating the bullet properly. A fired cartridge case expands to fit the chamber walls then returns almost to its original shape. If the case is to be used in the same rifle, then only the neck needs to be resized. But if it will be used in a different rifle, then the case should be full length-resized to return it to its original diameter.

Next, the case should be trimmed to the proper length. When the case is fired, pressure and temperature cause the brass to flow. Since the diameter is confined by the chamber walls, the tendency is for the case to lengthen, or stretch. By trimming the neck, the proper case length is reestablished and it will fit into the magazine and chamber without problem.

Before the bullet is inserted, a powder charge must be dropped into the case. And this in itself is a can of worms. Some match shooters weigh every charge on a digital or balance scale to a 0.1 of a grain or less. Others depend on a powder measure to drop a consistent charge from round to round. The latter is certainly less time-consuming than weighing each charge but may not be as accurate, especially in a small capacity case like the .223. Again, you should experiment for yourself. And if you elect to use a powder measure, you should weigh out ten consecutive charges and average them several times during a reloading session to make certain the charger is "throwing true."

Finally, the bullet must be fitted into the case in line with the axis of the neck. It must not lean to one side or the other

nor must it be seated to one side or the other. Crimping is part of the bullet seating process and is accomplished to secure the bullet in the mouth of the case, especially important with semi-automatic and automatic weapons. Taper crimps usually work best if applied evenly around the case mouth. Again, the key is the best reloading dies you can find.

Testing the Results

If you are a serious match competitor, you will want to develop your hand loads very carefully. Make a list of all the variables — case capacity, case length, powder charge, neck diameter, chamber dimensions, etc. — to be investigated but do not make your testing protocol for complicated that you lose track of what you are doing.

For instance, a few years ago, a friend decided that he wanted to test three brands of cartridge cases all sized to the same dimensions against powder charges varying by 0.1 grain over a range of 1.5 grains against one bullet weight and three brands of powder. I pointed out to him that this entailed 135 variables and that he would need a minimum of ten to fifteen cartridges per variable for just for the initial screening. That meant loading and testing 1,350 to 2,025 cartridges.

I recommended that he start with one load from a good reloading manual as a base and work with his reloading dies until he could produce consistent batches of ammunition from the same case lot, powder lot, type of bullet and powder load. At that point, he could then think about a devloping a simpler plan for developing his own hand loads. The plan he eventually worked out used a receipe from a well-known reloading manual, a 68 grain Sierra bullet and varied only the powder load by 0.1 of grain over a 1 grain range. When he was satisfied that he had acheived the best accuracy with that, then trying seating the bullet at various depths — against the lands, slightly back from the lands, etc. After that, he tried different primer brands to see what effect they might have on accuracy. When felt he had mastered that bullet weight/powder load/primer/case combination, he went on to try different bullet weights for longer distance shooting. The point being, that virtually any combination of case, bullet, powder and primer can be made to shoot accurately if you pay attention to the details and are willing to test various combinations under controlled conditions.

Once you get a load that you like, use that as your base line to begin further testing on the more esoteric factors that will lead you to that "golden" load.

APPENDIX E
HEAD SPACE CONSIDERATIONS

Head space specifications are set by different institutions. In the United States, they are most commonly set by the Small Arms and Ammunition Manufacturer's Institute (SAMMI) for civilian firearms. SAMMI specifications are derived with the idea that ammunition of a specific caliber from a wide number of manufacturers will be fired in a large number of firearms of that same caliber, made by many manufacturers. SAMMI specifications are therefore slightly more of a compromise than specifications set by the U.S. military which can control the type and variety of ammunition fired in its small arms. As a result, military head space specifications tend to be slightly tighter.

Proper head space is extremely important to the safe functioning of a firearm. If too loose, extremely hot, high pressure chamber gas may leak around the cartridge case. The case will stretch lengthwise and may split open, allowing combustion gases to blow into and through the action to injure, blind or even kill the shooter.

If head space is too tight, the case may stick in the chamber and not extract properly. It may even raise chamber pressures sufficiently to rupture the barrel or cause the bolt head to fail. Either will produce catastopic and deadly results. At the least, it will increase wear and tear on the rifle causing parts to fail prematurely.

Don't fool around. Never install a new or different bolt in a rifle without having the head space check properly. Periodically check fired cartridge cases for any signs of pressure and always check the chamber every few hundred rounds for signs of erosion.

Table E1 M16/AR15 Head Space Gage Dimensions SAMMI and U.S. Army/Marine Corps	
Go Gage	1.464
No Go Gage	1.470
Field Gage (Military) (Civilian (SAMMI))	1.473 1.474

APPENDIX F
ACCESSORIES AND PARTS

Accessories

A.H. Merchant (AR15 accessories available through Brownells.

A.R.M.S. Inc. 230 West Center St., West Bridgewater, MA 02379. 508 584-6816, FAX 508 588-8045.

B. Jones Lens Systems, 5115 E Edgemont, Phoenix AZ 85008. 602 840-2176. Website: http://www.bjonessights.com; Email: bjonessights@uswestmail.com

The Boyt Harness Company, 220 South Main Street, Osceola, IA 50213 800 550-2698, FAX 515 342-2703; Website: http://www.boytharness.com; Email: sales@boytharness.com

Brownells, Inc. Rte 2, Box 1, Montezuma, IA 50171. 515 623-4000, FAX 623-3896. Website: http://www.gunsmith-tools.com. Gunsmithing tools, jigs and aids, M16/AR15 barrels, stocks and parts. Indispensable.

CDNN Inv. Inc. PO Box 6514, Abilene, TX 79608. 800 588-9500

Centerfire Systems, 102 Fieldview Drive, Versailles, KY 40383. 800 950-1231

Century International Arms, PO Box 714, St. Albans, VT 05478. 800 258-8879; Website: http://www.centuryarms.com

Champion's Choice, Inc., 201 International Blvd., La Vergne, TN 37086. 615 793-4066, FAX 793-4070. Scoring books, wide assortment of shooting accessories.

Civilian Marksmanship Program of the Corporation for Rifle Practice and Firearms Safety was established by Congress in 1996 to replace the Civilian Marksmanship Program. At the time this listing was compiled, they had no M16/AR15 parts available to the public but AR15-type rifles were available for sale to affiliated rifle clubs. And they do have shooting supplies. To use the CMP services, you must be a member of the NRA and a local DCM-affiliated club (virtually all state rifle and pistol associations) and request an official order form from the above address. You may order two of any available parts in any fiscal year. PO Box 576, Port Clinton, OH 43452, 419 635-2141, FAX 419 635-2565, Website:http://www.odcmp.com.Email: custserv@odcmp.com.

Creedmoor Sports, Inc., PO Box 1040, Oceanside, CA 92501 888 273-3366, FAX 760 757-5558, Email: shoot@creedmoresports.com. Wide selection of shooters supplies including the best shooting coats made. Accurized AR15 match rifles.

Cryogenic Tempering /-300, PO Box 404 Center & Market Streets, Seville, OH 44273. 216 769-1495, FAX 216 769-1496. Cryogenic rifle barrel tempering.

Dewey Manufacturing, Inc., PO Box 2014, Southbury, CT 06488. 203 264-3064, FAX 203 598-3119.

Entréprise Arms, Inc. 15861 Business Center Drive, Irwindale, CA 91706. 626 962-8712, FAX 626 926-4692; Website: http://entreprise.com. Scopes, mounts and other accessories for the M16/AR15 and other service rifles.

Federal Arms Corporation of America, 7928 University Avenue, Fridley, MN 55432. 800 486-5671, FAX 612 780-5647

Gun Parts Corporation, PO Box 299, West Hurley, NY 12491. 914 679-2417, FAX 679-5849.

GRSC, PO Box 1246, Yucaipa, CA 92399 909 446-0272; Website: http://www.grsc.com; Email: snapsling@grsc.com

J.P. Enterprises (AR15 products) available through Brownells

J.&T. Distributing, PO Box 430, Winchester, KY 40391 606 745-1757

Kiesler's Wholesale, 3300 Industrial Parkway, Jeffersonville, IN 47130-9634 888 543-7537, FAX 812 285-5095

Leupold & Stevens, PO Box 688, Beaverton OR 97075-0688 503 526-5195; Website: http://www.leupold.com

Lyman Products Corporation, 475 Smith Street, Middletown, CT 06457 800 22-LYMAN, 860 632-2020 FAX 860 632-1699; Website: http://www.lymanproducts.com

Milazzo Accuracy Products, N9178 Walnut St, East Troy, WI 53120 414 363-8799

Oehler Research, Inc., PO Box 9135, Austin, TX 78766 800 531-5125

OK Weber, Inc. PO Box 7485, Eugene, OR 97401 541 747-0458, FAX 541 747-5927; Email: okweber@pacinfo.com (rpa height adjustable front sight).

R Guns, 140 N Western Avenue, Rte 31, Unit B, Carpentersville, IL 60110. 847 428-3569, FAX 847 428-0029; Email: rguns@starnetusa.com

SARCO, Inc., 323 Union Street, Stirling, NJ 07980. 908 647-3000, FAX 647-9413. A major supplier of parts for the M16/AR15 and other U.S. military firearms.

Smith Enterprises, 1701 W 10th St, Tempe AZ 85281 480 964-1818 FAX 921-9987; http:// www.smithenterprise.com

TAPCO, 3615 Kennesaw North Industrial Parkway, Kennesaw, GA 30144. 800 544-1445; http://tapco.com. Wide variety of new and surplus parts and ammunition.

Trigicon Inc., PO Box 930059, Wixom, MI 48393-0059. 248 960-7700 FAX 248 960-7725

Uncle Mikes, 1710 Red Soils Court, Oregon City, OR 97045. 800 84502444 FAX 503 722-5701

Young Manufacturing, Inc., 5621 N 53rd Avenue #1, Glendale AZ 85301. 623 915-3889 FAX 914 3746

Z-M Performance, makers of the ACCU-Wedge. Available through Brownells and retail gun shops.

Ammunition
Bartlett, Jeff, 1309 W 9th Street, Owensboro KY 42301, 800 714 6348, FAX 270 684-6348. Website: http:// www.gibrass.com. An excellent source for reloading components — brass, powder and projectiles.

Berger Bullets, Ltd. 5342 West Camelback Rd., Ste 200, Glendale, AZ 85301. 602 842-4001, FAX 602 934-9083; Website: http://www.bergerbullets.com. Email, bergerbullets@bergerbullet.com.

Black Hills Ammunition, Inc. PO Box 3090, Rapid City, SD 57709-3090. 605 348-5150, FAX 605 348-9827. A excellent line of ammunition for the M16/AR15, including molly-coated bullets.

Federal Cartridge Company 900 Ellen Drive, Anoka MN 55303. 612 323-2300. Considered by many to be the standard against which match ammunition is measured.

Hammets VLD Bullets PO Box 479, Rayville, LA 71269. 318 728-2019.

Hornady Match Bullets and Ammo, PO Box 1848, Grand Island, NE 68802-1848. Website: http://www.hornady.com

HSM, Missoula, MT 406 777-2106; Website: http://www.Huntingshack.com

Hornady Manufacturing Company PO Box 1848, Grand Isle, NE 68802. 800 338-3220. FAX 308 382-5761. Complete line of hunting and match ammunition.

Ultramax Ammunition, 2112 Elk Vale Rd, Rapid City, SD 57701-8526. 605-342-4141. Complete line of hunting and match ammunition.

Sierra Bullets, 1400 West Henry St, Sedalia, MO 65301. 800 223-8799, FAX 816 827-6300; website: http:// sierrabullets.com; Email: sierra@sierrabullets.com

Barrels
Douglas Barrels, Inc., 5504 Big Tyler Road, Charlestown, WV 25313. 304 776-1341, FAX 304 776-8560. Website: http://www.benchrest.com. Website with video describing their products.

Hart Rifle Barrels, Inc. PO Box 182, Lafayette NY 13084. 315 677-9841, FAX 315 677-9610.

K & P Barrels, 740 Nevada Ave, Raton, NM 87740. 505 445-1311 FAX 505 445-1312

Krieger Barrels, Inc., N114 W 18697 Clinton Dr., Germantown, WI 53022. 414 255 9593, FAX 414 255-9586.

Obermeyer Rifle Barrels, 23122 60th St, Bristol, WI 53104. 414 843-3537, FAX 414 843-2129.

Shilen Rifle Barrels, Inc., 12202 N 62nd Place, Scottsdale, AZ 85254. 602 948-2525

Complete Rifles
American Spirit Arms Corporation, 15001 N. Hayden Rd. Suite# 112, Scottsdale, AZ 85242, Voice 888-486-5487, Fax 480-483-5301, Web Site:http://www.gunkits.com

ArmaLite, Inc., PO Box 299, Geneseo, IL 309 944-6939, FAX 309 944-6949; Website: http://www.Armalite.com; Email: (Sales) hale.strasser@armalite.com

Colt's Manufacturing Company, Inc., PO Box 1868, Hartford, CT 06144-1868 800 962-2658; FAX 860 244-1449; website: http://www.Colt.com; Email: None.

DPMS, 13983 Industry Avenue, Becker, MN 55308; Voice

612 261-5600, FAX 612 261-5599; Email, dpmsinc@aol.com; Website: http://www.dpmsinc.com

Knights's Manufacturing Co., 7750 9th Street Southwest, Vero Beach FL 32968 561 778-3700, FAX 561 569-2955.

Leitner-Wise Rifle Company, 1033 North Fairfax Street, Suite 402, Alexandria VA 22314; Voice 703 837-9390; FAX 703 837-9686; Email, info@leitner-wise.com.

Olympic Arms, Inc., 620-626 Old Pacific Highway, SE, Olympia WA 360 459-7940, FAX 360 491-3447; Website, http://www.olyarms.com

Parker-Hale, Ltd, Golden Hillock Road, Birmingham B11 2PZ, England 44 121 766 6996, FAX 44 121 772-0129.

Professional Ordnance, Inc., 1070 Metric Drive, Lake Havasu City, AZ 86403; Voice 520 505-2420, FAX 520 505-2141; Email, dlocketett@professional-ordnance.com; Website, http://www.ProOrd.com.

Quality Parts/Bushmaster Firearms, 999 Roosevelt Trail, Windham ME 04062 207 892-3594,FAX 207 892 8069; website: http://www.bushmaster.com; Email bushmaster@maine.com

Rock River Arms, Inc., 101 Noble Street, Cleveland, IL 61241; Voice 309 792-5780, FAX 309 792-5781; Email, rockriverarms@revealed.net;Website: http://www.rockriver-arms.com.

Cryogenic Treatment Services
Accurizing Cryo, Division of 300° Below, Inc., 1160 S. Monroe, Decatur, IL 62521. Computer-controlled cyrogenic barrel accurizing.

Amtreat Cryogenics, 24374 Clipstone St., Woodland Hills, CA 92666, 818 888-8664. Computer-controlled cryogenic barrel tempering.

M16/AR15 Gunsmithing Services
Accuracy Speaks Gun Smithing, 3960 N Usery Pass Rd, Mesa, AZ 85207. 480-373-9499

Grúning Precision, 7101 Jurupa Ave., Ste 12 Riverside, CA 92500. Contact Jim Gronning 909 689-6692 (Office) FAX 909 689-7791; Email: groanin@ca.freei.net.
Custom AR15 service and match rifles, full range gunsmithing services. Specializing in M16/AR15, M14-type, M1 Garand and bolt action precision rifles for civilian and military match shooters and sniper rifles for law enforcement and the military. Grúning Precision has about wrapped up the Southern California precision rifle and police sniper market.

Compass Lake Engineering, 719 White Dr., Alford, FL 32420 850 579-1208, FAX 850 579-2930; Website: http://compasslake.com; Email: email@compasslake.com. Frank White has been building match quality AR15s longer than most and his customers swear by his work.

Tim La France, P.O. Box 178211, San Diego 92177 CA 619 293-3373 FAX 619 297-0577. Custom built high power match rifles, custom building services.

Fulton Armory, 8725 Bollman Place #1, Savage, Maryland 20763. 301 490-9485. Website: http://www.fulton-armory.com/Fulton1.htm. Clint McKee has a package of three custom AR15 rifles; check out his website.

Smith Enterprises 1701 W 10th St, Tempe AZ 85281. Provides custom services for M14/M1A and AR15 match rifles including rear sights and chrome-plated AR15 bolt carriers. 602 964-1818 FAX 921-9987; Internet: http://www.smith-enterprise.com

Wilson Trigger Specialities, 111 East South Street, Atwood, Illinois 61913. 217 578-3026

Internet Sites
http://www.AR15.com One of the best sites on the web for information and documentation for the M16/AR15 rifle.

http://www.northcapepubs.com Firearms books for shooters and collectors.

http://www.nra.org If you don't belong to the National Rifle Association, you are not doing your part to support our 2nd Amendment rights. The latest services, news, commentary and legislation.

http://www.nraila.org The legislative and legal side of the NRA. A very important site and one you should monitor regularly.

http://www.nssf.org The National Shooting Sports Federation web site. The leading trade association of the firearms and recreational shooting sports industry.

http://www.pla-net/~recomer Internet Shooting Directory.

http://www.teleport.com American Firearms Page. Links to dozens of firearm's related sites.

http://www.webring.org A directory to dozens of firearms web sites.

Reloading Equipment and Supplies

Dillon Precision Products, Inc., 8009 E Dillon's Way, Scottsdale, AZ 85260. 800 223-4570, FAX 602 998-2786. A range of shooting supplies and reloading equipment.

RCBS, PO Box 856, Cession, ID 83501. 800 725-9212

Redding Reloading Equipment, 1089 Starr Road, Courtland, NY 13045. 607 753-3331, FAX 607 756-8445; Website: http://www.redding-reloading,com

Training

Front Sight Firearms Training Institute, Bakersfield, CA and Las Vegas, NV 800 987-7719, FAX 831 684-2137; Website: http://www.frontsight.com; Email: info@front-sight.com

APPENDIX G
THE LEGAL RAMIFICATIONS
OF BUILDING SEMIAUTOMATIC RIFLES

The Bureau of Alcohol, Tobacco and Firearms has recently clarified federal firearms regulations regarding the assembly from parts kits of semiautomatic rifles which are banned from federal *importation* or manufacture under the provisions of the 1994 Violent Crime Act.

Domestic Semiautomatic Firearms
Banned From Manufacture

The 1994 "Violent Crime Act" restricts the manufacture of domestically produced semiautomatic rifles. You are no longer allowed to assemble such a rifle if it includes two or more of the following "banned" items: folding or telescopic stock, pistol grip, bayonet mount, flash suppressor (flash hider) or threaded barrel (at the muzzle) and a grenade launcher. Also, any detachable magazine with a capacity greater than 10 rounds cannot be used.

In short, the law now prevents you from purchasing a "parts kit" and assembling it, or having it assembled to a receiver, either original, reproduction or replacement, whether manufactured in this country or a foreign country, if the completed firearm is identical to the original proscribed rifle or uses more than ten imported parts if manufactured abroad.

The M16 as originally built did not have a folding stock but did have a telescopic stock; also a pistol grip, bayonet mount and compensator, which the ATF has defined as a flash hider, and a threaded barrel. To conform to provisions of the 1994 Violent Crime Act, any AR15 rifle manufactured after September, 19994 must not have a compensator, threaded barrel or bayonet mount, nor can it accept a magazine with more than a ten-round capacity. You cannot add a telescoping (collapsible stock). And, of course, refrain from mounting a grenade launcher.

Imported Semiautomatic Firearms

Paragraph 178.39 of Section 27 of the Code of Federal Regulations states that no one can assemble a semiautomatic rifle or any shotgun using more than ten *imported* parts. The BATF lists twenty parts of which no more than ten can be used: 1) frames, receivers, receiver castings, forgings or stampings, 2) barrels, 3) barrel extensions, 4) mounting blocks (trunnions), 5) muzzle attachments, 6) bolts, 7) bolt carriers, 8) operating rods) 9) gas pistons, 10) trigger housings, 11) triggers, 12) hammers, 13) sears, 14) disconnectors, 15) buttstocks, 16) pistol grips, 17) forearms or handguard, 18) magazine bodies, 19) followers, 20) floorplates. The only exceptions allowed to this rule are the assembly of rifles for sale or distribution to a governmental body, or for testing or experimentation with the permission of the BATF, *or the repair of, or the replacement of* any part on a now-banned rifle or shotgun that was imported into the United States *prior* to November 30, 1990. It was on this date that President George Bush issued an executive order banning the importation or manufacture of "assault rifles."

The semiautomatic firearms currently listed as "assault rifles" included all models of or copies of the Norinco, Polytech or Mitchell AK47, UZI, Galil, Beretta AR70 (SC70), Colt AR-15, FAL, FNC, MAC 10,11 or 12, Steyr AUG, INTRATEC TEC-9 and variations; all variations of the Striker, Street Sweeper or USAS 12 shotgun. The current ban further includes any semiautomatic rifle that can accept a detachable magazine and has at least two of the following parts: folding or telescopic stock, pistol grip, bayonet mount, flash suppressor or threaded barrel and grenade launcher. The ban further includes pistols with any of the above parts plus a barrel shroud and which weighs 50 ounces or more, unloaded. Also any semiautomatic shotgun that has any of the above parts plus a fixed magazine capacity in excess of five rounds, or a detachable magazine.

State Semiautomatic Firearms Regulations

The number of states and local governments which have banned or restricted semiautomatic firearms has become too extensive to list here. The most prominent examples are of course, California and New Jersey. If there is any question, ask your dealer or call your state's Department of Justice.

Whatever the firearms laws that exist in your state, obey them. We may not like them, but the law is the law and gun owners are the most law-abiding citizens in this country.

APPENDIX H
BIBLIOGRAPHY

____, "Alliant Techsystems 1999 Annual Report,", Alliant Techsystems, 600 Second Street N.E., Hopkins, MN 55343.

Blunt, Captain Stanhope E., "Firing Regulations for Small Arms for the U.S. Army," Charles Scribner's Sons, New York, 1889.

Brown, Gary, "The History and Evolution of Colt's Sporter Rifle," *Guns*, January 1991.

Canfield, Bruce, "Winchester in Service," Andrew Mowbray, Inc., Lincoln, RI 02865.

Crossman, Captain Edward C., "The Book of the Springfield," Small Arms Technical Publishing Company, Marines, NC 1932.

Cutshaw, Charlie, "H&K's Revolutionary G-36 Rifle," *American Rifleman*, National Rifle Association, 11250 Waples Mill Rd, Fairfax VA 22030-9400, September 1999.

___, "Defense Highlights: Big Job for Small Rifle," *Ordnance*, May-June, 1963.

Duff, Scott A., "The M1 Garand: Owner's Guide," Scott Duff Publications, Export, PA 15632, 1994.

Duff, Scott A., and John M. Miller, "The M14 Owner's Guide and Match Conditioning Instructions," Scott Duff Publications, Export, PA 15632, 1996.

Ezell, Edward C., "Cracks in the Post-War Anglo-American Alliance: The Great Rifle Controversy, 1947-1957," *Military Affairs*, December 1974.

Ezell, Edward Clinton, "The Great Rifle Controversy," Stackpole Books, Harrisburg, PA 17105 1984.

Faatz, Wayne, "The Mysterious Slam Fire," *American Rifleman*, 11250 Waples Mill Road, Fairfax VA 22030, Phone 800 336-7402. October 1953.

____, "Federal Firearms Regulations Reference Guide," Department of the Treasury, Bureau of Alcohol, Tobacco and Firearms," ATF P 5300.4 (10-95), U.S. Government Printing Office, Washington DC, 20402-9328, 1995.

Feamster, John, "Black Magic," Precision Shooting, Manchester, CT 06040, 1998.

Fuller, Claude E., "The Breechloader in the Service, 1816-1917," N. Flayderman and Company, New Milford, CT., 1965.

Gilbert, Glenn M., "The Making of A Match Rifle," *American Rifleman*, National Rifle Association, 11250 Waples Mill Rd, Fairfax VA 22030-9400, July 1999.

Hale, Captain H.C., "New Firing Regulations for Small Arms," *Journal of the U.S. Infantry Association*, July 1904.

Harrison, E.H., "New Service Rifle," *American Rifleman*, June 1957.

Hatcher, General Julian S., "The Book of the Garand," Infantry Journal Press, Washington DC, 1948.

Hatcher, Julian S., "Hatcher's Notebook," Stackpole Books, Harriburg, PA 1947, rev. ed. 1966.

Hicks, James C., "US Firearms, 1776-1965: Notes on US Ordnance, Vol. 1," James E Hicks and Son, La Granada, CA 1957.

Horn, Captain R..O., "Fire Discipline, Control and Direction," *Infantry Journal*, January-February 1913.

____ "Instructions for the Operation of the Colt Armalite AR015 Automatic Rifle, Caliber .223," Colt's Patent Fire Arms Mfg. Co., Inc., Hartford 15, Conn., USA.

James. Frank, "Colt's Sporter Rifle," *Guns*, January 1991.

Kuhnhausen, Jerry, "The U.S. .30 Caliber Gas Operated Service Rifles, A Shop Manual, Volumes I and II," Heritage Publishers, Box 887, McCall ID 83638, 1995, Phone 208 634-4104. Fax 208 634-3101.

Laidley, Colonel T.T.S., "Course of Instruction in Rifle Firing," J.B. Lippincott and Company, Philadelphia 1879.

Lippincott, Colonel Aubrey, "Firepower," *Cavalry Journal*, July 1928.

Lippitt, Francis J., "A Treatise on the Tactical Use of the Three Arms," D. Van Nostrand, New York, 1865.

Lissak, Ormand M., "Ordnance and Gunnery," John Wiley and Sons, New York, 1915.

Mayer, Scott E., "Cryo Update," *American Rifleman*, National Rifle Association, 11250 Waples Mill Rd, Fairfax VA 22030-9400, July 1999.

McNaugher, Thomas L., "Marksmanship, McNamara and the M16 Rifle: Organizations, Analysis and Weapons Acquistions," Delivered at the March 21-24, 1979 International Studies Association, Toronto, Ontario. From the Rand Corporation Collection.

___, "The M1 Rifle," American Rifleman Reprint, National Rifle Association, 11250 WaplesMill Rd, Fairfax VA 22030-9400.

___, "M-14 Rifle Accurization, Guide to National Match Accurizing as Performed by U.S. Army Shooting Team Gunsmiths," U.S. Army Marksmanship Unit, Fort Benning GA 31905.

___, "M16A2 Rifles and Carbines, Operation and Unit Maintenance Instructions," Colt Manual No. CM101, Colt's Manufacturing Company, Inc., Hartford, CT, 2nd Edition, 1998, Revised August,1995.

___, "M16A2 Rifles and Carbines, Armorer/Depot Maintenance and Repair Manual," Colt Manual No. CM102, Colt's Manufacturing Company, Inc., Hartford, CT, 2nd Edition, 1991 Revised August,1995.

___, M16/AR15 , Assembly, History, Ballistics and Reloading Data for the U.S. Service Rifle and Commercial Model," *American Rifleman Reprint*, National Rifle Association, Fairfax, VA

MIL-R-63997B(AB), "Military Specification, Rifle 5.56MM: M16A2," Notice 1, 20 February 1997.

MIL-C-70599A(AR), "Military Specification, Carbine 5.56MM: M4," 1 April 1987.

MIL-R-71186(AR), "Military Specification, Carbine, 5.56MM: M4A1," 31 January 1994.

___, "NRA High Power Rifle Rules," National Rifle Association of America, 11250 Waples Mill Road, Fairfax VA 22030, 1997, Phone 800 336-7402.

Moore, Lt. Colonel Roy E., " Shoot, Soldier," *Infantry Journal,* April 1945.

Naisawald, Lt. Colonel, L. Van Loan, "The High Cost of a Casualty," *Army*, September 9, 1968.

___, "1967 National Match Rifles, U.S. Cal. 7.62 mm M14 and U.S. Cal. 30 M1 National Match Ammunition," U.S. Army Material Command, U.S. Army Weapons Command, U.S. Army Munition Command.

___, "Operating and Maintenance Manual, Rifle, 5.56-MM, AR-18," Armalite, Inc., 118 East 16th Street, Costa Mesa, California, 92627.

___, "Operation & Maintenance, Armalite's AR-180," ArmaLite, 118 East 16th Street, Costa Mesa, California, 92627.

Pikula, Sam, Major, USAR, "The Armalite AR-10," Regnum Fund, uksmino 8/3, 2600, Vilnus, Lithuania, 1998. (Available from North Cape Publications®, Inc.)

Pullum, Bill and Frank T. Hanenkrat, "Position Rifle Shooting," Privately Printed, Available through the National Rifle Association, 11250 Waples Mill Road, Fairfax, VA 22030-9400,1985, Phone 703 267-1600.

Rocha, John G., "Technical Notes, Small Arms Weapons Design," Rock Island Arsenal, Rock Island, IL., May 1968. Reprinted by ArmaLite, Inc., PO Box 299, Geneseo, IL 61254

Senich, Peter R., The Complete Book of U.S. Sniping," Paladin Press, Boulder, CO 80306, 1988.

Senich, Peter R., The Long Range War —Sniping in Vietnam," Paladin Press, Boulder, CO 80306, 1994.

___, Small Arms Repair Course, 45B10-B-1, Supplement No. 1, Rifle 5.56MM, M16A1, U.S. Army Ordnance Center and School, Aberdeen Proving Ground, MD, July 1976.

Shea, Dan, "Father of the AR15," American Rifleman, National Rifle Association of America, 11250 Waples Mill Road, Fairfax VA 22030, November/December 1997.

Stephen, Lewis, "The M14 and its Civilian Counterpart, the M1A," *Banned Guns 2*, Challenge Publications, Canoga Park, CA 91304, 1995.

Stevens, R. Blake and Edward C Ezell, "The Black Rifle, M16 Retrospective," Collector Grade Publications, Toronto, CA, Enhanced edition, 1992.

Stevens, R. Blake, "U.S. Rifle M14, from John Garand to the M21," Collector Grade Publications, Toronto, CA, 1983.

Sweda, Charles, "No Place to Hide, The OICW Goes to War," *Small Arms Review*, Vol. 2, No. 9, June, 1999.

TM-9-1005-222-12, "Operator and Organizational Maintenance Manual Including Repair Parts and Special Tools List, Rifle Caliber .30: M1, W/E (1005-674-1425), Rifle, Caliber .30: M1C (Sniper's) W/E (1005-674-1430), Rifle, Caliber .30: M1D (Sniper's) W/E (1005-674-1431), Headquarters, Department of the Army, 1969.

TM9-1005-222-12P/1, "Operator and Organizational Maintenance Repair Parts and Special Tool Lists for Rifle 7.62 mm, M14 National Match and Rifle 7.62 mm, M14(m) Headquarters, Department of the Army, Washington D.C., February 1968.

TM9-1005-223-12P, "Operator and Organizational Maintenance Repair Parts and Special Tool Lists for Caliber .30 U.S. Rifle M1 (National Match), Headquarters, Department of the Army, Washington D.C.,1963.

TM 9-1005-223-20, "Organizational; Maintenance Manual Including Repair Parts and Special Tool Lists for Rifle, 7.62 mm, M14, W/E/ (1005-589-1271); Rifle, 7.62 mm, M14A1, W/E/ (1005-072-5001); Bipod, Rifle M1 (1005-711-6202), Headquarters, Department of the Army, August 1972.

TM 9-1005-223-35, "Direct, Support, General Support, and Depot Maintenance Manual Including Repair Parts and Special Tools List: 7.62 mm, M14, W/E/ (1005-589-1271); Rifle, 7.62 mm, M14A1, W/E/ (1005-072-5001); Bipod, Rifle M1 (1005-711-6202), Headquarters, Department of the Army, August 1968.

TM 9-1005-249-14, T.O. 11W3-5-5-1, NAVWEP O.P. 333 and MC I.D. 05538A. Technical Manual, Operation, Repair and Replacement Parts Rifle, 5.56-MM, M16; Rifle 5.56-MM, XM16E1; and Launcher, Grenade, 40-MM, XM148, Published under the Authority of the Secretaries of the Army, Navy and Air Force. 1 August 1966.

TM 9-1005-309-23&P, "Technical Manual, Organizational and Direct Support, Maintenance Manual (Including Repair Parts and Special Tools List) for Submachine Gun, 5.56-MM: Port, Firing, M231 (1005-01-081-4582), Headquarters, Department of the Army, March 1983.

TM 9-1005-319-10, "Operator's Manual W/Components List, Rifle 5.56-MM, M16A2 W/E and Carbine, 5.56-MM, M4 W/E, Headquarters, Department of the Army, May 1994.

TM 9-1005-319-23&P/TO 11 W3-5-5-42, "Technical Manual, Unit and Direct Support Maintenance Manual, Rifle 5.56MM, M16A2 W/E, Carbine, 5.56 MM, M4, and Carbine, 5,56 MM, M4A1, Departments of the Army and Air Force, May 1991.

TM 9-6920-363-12&P, Technical Manual, Operator's and Organizational Maintenance Manual Including Repair Parts and Special Tools List Conversion Kit (Caliber .22 Rimfire Adapter) M261 (NSN 1005-01-010-1516) for Rifle, 5.5-MM, M16 and M16A1. Headquarters, Department of the Army, September 1980.

U.S. War Department, "War Department Equipment Board Report, 22 May 1946," NARC #319, Box 334 "W". This board is known as the "Stillwell Board."

Zediker, Glen D., "The Competitive AR-15," privately published and available from Brownells, 200 South Front Street, Montezuma, IA 50171 515 623-4000.

About the Author

Joe Poyer is the author of more than 400 magazine articles on firearms, the modern military, military history and personal security. He written and published twelve novels with worldwide sales exceeding five million copies and authored or co-authored nine non-fiction books on the modern military.

He is the owner and publisher of North Cape Publications®, Inc. which publishes the "For Collectors Only" and "Shooter's and Collector's Guide" series of books for firearms collectors and shooters. In these series, he has written or co-authored, "The .45-70 Springfield," "U.S. Winchester Trench and Riot Guns, and other U.S. Combat Shotguns," "The M1 Garand 1936 to 1957," "The SKS Carbine," "The M14-Type Rifles," "The SAFN-49 Battle Rifle," "The Swedish Mauser Rifles" and "The M16/AR15 Rifles."

Mr. Poyer has served as editor of the following magazines: *Safe & Secure Living*; *International Military Review*, *International Naval Review* and as field editor for *International Combat Arms*. He is currently at work on a new book in "The For Collectors Only" series; "The Colt Single Action: Four Generations" and in "The Shooter's and Collector's Guide" series, "The American Sniper Rifle; Revolutionary War to Kosovo."

Mr. Poyer was the on-camera Military Affairs Analyst and Reporter for a major television station in Los Angeles, California. He also imported the very fine L1A1A inch pattern FAL rifles from Australia in the late 1980s.

Other Books from North Cape Publications®, Inc.

The books in the "For Collectors Only" series are designed to provide the firearm's collector with an accurate record of the markings, dimensions and finish found on an original firearm as it was shipped from the factory. As changes to any and all parts are listed by serial number range, the collector can quickly assess not only whether or not the overall firearm is correct as issued, but whether or not each and every part is original for the period of the particular firearm's production. "For Collectors Only" books make each collector an "expert."

The .45-70 Springfield by Joe Poyer and Craig Riesch ($16.95) covers the entire range of .45 caliber "trapdoor" Springfield arms, the gun that really won the west. "Virtually a mini-encyclopedia . . . this reference piece is a must." Phil Spangenberger, *Guns & Ammo*

U.S. Winchester Trench and Riot Guns and other U.S. Combat Shotguns by Joe Poyer ($15.95). Describes the elusive and little-known "Trench Shotgun" and all other combat shotguns used by U.S. military forces. "U.S. military models 97 and 12 Trench and Riot Guns, their parts, markings [and]

dimensions [are examined] in great detail . . . a basic source of information for collectors." C.R. Suydam, *Gun Report*

The M1 Carbine: Wartime Production by Craig Riesch ($16.95) describes the four models of M1 Carbines from all ten manufacturers. Complete with codes for every part by serial number range. "The format makes it extremely easy to use. The book is a handy reference for beginning or experienced collectors." Bruce Canfield, Author of "M1 Garand and M1 Carbine"

The M1 Garand 1936 to 1957 by Joe Poyer and Craig Riesch ($19.95). "The book covers such important identification factors as manufacturer's markings, proof marks, final acceptance cartouches stampings, heat treatment lot numbers . . . there are detailed breakdowns of . . . every part . . . in minute detail. This 216 page . . . volume is easy to read and full of identification tables, parts diagrams and other crucial graphics that aid in determining the originality of your M1 and/or its component parts." Phil Spangenberger, *Guns and Ammo*

Winchester Lever Action Repeating Firearms, by Arthur Pirkle.
    Volume 1, **The Models of 1866, 1873 & 1876** ($19.95)
    Volume 2, **The Models of 1886 and 1892** ($19.95)
    Volume 3, **The Models of 1894 and 1895** ($19.95)
These famous lever action repeaters are completely analyzed part-by-part by serial number range in this first new book on these fine weapons in twenty years. ". . . book is truly for the serious collector . . . Mr. Pirkle's scholarship is excellent and his presentation of the information . . . is to be commended." H.G.H., *Man at Arms*

The SKS Carbine, by Steve Kehaya and Joe Poyer ($16.95).The "SKS Carbine" is profusely illustrated, articulately researched and covers all aspects of its development as well as . . . other combat guns used by the USSR and other Communist bloc nations. Each component . . . from stock to bayonet lug, or lack thereof, is covered along with maintenance procedures . . . because of Kehaya's and Poyer's book, I have become the leading expert in West Texas on [the SKS].Glen Voorhees, Jr., *Gun Week*

British Enfield Rifles, by Charles R. Stratton
    Volume 1, **SMLE (No. 1) Mk I and Mk III** ($16.95)
"Stratton . . . does an admirable job of . . . making sense of . . . a seemingly hopeless array of marks and models and markings and apparently endless varieties of configurations and conversions . . . this is a book that any collector of SMLE rifles will want on his shelf." Alan Petrillo, *The Enfield Collector's Digest*

Volume 2, **The Lee-Enfield No. 4 and No. 5 Rifles** ($16.95)
In Volume 2, "Skip" Stratton provides a concise but extremely thorough analysis of the famed British World War II rifle, the No. 4 Enfield, and the No. 5 Rifle, better known as the "Jungle Carbine." It's all here, markings, codes, parts, manufacturers and history of development and use.

The Mosin-Nagant Rifle by Terence W Lapin ($19.95). For some reason, in the more than 100 years that the Mosin-Nagant rifle has been in service around the world, not a single book has been written in English about this fine rifle. Now, just as interest in the Mosin-Nagant is exploding, Terence W. Lapin had written a comprehensive volume that covers all aspects and models from the Imperial Russian rifles to the Finnish, American, Polish, Chinese, Romanian and North Korean variations. His books set a standard that future authors will find very difficult to best.

M14-Type Rifles, A Shooter's and Collector's Guide, by Joe Poyer ($14.95). A study of the U.S. Army's last and shortest-lived .30 caliber battle rifle which became a popular military sniper and civilian high power match rifle. A detailed look at the National Match M14 rifle, the M21 sniper rifle and the currently-available civilian semiautomatic match rifles, receivers, parts and accessories, including the Chinese M14s. A guide to custom-building a service type-rifle or a match grade, precision rifle. Includes a list of manufacturers and parts suppliers, plus the BATF regulations for building a "banned" rifle look-alike.

The SAFN-49 Battle Rifle, A Shooter's and Collector's Guide, by Joe Poyer ($14.95). The SAFN-49, the predecessor of the Free World's battle rifle, the FAL, has long been neglected by arms historians and writers, but not by collectors. Developed in the 1930s at the same time as the M1 Garand and the SVT38/40, the SAFN-49 did not reach production because of the Nazi invasion of Belgium until after World War II. This study of the SAFN-49 provides a part-by-part examination of the four calibers in which the rifle was made. Also, a thorough discussion of the SAFN-49 Sniper Rifle plus maintenance, assembly/disassembly, accurizing, restoration and shooting. A new exploded view and section view are included.

Campaign Clothing: Field Uniforms of the Indian War Army
    Volume 1, 1866 to 1871 ($12.95)
    Volume 2, 1872 to 1886 ($14.95)
Lee A. Rutledge has produced a unique perspective on the uniforms of the Army of the United States during the late Indian War period following the Civil War. He discusses what the soldier really wore when on campaign. No white hats and yellow bandanas here.

A Guide Book to U.S. Army Dress Helmets 1872-1904, by Mark Kasal and Don Moore ($16.95).
From 1872 to 1904, the men and officer's of the U.S. Army wore a fancy, plumed or spiked helmet on all dress occassions. As ubiquitous as they were in the late 19th Century, they are extremely scarce today. Kasal and Moore have written a step-by-step, part-by-part analysis of both the Model 1872 and 1881 dress helmets and their history and use. Profusely illustrated with black and white and color photographs of actual helmets.

All of the above books can be obtained directly from North Cape Publications®, Inc, P.O. Box 1027, Tustin, CA 92781 or by calling Toll Free 1-800 745-9714. Orders only to the toll free number please. For information, call 714 832-3621. Orders may also be placed by FAX (714 832-5302) or via Email to ncape@pacbell.net. CA residents add 7.75% sales tax. Postage is currently $2.75 for 1-2 books, $3.25 for 3-4 books, $4.95 for 5-8 books. Call for postage on quantities for 9 books and more.

Also, visit our Internet web site at **http://www.north-capepubs.com**. Our complete, up-to-date book list can always be found there. Also check out our linked On-Line Magazine for the latest in firearms-related, magazine-quality articles and excerpts from our books.